The Biochemistry of Memory

The Biochemistry of Memory

WITH AN INQUIRY INTO THE FUNCTION OF THE BRAIN MUCOIDS

SAMUEL BOGOCH, M.D., Ph.D.

Director, Foundation for Research
on the Nervous System, and
Associate Research Professor
of Biochemistry and Psychiatry,
Boston University School of Medicine

New York

OXFORD UNIVERSITY PRESS
London   Toronto   1968

Copyright © 1968 by Oxford University Press, Inc.
Library of Congress Catalogue Card Number: 68-19766
Printed in the United States of America

Acknowledgments

Many investigators who have contributed to the development of this rapidly growing field are represented in the bibliography, although the list by no means claims to be exhaustive. My co-workers, to whom I am greatly indebted, are my co-authors in papers in the bibliography. The balance achieved by the attempt to present both a review of the work of others and sufficient supporting data for the principal thesis of a particular book is always open to criticism. The description of the work directly relevant to the hypothesis presented in this book occupies approximately one-half of the total text, while the work of other laboratories in the general field of memory occupies 532 of the 585 references. The Foundation for Research on the Nervous System provided the facilities and support for much of our work. The Massachusetts Mental Health Center, Harvard Medical School, Massachusetts General Hospital, Boston Lying-In Hospital, Children's Medical Center, Metropolitan State Hospital, Foxboro State Hospital, Boston State Hospital, and Boston University School of Medicine, all of Boston and vicinity, together with St. Vincent's Hospital, Rockland State Hospital, and the New York Psychoanalytic Institute, all of New York, are the other institutions whose facilities have helped make various aspects of this work possible. Mrs. Louis S. Gimbel, Jr., Mr. John K. Norwood and Mrs. Katherine Norwood, Dr. A. Baird Hastings, Dr. William H. Sweet, Dr. Harry C. Solomon, Dr. Paul Yakovlev, Dr. Francis O. Schmitt, Dr. F. Marott Sinex, Dr. Bernard Bandler, Dr. William Malamud, Dr. Nathan Kline, the late Dr. Siegfried Thannhauser, and the late Dr. Heinrich Waelsch were often interested and helpful. The continuous financial support of this work by the National Institutes of Health, the U.S. Public Health Service, the National Science Foundation, and the Scottish Rite Freemasons, is also gratefully acknowledged.

Boston, Massachusetts   Samuel Bogoch
March, 1967

Permissions

We are grateful to the following individuals and publishers for granting us permission to reproduce copyrighted material:

Academic Press, Inc., New York, for Figs. 22 and 23, which appeared in *Virology*, 7, 161, 1959.

The *American Journal of Psychiatry*, for Fig. 30 and Table XIV, which appeared in that journal, 119, 128, 1962; and for Fig. 31, which appeared in that journal, 123, 952, 1967.

The American Psychological Association, for the quotation on pp. 8 and 9 (ref. 524), which appeared in *Psychological Reviews*, 64 (Suppl.), No. 6, Part 2, 20, 1957.

The *Biochemical Journal*, for Figs. 3 and 4, which appeared in that journal, 68, 319, 1958.

The Cold Spring Harbor Laboratory of Quantitative Biology, Cold Spring Harbor, L.I., New York, and Dr. J. Wersall, for Fig. 2, which appeared in the *Cold Spring Harbor Symposium on Quantitative Biology*, 30, 115, 1965.

Harvard University Press, Cambridge, Mass., for the quotation on pp. 215-16 (ref. 114), which appeared in *The Integrity of the Body, A Discussion of Modern Immunological Ideas*, by F. M. Burnet, Harvard University Press, Cambridge, Mass., 1963.

Elsevier Publishing Co., Amsterdam, for Figs. 11, 19, 20, and 35, which appeared in *Protides of the Biological Fluids*, H. Peeters (ed.), Vol. 15, Elsevier, Amsterdam, 1968, pp. 131-41, and for

Fig. 10, which appeared in *Protides of the Biological Fluids*, H. Peeters (ed.), Vol. 13, 1966, pp. 211-16.

McGraw-Hill Book Co., for the quotations on p. 211 (ref. 337) and on p. 212 (ref. 337), which appeared in *Psychology: A Study of a Science*, S. Koch (ed.), 1959, p. 94.

Macmillan (Journals) Ltd., London, for Fig. 8, which appeared in *Nature*, 304, 73, 1964, and for Fig. 21, which appeared in *Nature*, 185, 392, 1960.

Neurology, for Fig. 3, which appeared in that journal, 10, 439, 1960.

The *Neurosciences Research Program Bulletin*, for Fig. 1 (ref. 393), which appeared in that journal, 7, 77, 1964; for the quotation on page 83 (ref. 185), which appeared in that journal, 3, 43, 1965; and for the quotation on p. 87 (ref. 261), which appeared in that journal, 2, 33, 1964.

The *New England Journal of Medicine*, for Figs. 24, 25, 28, and 29, which appeared in that journal, 264, 521, 1961.

Pergamon Press, Inc., for Figs. 16, 17, and 18, which appeared in *Inborn Disorders of Sphingolipid Metabolism*, S. M. Aronson and B. W. Volk (eds.), Pergamon Press, Inc., New York, 1967, p. 273.

Sigmund Freud Copyrights, Ltd., The Institute of Psychoanalysis, and Mrs. Alix Strachey, and the Hogarth Press, Ltd., London, and to Basic Books, Inc., for the quotations on p. 82 (ref. 207) and on p. 85 (ref. 206).

Science and Behavior Books, Inc., for the quotation on p. 85 (ref. 171), which appeared in *The Anatomy of Memory*, D. P. Kimble (ed.), 1965, p. 12; and for the quotation on p. 9 (ref. 502), which appeared in *Learning and Its Disorders*, I. N. Berlin and S. A. Szurek (eds.), 1965, p. 3.

Springer-Verlag, New York, Inc., for Figs. 6 and 7, adapted from material which appeared in *Reviews of Physiology, Biochemistry and Experimental Pharmacology*, 57, 190, 1966.

Contents

I Introduction, 3

   1. Brain-mind, 3
   2. An Hypothesis, 5

II Approaches to the Study of Learning and Memory, 8

   1. Definitions of Learning, 8
   2. An Operational Concept of Learning and Memory, 10
   3. Phases of the Memory Process, 10
   4. Experimental Systems Used in the Study of Learning and Memory, 12

III Surgical, Electrical, and Pharmacological Means of Studying Learning and Memory, 21

   1. The Effect of Surgical and Natural Brain Lesions on Learning and Memory, 22
   2. Electrical Means of Studying Learning and Memory, 26
   3. The Influence of Drugs on Learning and Memory, 32

IV Biochemical Studies on Learning and Memory, 39

   1. Attempts To Measure Biochemical Changes in the Nervous System in Learning, 39
      Some Reasons for Studying Transduction in Sensory Receptors; Mechanoreceptors; Hearing; Olfactory Receptors; Electrical and Chemical Receptors; Photoreceptors, 39

Studies on Nucleic Acids in the Nervous System in Learning, 47
Studies on Acetylcholine and Acetylcholinesterase in the Nervous System in Learning, 56
Studies on Proteins of the Nervous System in Learning, 61
2. Attempts To Achieve "Passive" Biochemical Transfer of Information, 69
Studies in Planaria, 69
Studies in Rats, 71
Studies in Humans, 74

V   Some Current Non-molecular and Molecular Theories of Memory, 76
Introduction, 76
Non-molecular Theories, 76
Molecular Theories of Memory, 80

VI   Central Nervous System Mucoids in Learning and Memory, 91
Introduction:
Some Requirements for Prospective Coding Molecules, 91
Nomenclature for the CNS Mucoids, 93
The Constituents of the CNS Mucoids, 94
1. Heterogeneity of CNS Mucoids, 107
Human Brain Aminoglycolipids, 107
Human Cerebrospinal Fluid Glycoproteins, 110
Brain Glycoproteins, 111
2. Location of CNS Mucoids, 125
3. Prenatal and Postnatal Development of Human Brain Proteins, 134
4. Pathology of the CNS Mucoids, 139
5. "Chemistry of Recognition" and CNS Mucoids, 155
Mucoids as Antigens, 155
Mucoids as Specific Receptors, 162
Mucoids as Stimuli, 168
6. Biosynthesis and Regenerative Potential of CNS Mucoids, 173
7. CNS Mucoids Change with Behavioral Change, 179
8. Pigeon CNS Mucoids in Learning Situations, 185
Change in the Concentration of Certain Pigeon Brain Glycoproteins in Learning, 185

Identification and Concentration of Sugars Bound Glycosidically in Nondialyzable Mucoids of Pigeon Brain: At
Rest, and Training, 195
Incorporation of 1-^{14}C-glucose into Pigeon Brain Mucoids,
201

VII   Toward a Comprehensive Biochemical Theory of Memory, 209

Time Dependency and Hierarchies of Storage, 209
Repair and Sleep, 210
Plasticity, Redundancy, and Economy, 210
Organizers, 211
Development, 212
The Function of the Brain Mucoids, 213
         The "Sign-post" Mechanism, 214
         The "Spell-out" Mechanism, 217
         Combined Mechanism, 217

References, 219

Index, 245

The Biochemistry of Memory

I

Introduction

1. Brain-mind

The idea that there is a biochemistry of memory is gaining acceptance, partly because of work in the field itself, and partly because of a number of developments in biology in general. First, the recent recognition that certain chemical substances, the deoxyribonucleic acids, carry at least part of the informational content of genetics has represented a major conceptual advance, in that it has shown chemical structure to be linked so closely to informational and instructional content that the word "code" (549) can be used. Second, the advances in classical immunology have been increasingly discussed in the language of what might be called the chemistry of recognition and recall for the cells of the body, and for substances which on entering the body are recognized as foreign, or non-self. Third, the realization that certain physical and chemical agents, such as electroconvulsive shock, sodium amytal, and puromycin, have an influence on memory has increased the conviction that there are direct but unknown organic links between the concepts of memory formulated in terms of "brain" and those formulated in terms of "mind." Finally, there are some indications that we are moving in a direction which permits and even encourages further biological inquiry into the nature of man's behavior, wherein the idea that there is a molecular basis for memory may not be so frightening as it formerly was.

What is learning? How is memory studied? Is man's memory

3

just a specialized example of information handling by natural mechanisms akin to those used in molecular genetics or in molecular immunology, but with an extra macro systems component of nerve net organization? If this is indeed the case, what are the molecular substrates for nervous system memory? What is the chemical basis of the code? How are storage, retrieval (remembering), and non-retrieval (forgetting) accomplished, and what is the basis for selectivity in these functions? These are the questions with which this book is concerned. It hardly needs to be stated that these questions will not be answered here, but some of the approaches to solutions will be outlined.

The mucoids are one of the groups of brain substances which might be considered in terms of the primary as well as the secondary or supporting reactions constituting the molecular bases of memory. This book describes studies on the mucoids of the nervous system: on their structure, metabolism, pharmacology, immunology, pathology, development, and their changes in learning situations and in various behavioral states.

The work of our laboratory over the past ten years has led to the development of an hypothesis which has two separate but closely related parts: first, that the mucoids are involved in cell integrity functions, i.e. membrane, receptor, barrier, transport, and transmission functions; second, that they are involved in the chemical coding of experiential information, and that a disturbance in these functions may be fundamental to or associated with disturbances in nervous system activity as seen in behavioral disturbances. Experimental findings in other organisms, in other organs, and in other disorders which appear to be relevant to this hypothesis are reviewed, and the possible significance of these studies for pathogenesis and therapy in psychiatric and neurologic disorders is discussed.

The unitary biological orientation observed throughout this book is that the behavioral and the biochemical characteristics of an organism are distinct and separable only because the methods utilized to observe them differ. Each method illuminates only a particular property of the organism in a small part of its complexity. In keeping with an orientation toward the unity of biology, the phenomena of "brain" and "mind," the subject of divisive controversy since antiquity, should be referred to as "brain-mind." It is not intended that the hyphenation of the words for two of the most complex concepts in nature should diminish appreciation for the magnitude of the task faced in even beginning to understand them scientifically. The fact, however, that there is no single word to describe their unity seems to have provided an additional irrational obstacle to their study. Contrary opinions to this unified concept have been expressed in the past (474), but it is encouraging to note that others working in this field (337) have independently proposed "brain-mind" as a word which more adequately represents the phenomenon than does either part of the word alone.

2. An hypothesis

The suggestion that the mucoids are involved in membrane, receptor, barrier, and transmission functions was first made when the partial elucidation of the structure of a preparation of bovine brain ganglioside indicated the suitability of orientation of its constituents to interphase or membrane functions. This hypothesis has been supported by the following further observations: the study of the antigenic properties of gangliosides and the consideration of their structural analogy to the group-specific blood group substances and bacterial cell wall constituents; the observation that gangliosides interact with influenza PR8 and NWS viruses in a manner suggesting that they are structurally similar to or identical with the *in vivo* brain receptor for these viruses; the observation that brain gangliosides stimulate smooth muscle preparations and that the specificity of this effect is lost when terminal neuraminic acid is hydrolytically removed; and the detection of structurally analogous substances which are released from membranes in the first minutes of virus infection in the chick egg (55-87).

In addition, work from other laboratories, although not yet completely elucidating the structure of all of the variants of gangliosides, first, confirmed the findings which indicated that the basic unit of gangliosides is a cerebroside (predominantly or entirely

glucocerebroside) to which galactose, galactosamine, and neuraminic acid moieties were glycosidically attached; second, confirmed
the receptor-like properties demonstrated by the interaction of
ganglioside with viruses, and extended this property to tetanus
toxin, bacterial toxins, and serotonin; and third, confirmed the
effect of ganglioside on smooth muscle, extended the range of its
demonstrable pharmacological activity to brain slices, and made
observations on the histological localization of gangliosides, actually
identifying them with isolated membrane structures of brain.
While there has been no negative evidence as yet, the discussion
of this work in some detail in the following pages will indicate that
much work is still required before anything approaching a comprehensive understanding is attained of the chemistry, histology, and
function of the gangliosides, or of their metabolic relationship to
the glycoproteins and other mucoids.

With the mucoids increasingly implicated in membrane integrity and recognition functions, it was proposed that they may be
the substances (or one of the substances) in which experiential
information is encoded in the nervous system (68, 69, 75). White
Carneaux pigeons, the subject of much intensive instrumental
learning studies for years, now have been studied for changes in
brain proteins accompanying learning. Some apparently non-specific
changes in particular brain glycoproteins have been observed which
correlate with training rather than with learning, and some apparently specific changes in other brain glycoproteins relate to learning itself. The brain mucoids will be seen to exhibit heterogeneity,
location, development, pathology, recognition functions, biosynthesis, and change with behavior and learning consistent with requirements for coding functions (Chapter VI). Some ways in which
the hypothesis can be made more explicit are examined in Chapter
VII. Since this book was written, inhibition of synthesis of brain
gangliosides has been demonstrated to occur with the memory-
inhibitor puromycin, and mucoids have recently been visualized at
synaptic junctions (284a, 430a, 430b).

The evidence at hand thus suggests a role for the brain mucoids
in the coding of experiential information in the nervous system.
Beyond the confirmation or negation of a particular aspect of the

hypothesis on the function of the mucoids, however, some require-ments are illustrated for the design of experiments which might be-gin to establish the relationship, or lack thereof, of behavioral and chemical phenomena in nervous system function, both normal and abnormal, whether it be in planarian, pigeon, or man.

II

Approaches to the study of learning and memory

1. Definitions of learning

It should be recognized at the outset that attempts to make precise definitions of learning have met with objections. On the one hand there is the legitimate complaint that an area of work which is not subject to precise definition must be marked by the confusion of a lesser science; on the other hand there is the recognition that transitory and imperfect definitions may serve useful purposes in the course of research.

There are considerable variations among the following few examples of definitions. One view states that something like learning takes place in tissue culture where there are plastic changes in the excitability properties, lasting for minutes, which can be produced by simple combinations of input stimuli (150, 149). Conditioning learning has been defined as "the ability to code and retain different patterned sensitivities to the same stimulus" (178, 177). Learning has also been defined as follows: "To exhibit a change in behavior between two successive exposures to the same environment that cannot be attributed to manipulation of drive operations, alterations in the environment, sensory adaptations, disease, surgical interference, physical trauma, or growth—although the propriety of these exclusions may be questioned. (When we say that an animal learns, we are stating at least that, other things being equal, some behavior now occurs in a situation in which it had not occurred previously, or that the behavior now occurring in a given situation is different from the behavior that occurred in the last occasion the animal was in that situation. The behavior need not change, nor the situation, but the relation between them has changed. . . .)" (524).

An example of a complicating experimental problem involves "latent" learning; that is, learning which at one time of testing is not apparent in terms of performance, but which later does become apparent, as when rewards are introduced (506).

As the organism studied becomes more complex, so naturally does the attempt to describe learning (the attempt to define it has usually been given up by this time). The following passage expresses some aspects of the complexity of the problem at the human level: ". . . whatever the endowed potentiality for learning, opportunities for study and stimulating teaching are essential for the fullest growth of that power in which the human being is preeminent among living things. It is a long and slow road each child travels from converting the vocal noises of infancy and early childhood into the more precise signals we call words, language, . . . His language and developed capacity for abstraction permit him . . . to learn how his ancestors dealt with problems and creatively to solve his own . . ." (502).

The distinction (or lack thereof) between innate (genetic, instinctual) and experiential behavior continues to be argued at the behavioral and ethological levels (339, 244).

At the biochemical level the complex interaction between genetic and experiential information is just beginning to be explored (379).

From the view of experimental psychology, learning is operationally defined. The types of operations usually employed are described in terms of the classical conditioning idiom (404) or in the idiom of instrumental learning (508, 475). There is disagreement over whether these two modes of studying learning are different at some fundamental level (310, 475) or whether the laws of classical conditioning and instrumental learning are fundamentally similar (373, 376). Even if the differences are not so much fundamental as they are the effects of different conditions of learning, the design and description of a given learning experiment require utmost care

and attention to detail if the experiment is to be correctly interpreted, especially when the aim is the correlation of observations
on learning with particular biochemical observations.

2. An operational concept of learning and memory

From the "learning" which is involved in immunological recognition by the organism of a foreign protein on second presentation
and mobilization of the synthesis of antibodies to it, through single
cell "learning" in tissue culture and *in situ* in nerve cell collections,
through earthworms, through pigeons, up to learning in man from
infancy to adulthood, there is a transition over many hierarchical
levels of molecular organization. And yet there is something in the
sense of the word "learning" which fits all of these levels appro-
priately. It is not through some semantic trick that they fit, but
because at the fundamental level of basic requirements there appears to be an operational affinity. That is, all of these cases deal
with the handling of information; in all there must be a stimulus, a
mechanism to receive the informational content of the stimulus
and "recognize" it, a mechanism to classify it, one to code it, one
to store it, one to retrieve it, one to associate it, and one to discharge the information or its derivative as response. Not that there
may not be more than one of each, as well as overlapping of these
functions, but each must be present as a minimal requirement for
learning and memory to occur.

3. Phases of the memory process

In the previous section, some of the basic requirements for the phenomena of learning and memory to be invoked were mentioned. An
important distinction that must be made, but rarely is, is the distinction between primary or fundamental processes and secondary
or supportive processes. Our ignorance prevents us at this stage
from separating these two sets of phenomena in all cases, but some
are obvious. Thus for example, when energy-generating or energy-

storing mechanisms in the organism or cell are interfered with experimentally, and the processes of learning and memory are concurrently interrupted, one clearly cannot say that the energy mechanism is synonymous with the memory mechanism. Interference with the synthesis of adenosine triphosphate production may interfere with literally thousands of biochemical processes, the maintenance of cell membrane and cytoplasmic constituents of all types, and all of these may be essential to the maintenance of certain biological structures without which learning cannot occur. This, however, is a different matter from the identification of particular molecules which actually mediate the transmission of an electrical signal between two components of a nerve net. This subtle, demanding, and continuous task of distinction between primary and secondary supportive dimensions is present in the experimental and the hypothetical aspects of all studies of learning and memory.

Table I. Required Mechanisms* for processing of information in the nervous system: (phases of the memory process) (69)

1. *Sensory input reception.*

2. *Encoding for transmission:* Transduction from primary sensory modalities (sound, light, etc.) to electrochemical equivalents utilized by nervous system cells.

3. *Association and Abstraction:* Association with information previously stored, pattern recognition, abstraction, synthesis of new constructs: Conscious and unconscious.

4. *Storage:* (a) Further encoding, or same as 2?
   (b) Same process for short and long duration?

5. *Retrieval:* Remembering—forgetting.

6. *Effector Consequences of Retrieval:* Further association and abstraction; discharge in thought, language; motor and affective accompaniments.

7. *Supporting chemical reactions* for 1 through 6.

* Immediate chemical reactions are expected to be defined for each of the primary mechanisms 1 through 6. In addition, "second order" supporting reactions are expected for each (7. Supporting Chemical Reactions).

Table I summarizes some of the major components of the memory process which, although overlapping in some parts, appear now to require at least partially separate definition.

When the stimulus outside the organism, whether it be light, sound, smell, mechanical pressure, etc., reaches the receptor cells of the organism, the first series of biochemical transformations must occur; these transformations will eventually result in the processing of the message borne by the stimulus into an electro-chemical currency that will then be propelled, associated, stored, retrieved, and discharged. These first "biochemistries of memory," these first transductions from the language of the outside world to those inside the nervous system, are as unknown as are those later biochemistries of code transmission, storage, retrieval, and discharge. They are all a part of the biochemistry of information handling, and thus of learning and memory.

Some of the implications of these considerations to non-molecular and molecular theories of memory will be discussed in Chapter V.

4. Experimental systems used in the study of learning and memory

Each experimental system has certain operational and conceptual advantages and limitations. All are potentially useful. None are reviewed in detail here, but each is outlined with a few examples and some critical comments.

IMMUNOLOGICAL SYSTEMS

To a large extent the denotation of a given system as simple or complex depends upon the minimal system which one accepts as capable of demonstrating all of the necessary and sufficient characteristics of learning. Thus if the ability to synthesize and abstract information is deemed essential, then the immunological system with transplanted lymph nodes challenged *in vitro* by molecules which are to be recognized for the first or second time may seem inadequate, and nothing infrahuman will suffice. And yet even in this example, the ability—or is it the inadequacy?—of the immunological system to generalize a response to other substances of closely related structure to the one it has "learned" to "recognize" may be considered to represent a kind of abstraction. In all instances of learning some form of stimulus and some form of response must be measured. In this instance the stimulus is the foreign or "not me" substance presented, and the "response" or "behavior" of the organism, organ, or cell which is actually measured is the production of specific proteins called antibodies.

The mechanisms by which organ-specific substances live in immunological isolation side by side in the same organism, and the breakdown of this isolation which leads to "autoimmune disease," are fascinating and still poorly understood aspects of the handling of immunological information that may have parallels in the compartmentalization of information in the nervous system and its breakdown.

In its grosser aspects this might refer to the development extraneurally of antibodies to neural substrates (234). In other ways it might refer to the immobilization or change in function of a neural molecule, normally insulated from a neighboring molecule, when the insulating mechanism fails. If, for example, engram A does not normally associate with engram B in realistic daytime (secondary process) thinking, then the failure of the insulating mechanism may lead to the "looseness of associations" characteristic of thinking disturbances (49) in certain brain-mind disorders. This parallel, of course, can only be regarded as an analogy in the absence of any evidence bearing on it.

TISSUE CULTURE

Tissue derived from fetal rat spinal cord and neonatal mouse cerebral cortex (150, 149) provides an *in vitro* system in which the electrical activity of cells can be studied. The input stimuli can be electrical, and the plastic changes in the excitability properties and the nature of the electrical response are measured. It has been noted (113) that while this system might reflect learning in terms of an altered responsiveness to the same input, the change due to repeated electrical stimulation of previously quiescent cells has not yet been sufficiently quantified to provide a well-defined physicochemical "control" state needed in the evaluation of learning phenomena. While electrical phenomena are the responses here measured, the vast literature on chemical changes in tissue culture bears evidence to the fact that it is a rare study in which the culture media and conditions are sufficiently well defined that chemical products may be compared in different experimental situations. Intrinsic to this system also are the problems of de-differentiation of cells, a time-related phenomenon. Thus one constant worry in the study of learning in growing and differentiating systems such as young animals is the question of whether a behavioral change attributed to experiential learning might in fact be caused by genetically programmed responses that appear at that moment. In tissue culture one observes both that problem, due to cell division, and the reverse problem of the plastic electrical and chemical changes occurring as a consequence of de-differentiation and then death of cells. Much attention is being given to establishing morphological and chemical criteria for the identification of stable differentiated states in viable cells in tissue culture, but until these relatively stable states have been better achieved and defined, the system remains open to considerable challenge in terms of its utility for learning studies.

SINGLE NERVE CELLS AND SYNAPSES IN SITU

Because of the anatomical nature of nerve cells, even in primitive organisms, the single nerve cells *in situ* can hardly be studied independently of the influences of processes from neighboring cells through both excitatory and inhibitory synapses. If the input influences of a given process from another cell can be adequately measured, the system becomes a potentially elegant one (169). In such cases the study is actually of the inhibitory and excitatory effects of one nerve cell upon another and the central focus is on their area of juncture, the synapse. While the analysis of the electrical events in pre- and post-synaptic regions is sufficiently complex in itself, it is not the immediate subject of this book. Chemically one can analyze the concentrations of transmitter substance in a general synaptic locus, but the complex three-dimensional intertwinings of the submicroscopic portions of even one synaptic region (316, 397) help to explain why chemical methods have not yet been devised for the analysis of events in pre- and post-synaptic membranes as well as in the synaptic cleft.

Studies using conditioning (284, 490, 503) in the single giant cell of the abdominal ganglion of the mollusk *Aplysia depilans* ("sea hare") attempt to describe the electrical events of nervous function at the cellular level, but have been limited to date to studies of response in terms of electrical activity. While some neurophysiologists are as little interested in the underlying molecular mechanisms in habituation phenomena in these single ganglion studies as are some behavioral psychologists in any of the biological mechanisms inside the whole organism emitting responses, many treat such experiments as preliminary ways to define the parameters of relatively simple systems which can then be more fruitfully studied from the biochemical point of view. Among the objections to this type of system are that while only the input to the cell is under experimental control, the nature of the synapse is not fully understood, presynaptic inhibition remains a possibility, and it may not be possible to generalize to other cells from what may be an "atypical" isolated cell (112). The single cell biochemical studies in higher organisms are discussed in Chapter IV.

WHOLE GANGLIA IN PRIMITIVE ORGANISMS

Studies of the headless cockroach or locust have demonstrated that only a part of the insect was necessary to demonstrate conditioning effects (253). The system then was further simplified so that only the metathoracic ganglion, the anterior coxal adductor muscle, and the nerve fibers connecting the two are studied electrophysiologically (255).

Similar learning studies on these ganglia were made in an attempt to identify a given cell body with a given peripheral axon in the leg nerve, by using retrograde chromatolysis of the cell body when the axon is cut (178). The addition of a histochemical dimension to this study by the use of staining techniques for cytoplasmic RNA (140) is now being employed to determine whether muscular use alone may result in increased staining of RNA.

RELATIVELY INTACT NERVOUS SYSTEM

Use of an essentially intact nervous system with behavioral and electrical responses measured is exemplified by the studies on the *cockroach*, where the usual cleaning behavior using one leg is required to be relearned for another leg (342). When this preparation is simplified so that a preganglionic connective is stimulated, recordings are made from a branch of a peripheral nerve containing a small number of motor axons. After learning an efferent response is given, which has been considered to be related to the relearning phenomenon. Such studies must be accompanied by cautious interpretation because of the unknown effects of peripheral amputation on the background electrophysiological properties of the central ganglia (133). However, good controls are feasible, and since the central nervous system is left essentially intact, there are potential advantages to this and similar systems.

Spinal cord preparations in which higher centers are surgically removed can be considered to be relatively intact large segments of nervous system in learning studies. In certain studies of this type, which test the development of a conditioned motor response (108), pharmacological agents such as Flaxedil, which blocks neuromuscular transmission, have been added, and thus chemical phenomena have been included in the accounting.

In many of these relatively intact systems, *individual nerve cells* are singled out for electrode implantation and recording of effector response (396), and the nature of the input is not determined as it is in isolated single cell studies.

Decapitated earthworms have been studied to test their ability to retain old learning and even learn anew through experience or through the so-called chemical transfer of information (270, 353). Many problems exist in the evaluation of response even in the intact worm because of observer bias, comparability of worms, and great fluctuations in baseline behavior of individual worms, as documented in most of the studies on the chemical transfer of learning (111). (See Chapter IV.)

INTACT ORGANISMS

Studies in this group range from *Paramecium* to man; from organisms where no nervous system exists, yet something like learning apparently occurs, to man, where the most complex organ in nature mediates learning. It is in the comparison of members of this group that most difficulty arises in the definition of learning, for how does one compare *Paramecium* to the rat, the rat to the pigeon, or any of these to man? The return to the simplest criteria of stimulus and response, with time, allows them all to be considered together at least in these fundamental terms. But from this point on, much discretion is required. As long as the intrinsic limitations of the system referred to are kept foremost, something probably can be learned by and from each.

Paramecia avoid a clean platinum wire, but aggregate at a source of bacterial food. After dipping a platinum wire coated with bacteria into a ciliate culture several times, dipping a clean platinum wire into the culture attracts Paramecia up to ten hours later (216). *Sea anemones*, which possess only a diffuse nerve net, can be taught to modify choice between contractile and swimming movements (456). *Starfish* can presumably learn a Y-maze (110). The antics of pigeons, rats, dogs, and man fill the archives of experimental psychology on learning.

There are certain *limitations imposed by complexity*. In the extreme, an individual human being studied for years in the clinical psychoanalytic situation may provide much data obtained by the sound naturalistic tradition of repeated observation, on the nature of remembering and forgetting, on the associative pathways operating between engrams relating memories regardless of their position in the life span of experience. And yet the way to make correlative electrophysiological or neurochemical observations relevant to these memory phenomena in man appears to be beyond our present imagination. Even in human subjects, however, some interesting and promising efforts in the recording of electroencephalographic changes relating to attention and expectancy have been made. These will be discussed later.

The study of critical periods in the development of birds or mammals is of great interest because of the temporal confluence of suddenly emerging genetic response with experiential learning (307). This will doubtless receive more biochemical attention in the future.

From the biochemical point of view the choice of a given organism for studies on the molecular basis of learning also depends largely upon the form of the initial hypothesis. Thus, if engrams are sought in discrete cell groups, dendritic nets, or fiber tracts, simpler organisms have certain advantages. If, on the other hand, change in a given substrate which is diffusely spread over anatomical groupings is considered more likely, any readily available representative portion of nervous tissue might suffice. If both general changes and discrete microhistological changes are contemplated for various phases of the memory process, both classes of "dissection" must be considered.

One thing seems certain regardless of the theoretical chemical orientation possessed by the investigator: an organism should be chosen for study about which a maximal amount of *quantitative* experimental data has been gathered in the behavioral realm, since then at least the behavioral criteria may be reliably used to fix one's position in the sea of memory and learning. Such is the case for the male white Carneaux pigeon, the subject of exhaustive operant conditioning studies for years (191, 247, 135) which has been selected for some of the biochemical studies reported in Chapter VI of this book.

NON-BIOLOGICAL SYSTEMS: COMPUTERS

The analogy which can be drawn between the way a computer operates and some functions of the nervous system has been the source of considerable attention for three decades. If there were no realistic basis whatsoever to this analogy, its heuristic value alone has more than justified the conceptual space which it has occupied. At the simplest level, both the computer and the nervous system are structures whose function is the handling of information. One occasionally unfortunate result of comparing these two data-processing machines is the forgetting that the one is non-biological, while the other is biological and requires the properties of life for its performance. That is, without biological energy, the nervous system fails. This is only occasionally unfortunate when it is forgotten in the course of hypothesis formation that a plasticity characteristic of living organisms is intrinsic to the nature of the nervous system; it is not invariably unfortunate since some of the very essence of the nervous system may have nothing more to do with the fact that it is living than that stable circuitry happens to have been produced by the biochemistry of a living process. Aspects of this analogy are discussed in the chapters on theoretical aspects of memory and learning.

Summary

A number of systems, both living and non-living, have been employed to study learning and memory. There are limitations to each at both the operational and the conceptual levels, and it is difficult to apply information obtained from one system to another. Immunological systems are elegant in their unimolecular simplicity, but lack the macro-systems integration characterized by the nervous system. Tissue cultures similarly have the advantage of single cell simplicity, but lack stable inter-cell geometry, and lack stable baselines because of continuous growth and death of cells. The study of single nerve cells and synapses *in situ* are difficult to generalize, and adequate biochemical methods are not yet available for the study of the pre- and post-synaptic membranes and the synaptic cleft. Whole ganglia and various isolated parts of the nervous system provide limited systems when compared to the intact nervous system, but the latter may be too complex for the adequate isolation of experimental variables. Non-living computers perform important analogy functions, but plasticity and other properties of living cells are not accounted for. Despite their limitations, each of the above systems probably can provide answers of direct relevance to learning and memory in the nervous system, provided that we ask each the appropriate questions.

III

Surgical, electrical, and pharmacological means of studying learning and memory

The history of the study of brain-mind and memory functions by surgical, electrical, and pharmacological means shows the transition from haphazard, frequently accidental observations to more controlled and more specific means of influencing the natural state. The idea that the jelly-like contents of the cranial cavity are somehow related to mental phenomena has been successfully resisted to a large extent, despite the repeated dramatic instances in which natural disease, violence, or, therapeutically, the surgeon's knife or stereotaxic probe has interrupted certain fiber tracts or destroyed certain cell groups with marked effects on memory and learning (190, 219, 407). The information derived from the therapeutic and experimental surgical literature is massive and of great importance for concepts of the anatomical organization of memory processes. From the point of view of the biochemistry of memory, however, the secondary effects of tissue trauma, both in the immediate region of the lesion and not infrequently also remote from it, place a heavy burden upon the interpretation of a given chemical finding in its relevance to the molecular basis of memory. This problem is particularly great where the lesion is a natural one without clear boundaries of influence, such as a brain tumor. Adequate controls are sufficiently difficult that if experiments are possible which exclude natural disease and surgical manipulation, these may well have first order preference in a biochemical search.

The same considerations apply to electrical, pharmacological, and nutritional interference with the nervous system. In these instances, both immediate and long-lasting structural disturbances may have primary and secondary molecular consequences which may be difficult or impossible to disentangle from the molecular changes directly related to the memory process. Even extraneural influences operate here; in the case of a nutritional lack, such as thiamin deficiency, or the diarrhea which follows puromycin administration, easier muscle fatiguability may interfere non-specifically with the behavioral performance used as an experimental measure of learning, or with the energy available for the learning process.

Nonetheless, any formulation of the nature of memory process, be it molecular or otherwise, which does not integrate with and conform to the knowledge derived from surgical, electrical, and pharmacological studies will be incomplete at best, or simply incorrect. These studies provide their own valid observations of the memory process even though subjects which have been through their procedures may be less useful for biochemical studies of memory.

1. The effect of surgical and natural brain lesions on learning and memory

The first published reports of a disturbance in memory after the partial or total loss of the *medial temporal lobes* were the results of studies made on monkeys, in 1888 (105), and observations of the condition in man, in 1900 (528). The memory defect in man was consequent to a natural process of bilateral softening of the cortex and underlying structures of the medial temporal lobes. Since those studies were made numerous reports have appeared in both human and animal studies confirming the relationship of the temporal lobes, especially the deep-lying hippocampus, to the memory process. Figure 1 shows a diagrammatic representation of those structures in human brain referred to in the discussion which follows.

The *uncus, amygdala,* and *anterior two-thirds of the hippocampus* have been shown to be involved in memory storage processes, especially in recent memory (377, 468, 469). With bilateral resec-

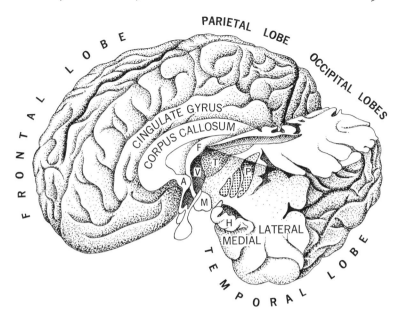

A = ANTERIOR COMMISSURE
F = FORNIX
H = HIPPOCAMPUS
M = MAMMILLARY BODIES
P = PUTAMEN
T = THALAMUS
V = THIRD VENTRICLE

Figure 1. Cutaway perspective drawing of some neuroanatomical structures whose functions appear to relate to memory (393). Putamen is shown as landmark structure only.

tion of these structures, the memory deficit is quite remarkable: patients are unable to learn the name of the hospital, are unable to learn by association, are unable to remember a series of only three numbers for more than a few minutes. At the same time, these patients retain quite good remote memory function, although the immediate past period of several months or a year just prior to the operation may be lost.

Other changes in behavior may occur if the *lateral aspects of the temporal lobe*—or especially if the entire temporal lobe—is resected bilaterally to a point approximately 7 cm. from the tip. Thus, the original Kluver-Bucy syndrome described in monkeys (305) and humans (504), includes in addition to the memory deficit some features of disorientation, possible alexia, agraphia, increased sexual activity, and changes in dietary habits and emotional behavior. On occasion, removal of a single temporal lobe may be accompanied by severe memory changes. In a few of these cases some evidence has been obtained that there is pathology in the opposite temporal lobe, so that the actual loss involves both temporal lobes (469, 408, 378).

There is some variance in results in cases where the *fornix* is sectioned bilaterally in humans. Some instances only result in memory disturbance (166, 500).

The presence of lesions in the *mammillary bodies* alone appear inadequate to produce memory defects; however, when pathology involves the thalamic nuclei as well, as occurs in the natural disorder of Korsakoff's syndrome (29, 525), memory deficits occur.

Stereotactic lesions placed in the *dorsal medial nucleus of the thalamus* may interfere with the acquisition of new information, as well as retention of previously learned material (484). Stereotactic lesions of *other thalamic areas*, for the treatment of intractable pain, have led to observations of recent memory disturbances of a transitory nature lasting up to ten days (349). Mice with lesions experimentally placed in the septal forebrain region showed little or no conditioning for passive avoidance (response inhibition) and fear. It was concluded that normal inhibitory influences of the passive avoidance type are mediated by the septal area (476).

Tumors in the region of the *third ventricle* have been reported to be associated with memory disturbances on several occasions, but the extent of the pathology is seldom delineated and the memory defect is not always well described. Among the defects reported for these cases are instances of inability to retain new impressions for any length of time, poor recall of past events, disturbances in recent memory, and inability to learn new sensory motor habits (561).

612.82 B634b
c./

While the *frontal lobe cortex* is doubtless involved in various aspects of learning, memory functions are only temporarily interfered with when the *cingulate gyri* are involved in bilateral lesions. In these cases individuals are transiently unable to organize remembered events in their correct temporal sequence (560). That life in a complex environment appears to increase the weight and thickness of the cerebral cortex in rats, and that these differences have been partially accounted for by an increase in the number of glial cells, are discussed in Chapter IV.

Sections of the *corpus callosum* and *anterior and hippocampal commissures* have been reported to result in failure to recall the memory of an event, but not in all cases nor under all conditions (481, 480, 52, 215).

There is, in addition, a large literature on the memory disturbances resulting from *head trauma* (562, 539, 100, 168), and *senile dementia* (100, 559). In many of these instances, as has been pointed out before, it is difficult to be certain of which anatomical structures are involved, but these cases serve as a general reminder, if one is still needed, that brain-mind function has observable gross neuroanatomical components as well as still unseen "micro" aspects.

Just as remarkable as all of the evidence which points to involvement of particular anatomical structures in learning and memory functions is the fact that some anatomical areas appear to have a lesser or no relationship to these functions. Thus lesions in the lateral temporal, parietal, and occipital lobes have not been associated with permanent alterations in memory function as a whole (393). In addition, brain damage associated with aphasia, apraxia, and agnosia, while they do involve certain special aspects of comprehension and memory (391), do not alter memory as a whole or, in particular, the storage aspects of memory.

The neuroanatomy of attention (347), and that of the appetites and emotions (346) have obvious relevance to the learning processes. In addition there is considerable evidence that information is rarely, if ever, stored in the nervous system without affective coding; it is as though equally important to the fact that an event happened in the past is the emotional response which accompanied that event. Events are apparently stored with identification as to whether they were experienced and interpreted in terms of pleasure —unpleasure. The structures of the "visceral brain" are therefore probably pertinent to the affective components of memory function.

Summary

The focus at present from an anatomical point of view is on the hippocampus, bilaterally, and its connections with the fornix, mammillary bodies, and thalamic nuclei. This information will need to be correlated with immediate and long-term requirements of memory mechanisms and with the biochemistry of memory as discussed in the last chapter of this book.

2. Electrical means of studying learning and memory

The use of electroconvulsive shock (ECS) as an effective treatment in certain mental disorders, especially in suicidal depressions and acute schizophrenic disorders, has provided some fascinating leads to the nature of the forgetting aspects of memory and its relationship to the disordered behavior. Depending on the number of such treatments, amnesia is an almost constant "side effect." The amnesia is most marked for recent events but may reach back for many years. Usually, however, the remote past is left untouched except for certain events. The appearance of amnesia concomitant with sudden improvement in the clinical status of patients treated with ECS naturally leads to the hypothesis that forgetting is integral to recovery, that the loss of certain "painful" memories relieves the disturbance in the equilibrium in some way, or that a simple "erasing" of circuit content is beneficial. Actually there are over forty hypotheses on how ECS works; needless to say, considering that number the actual mechanism(s) remains unknown (371). In studies in which the memory lost immediately following ECS was partially recovered with sodium amytal interviews, most of the patients maintained their improvement, but 2/17 immediately returned to the psychotic state which the ECS had reversed (53).

The amnesic effect of ECS has been a useful instrument in experimental studies of learning in animals as well. The clinical impression that the amnesia induced with ECS is due to the effect on brain of the electric current, and is present even when convulsions are inhibited, has now been confirmed in mice (362). The punishment factor in receiving multiple shocks has clouded interpretation of the data on several occasions (143). A partial solution to this dilemma is afforded by studies which demonstrate that amnesia can be obtained without the punishment factor of multiple ECS when only one electroshock is given after a single learning trial (363) or after massed trials (507).

Single ECS has been used also to test the hypothesis (218, 244) that intrinsic electrical activity is a necessary component of the early stage of memory consolidation. Thus, ECS given to mice 1 hour after reversal training showed that learning was retained. It was concluded that intrinsic electrical activity is not a necessary component of the early phase of memory consolidation (197). The mice were also treated with acetoxycycloheximide, an inhibitor of protein synthesis, however, and only a small proportion of the mice treated with ECS survived (suggesting a combination of debilitation due to heximide and too strong ECS). It might also be questioned whether the particular ECS given can be reliably judged to "erase" all electrical activity of alleged importance to memory consolidation.

The time after learning that ECS can be observed to interfere with memory consolidation is still somewhat in doubt. In one study, ECS produced "amnesia" only if given up to and including 30 seconds after learning (421). Another study reported ECS to be effective in producing amnesia for at least 1 hour and possibly 6 hours after learning (310). In particular learning situations there may well be differences in the duration of the "electrical" phase of memory consolidation, but it should be noted that in the last two studies mentioned the manner of administering the ECS differed, and there is some uncertainty that the actual current which passed through the brain in both studies was identical. Further, evidence of large individual differences in consolidation time has been reported.

The attempt to study and control appetitive behavior in animals by applying electrical stimuli through deeply implanted electrodes to particular nuclei or small groups of cells has had much success in recent years, especially with regard to thirst, temperature, hunger, respiration, and sexual centers (17, 395, 18, 372, 489).

"The ancient idea of centers—local brain areas in which specific and particular functions have special representation—appears to gain rather than lose ground" (213). This work is of interest to the retrieval or effector aspects of memory. That such studies need not simply be concerned with the artificial production of automatic "non-meaningful" behavior, as criticism sometimes states, is indicated, for example, by the fact that stimulation of the hunger area in the hypothalamus can elicit food-seeking habits which have been learned, and which have properties of the strong hunger that comes with fasting (374). Unfortunately, the use of finer-tipped probes to find more micro areas of response yields almost no response at all, presumably because a fairly large number of cells need to be recruited (375). In addition, a number of appetitive functions converge in the hypothalamus, and several effects, in relatively unpredictable combinations, may be obtained on stimulation (441).

Another approach in the use of electrical stimulation, both imposed and as self-stimulation, has been with regard to its function as a reward to reinforce learning and to maintain the performance of learned activities (394).

Studies in humans, in which both certain superficial and deep areas of the brain have been stimulated electrically, have resulted in the conscious perception by the subject of well-formed and detailed memories accompanied by appropriate affect. Parts of the temporal lobe and the insular area of the cerebral cortex are the chief sites of such effects. The well-documented studies of electrical stimulation of exposed areas of brain during neurosurgical procedures resulting in sudden vivid retrieval of memories in the conscious patient are provocative at the least (407). In addition, the stimulation of certain deep areas in humans has been reported to produce frequently more global, but strong, appetitive sensations, to interrupt the conscious flow of thoughts and to have characteristics of a reward (243).

The recording of spontaneous electrical events during learning is also of interest. With electrodes implanted in pyramidal cell and dentate granule cell layers of both dorsal and ventral parts of the cat hippocampus, as well as in the adjacent entorhinal zone of the hippocampal gyrus and in the amygdaloid complex, the distribution of slow-wave activity has been examined in the course of T-maze training (1). From the analysis of such experiments, a physiological basis has been suggested by which the hippocampal system may exert an influence on both non-specific ascending systems in the midbrain reticular formation and also on activity in the primary receptor areas of the visual cortex. This rhythmic regulatory activity may be essential to the process of laying down memory traces.

Observations have been made of the electroencephalogram (EEG) in somatic sensory areas indicating that the EEG controlling mechanisms are capable of accurate pitch discrimination. Behavioral responses were consistently associated with EEG "activation" effect, suggesting that the effect reflected changes that were necessary for the conditioned movements to occur. "Negative" tones produced "synchronization" of the EEG. The hypothesis was that the mechanism involved the following stages: (1) a receptor mechanism; (2) a trigger mechanism that determined whether the response would occur or not, fired by each pitch with characteristic probability; and (3) an effector mechanism that organized the conditioned response (109).

These studies have been extended to studies of the establishment of trace reflexes during natural sleep in the cat, in which it was concluded that an EEG "activation" effect can be used as an instrumental avoidance response, the trace of a tone having persisted in a sleeping cat. These experiments did not provide conclusive evidence that learning can occur during sleep, however (269).

Of interest in this regard also have been the studies on conscious cats with multiple implanted electrodes, when the cats were exposed to prolonged steady white noise. The summated electrical activity was recorded before, during, and after exposure to the unchanging stimulation. By this means it was possible to examine the major stations along the auditory pathway with respect to their dynamic responses to a standard form stimulation. Click responses could be obtained in many cortical and subcortical regions throughout the brain, but responses to sustained sound stimulation were limited to the classical auditory pathway. Sustained cortical responses were localized to a small region near the upper end of the posterior ectosylvian sulcus, an area much smaller than that usually considered as auditory cortex. Maximum sustained response amplitude decreased as one proceeded from round window to cortex. Following discontinuation of prolonged loud sound stimulation, every subcortical part of the central auditory pathway exhibited a profound, prolonged, reversible reduction in activity to below the level found prior to sound stimulation. Spontaneous activity tended to be stable, so that activity at each station along the auditory pathway was remarkably constant from day to day over a long period. Furthermore, activity shifted only slowly in response to environmental change and successively higher stations tended to be increasingly stable. These phenomena of non-correspondence between the sound stimulus and the response of the auditory pathway were interpreted as being due to active mechanisms resisting change. These electrophysiological phenomena were thought to be related to perceptual effects and aftereffects associated with long-continuing sensory stimulation. It was concluded that the analysis of the effects of prolonged stimulation may provide experimental access to some of the mechanisms underlying memory, learning, and other phenomena related to sensory experience (487).

A slow-wave potential shift has been recorded extracranially from human subjects who performed in a variety of stimulus-response tasks (540, 543, 541). This observation has been essentially confirmed in a study in which there was an interval between a warning stimulus (flash of light) and a burst of clicks which the subjects terminated by pressing a lever. When these subjects were not required to respond to the clicks, no slow-wave potential appeared. When the subjects were told to turn off the clicks, the slow-wave potential increased in amplitude at a rate that depended on their individual prior experience with the flash-clicks contingency. Omission of the clicks with no warning caused the slow-wave potential to increase in amplitude again. There was a significant negative correlation observed between the size of the slow-wave potential and the reaction time of the subjects (249). While the precise nature of this phenomenon is not understood, it appears to be related to expectancy of stimulus and the intention to act or decision to respond (542).

While the studies involving electrical stimulation and recording with deep electrodes in animals and humans suffer from some of the methodological crudeness of pioneer work, there seems to be little doubt that this will be a potentially fruitful approach to the study of learning and memory in the future. Such studies place limitations on concurrent biochemical investigations, as has been noted previously, but with future refinements in electrophysiological techniques even such combined studies may be feasible. The data from superficial electrode studies should be immediately useful in experiments seeking to define biochemical changes during the attention phase of learning.

Summary

The amnesia that follows the passage of an electric current through the brain has been of therapeutic use, and it is a constant reminder that physical processes underlie memory mechanisms. This induced amnesia has been increasingly employed in the controlled experimental interruption of consolidation of the memory trace in learning animals. The application of less intense electrical stimuli to deep brain areas has been useful in the study of appetitive and affective components which must relate to the broad understanding of learning and memory. Recording of spontaneous electrical events in deep and superficial areas of the brain have begun to indicate that there are changes in the early attention and later phases of learning. While electrical stimulation will be an increasingly important independent means of studying physiological processes in learning, concomitant biochemical studies on the same tissue are difficult because of the relatively crude influence of implanted electrodes, and the changes caused by the passage of strong electrical pulses through the tissue.

3. The influence of drugs on learning and memory

DRUGS WHOSE BIOCHEMICAL MECHANISM OF ACTION IS LARGELY UNKNOWN

When a pharmacological agent influences learning or memory, its substrate, if known, may become directly implicated in the molecular bases of these phenomena. Examples of these agents are given in the next section.

If the substrate is unknown, the effect is of greater interest for future studies on the molecular basis of memory than for those being made at the present. Nonetheless, the effect may be of considerable immediate use in certain cases for the dissection of parts of a behavioral complex, e.g. in separating facilitation of attention from facilitation of storage in the memory process.

Although something is known of the central depressant action of the *barbiturates* (368), and more recent studies have implicated several sites in the energy production sequence, the molecular site and mode of action remain essentially unknown. The barbiturates have been shown to impede learning. Early experiments were questioned because of possible secondary effects of changed food and water ingestion (364), but persistent impairment of performance was observed with repeated injections of *pentobarbital* (370). Pentobarbital in low doses does not affect simple discriminations, such as color of lights, but reduces the rate of response by pigeons, and does interfere with more complex discriminations in even smaller doses which do not interfere with the rate of response (162). Small doses of pentobarbital also retard problem-solving behavior in rats but do not seriously affect the performance of responses already learned. How much of the effect is related to the attention and focusing component of learning rather than to actual encoding and storage is unknown.

Sodium amytal (amobarbital sodium), has received much clinical and some experimental study because of its dramatic effect on the retrieval function of memory. It has been repeatedly suggested that the improvement of recall following amytal administration in cases of human amnesia is more pronounced in cases where "psychological" factors are more operant, in contrast to cases where the amnesia is the product of an "organic" process. The inadequacy of this type of division of causes of amnesia is underlined by studies in which much of the amnesia following electroconvulsive treatment in humans was reversed by a standard interview under sodium amytal (53). One problem in studies of this type in humans is the inability to account adequately for the punishing effects of the electroconvulsive treatment, which was discussed in Section 2, under electrical studies on learning.

To minimize the side effects of drugs on training and to delineate effects on memory storage itself, drugs are frequently administered after training rather than before. Thus the injection of *thiopental* into rats one minute after each trial in a water maze retarded their rate of learning (333). The punishing role of these repeated injections was not ruled out. The use of one-trial learning to avoid the punishing effect has been useful in the demonstration of the effect of *secobarbital* and *ether* as memory storage inhibitors when administered post-training (277, 276, 401). Even imprinting in chicks may be impaired if ether is administered immediately but not 15 minutes after the imprinting training session (233).

Chlorpromazine is another depressant drug the biochemical mechanism of action of which is unknown, and which has been reported to influence learning. The reports, however, are conflicting. Thus chlorpromazine was found to improve discrimination—reversal learning in rats (222), but elsewhere, also in rats, was claimed to interfere with memory consolidation (167).

Amphetamine, a sympathomimetic stimulant of the central nervous system, might be expected to improve memory and learning. Most studies indicate, however, that amphetamine either has no significant influence upon learning, as in T-maze learning (182), or impairs it, as in discrimination learning (7). The dose-dependency of some of these effects has been demonstrated (162). Amphetamine does increase activity (161), and small doses of *meth-amphetamine* (0.5 mg./kg.) facilitate discrimination learning in hamsters (423). Of possible relevance to understanding the manic patient who becomes less efficient as the rate of activity keeps increasing, the last named study showed that learning was impaired at a higher dose (2.0 mg./kg.), which produced a high activity level. The effects of amphetamine and methamphetamine appear to be more on the facilitation of attention than on memory storage.

Strychnine, the ancient medication and poison, has nervous system effects ranging from stimulant to convulsant, but its biochemical mode of action remains unknown. Rat maze learning was early shown to be improved with small doses of strychnine (325). Learning of a simultaneous visual discrimination task by rats has also been shown to be facilitated by strychnine (365). There is, however, also evidence, possibly dose-individual related, that strychnine may be disruptive to learning in some cases (409). There is some suggestion that the strychnine facilitation effect, in addition to strengthening certain response tendencies, includes "retrograde facilitation" of learning, and a possible effect on memory storage (366, 410). Post-trial injections of strychnine and *picrotoxin* enhanced avoidance learning of mice trained in a shuttle-box avoidance task. Post-trial administration of *nitrous oxide*, on the other hand, induced an impairment of performance. Learning was enhanced or impaired only when the treatments with these three agents were given within a few minutes after training, thus favoring the likelihood that these drugs directly influence memory consolidation processes (276). A synthetic, strychnine-like compound, *diphenyldiazadamantanol*, has also been reported to affect learning by enhancing inter-trial memory storage processes in rats (367).

Picrotoxin and *pentylenetetrazole*, two other stimulants, also have a positive effect on learning, with some suggestion that memory storage, as well as attention, are influenced (99, 360).

Caffeine seems to exert a positive effect on memory storage, in addition to its apparent effect through enhanced attention (424, 401). *Nicotine* had been shown to cause some impairment of rats' performance of learned responses (345), but in more recent studies has been shown to facilitate maze learning (443) and avoidance learning (94).

Deep anesthesia induced with *ether* administered within a few seconds after the task has been reported to interfere with memory with resultant amnesia for simple learned tasks (405).

Topical application of *potassium chloride* to the cerebral cortex, inducing "spreading depression," has resulted in retrograde amnesia (434, 406), and differential effects on "naïve" and "trained" hemispheres have been reported (6).

The studies with ether-induced and potassium chloride-induced amnesic effects should be compared with the retrograde amnesia produced with electroshock, since all of these studies provide clues to the time-dependent nature of memory processes (361).

DRUGS WHOSE BIOCHEMICAL ACTION IS BETTER KNOWN

A preliminary caution may be in order in discussing this group of drugs: Although a given drug is known to have even a primary biochemical action at a given biochemical site X, other actions of the drug need to be considered before it can be concluded that the influence on X is indeed what is responsible, in a given experimental situation, for an effect which the drug has on memory and learning. This simple caution is occasionally overlooked, and can be of great importance, as will be seen especially for drugs such as puromycin, which inhibits protein synthesis everywhere in the organism, and which has severe experimental side effects such as diarrhea, pyrexia, and muscular weakness.

The anticholinergic drugs, *atropine* and *scopolamine*, have been shown to interfere with learning and performance (558, 238, 127), but the effect appears to be more on perception or attention than on storage. At least these effects appear not to be extraneural, because related quaternary ammonium compounds such as *methylscopolamine* and *methylatropine* do not affect learning or performance (238).

Physostigmine, an anticholinesterase compound, facilitates learning in small doses before training, but impairs learning in large doses (116, 126).

Diisopropyl fluorophosphate, an anticholinesterase drug, when injected into the hippocampi of rats 30 minutes after escape learning, produced partial amnesia with full recovery 5 days after injection. There was no amnesic effect if the injection was given 3 days after learning. If this drug was given 5 days after learning, however, an amnesic effect was again obtained, and if given 14 days after learning, amnesia was complete even though no normal forgetting occurred within that period (160). It was concluded that older memories are more susceptible to the effects of this drug than are recent memories. This study, when compared to those in which short-term memory is affected more than long-term, may provide important clues to biochemical differences in the condensation, early storage, and maintenance of memory.

The above experiments give indirect evidence that learning depends upon levels of acetylcholine and acetylcholinesterase, but the fact that these substances are so ubiquitous makes the statement almost equivalent in terms of nervous function to one which would assert that adenosine triphosphate is required for learning to occur in biological systems. The subject has been referred to in the attempt to distinguish primary and secondary processes in memory (Chapter II, Section 3) and will again be considered in the discussion of theories of the molecular bases of memory.

Puromycin, the antibiotic, *cycloheximide*, and *acetoxycycloheximide*, interfere with various aspects of the learning and memory process presumably through their inhibition of protein synthesis in the brain, and *actinomycin-D*, through interference with RNA and protein, but these will be discussed in Chapter IV (197, 4).

Compounds such as *1,1,3-tricyano-2-amino-1-propene* (U-9189) which stimulate ribonucleic acid (RNA) and protein synthesis are of interest because of the possibility that they directly increase the level and function of RNA in brain. In studies of avoidance learning and spinal cord "fixation" of postural asymmetry in rats, while U-9189 did not affect these parameters on the first training day, on two subsequent days the performance of the experimental group was better than that of the controls. Injection of 8-*azaguanine*, an inhibitor of RNA synthesis, produced the opposite effect, i.e. it increased "fixation time" (127a).

Magnesium pemoline, a CNS stimulant, when injected in rats has been reported to enhance learning and memory of a conditioned avoidance response which was not positively influenced by metamphetamine and methylphenidate (411). Magnesium pemoline stimulates systems that synthesize brain nucleic acid, presumably through selective stimulation of true RNA polymerase (220). The same substance has been reported to improve memory functions in senile patients (121).

The technique of *chemostimulation through fine cannulae* placed deep in brain structures has produced some interesting results in terms of eliciting and blocking certain behavioral patterns such as "nest-building," care of the young, sexual behavior, and drinking and eating behavior (16, 192, 237, 157, 189, 232, 230, 231, 375). The results of such studies are frequently unpredictable, partly because of difficulties in exact placement, diffusion problems, the presence of multiple functions in small zones, and the use of rather large doses of various neuroactive compounds to get effects. A glance at recent electron microscopic photographs of even 0.1 to 1 microns of only two-dimensional space, in which several processes, perhaps with different chemical specificities, send membranes intertwining in a veritable maze of synaptic formations, makes one wonder how a crystal of visible size, shaken down a cannula, finds its way on solubilization to produce specific reproducible effects. On the other hand, some effects are reproducible, presumably as neural net field effects, and are promising. The technique has been little used as yet for learning and memory studies *per se*, but since it is, in principle, reversible, and since it can be addressed to specific neuroanatomic areas, it might well become a useful method in learning studies in the future.

The administration of *ribonucleic acids, protein,* and other naturally occurring biological substances will be considered separately in Chapter IV in the discussion of "passive transfer" of information.

When using pharmacological agents in any study, methodological problems occur, such as dissociation—i.e. the failure to transfer a response learned in the drugged state to the non-drugged state. In addition, the distinction must be kept in mind between peripheral and central effects of the drug, dose-response effects, problems of tolerance and sensitization, and strain and species differences, as well as various procedural problems (364).

Summary

Many drugs influence learning and memory, directly or indirectly. For insights into the molecular basis of memory processes, pharmacological agents with behaviorally defined modes of action doubtless will be increasingly useful. The ability to interfere with the memory process experimentally by means of chemical agents such as puromycin and actinomycin D has been a major stimulus to the biological study of memory. The side effects produced by these drugs may interfere with the learning process, and their specific modes of action are unknown, so that the precise correlation of the neurochemical with the psychological effects of these substances is still difficult.

IV

Biochemical studies on learning and memory

1. Attempts to measure biochemical changes in the nervous system in learning

SOME REASONS FOR STUDYING TRANSDUCTION IN SENSORY RECEPTORS

The phase of the chemistry of memory that deals with transduction in sensory receptors has been almost completely ignored by workers on memory. There are several good reasons for paying attention to this aspect of molecular events.

First, this is the initial event in the chronology of reception and recording of information by the nervous system, at least as far as experiential information is concerned. That is, while there is obviously a huge amount of information programmed in the nervous system genetically, all experiential information must first pass through the door of sensory transduction before entering into later transactions in the nervous system. There is, therefore, a logical argument for starting at this end of things in examining the molecular basis of memory.

Second, since we are totally ignorant of the chemical basis of all non-genetic encoding mechanisms in the nervous system, we cannot rule out the possibility that the chemical coding for experiential information is largely if not entirely accomplished at the input end in the process of sensory transduction. As previously stated, not all of the coding involved in association, memory storage, retrieval, and discharge functions is likely to be accomplished in the sensory transduction phase. Still, it may be that a large part of it, and perhaps the major part of it, is programmed at this stage. (For example, "Take these afferent fibers" is an instruction which determines a large portion of the future history of a given sensation by means of the neuroanatomic fiber and nucleus pathways subsequently followed. There is a mass of experimental data in perceptual psychology indicating that perception in the individual is influenced by the previous store of information. How much of this influence is exerted at the transduction phase is an open question, but it does appear likely that such influence does occur (336).

Third, from a practical point of view, the evaluation of chemical changes which are observed in other portions of the nervous system farther from the stimulus must be influenced by the chemical changes observed in the sense receptors. Thus, for example, the fact that an increase in the level of ribonucleic acid (RNA) in nerve cells of deep nuclear structures in brain occurrs with particular experiential input should be compared with the fact that certain cells of the retina show marked quantitative increases in RNA under certain conditions of stimulation by light. Do the same chemical changes occur in the first order of nerve cells servicing the actual receptor functions of the rods and cones as those observed in the third, fourth, fifth and nth order of cells in the nervous system chain? Are the RNA changes simply related to non-specific function of the nerve cell, and if not, how are RNA changes related to memory distinct from those of non-specific neuron activity?

Finally, the presence of discrete genetic disorders in sensation, as in color blindness and specific anosmias, provides experimental opportunities to examine some important propositions about genetic potential in nervous system function as they relate to what a given nervous system can learn experientially.

While the mechanism of transduction in sensory receptors is mostly unknown, some examples of recent progress in the field will be discussed below.

MECHANORECEPTORS

A mechanoreceptor cell is so arranged that the application of a suitable mechanical stimulus produces a nerve impulse (271). The sequence of processes involves a mechanical transformation of the stimulus, its conversion to an electrical signal, and the production of a nerve impulse. While this states the outline of the problem in electrical terms, and there is some indication that the usual confluence of ionic events and electrical events is present, nothing is known of the detailed chemistry of transduction.

The Pacinian corpuscle has been widely studied because it is a relatively circumscribed mechanoreceptor. It contains a hair which protrudes into the outside world to receive the stimuli, and the base of the hair is firmly imbedded in the corpuscular structure that carries out the transduction. It has been shown that the membranes of the Pacinian corpuscle respond to stretch stimuli with an increase of permeability to certain ions, a decrease in resistance, depolarization, and the setting up of an electrical current in the apposing nerve membranes. Which, if any, of these are the initial events, if in fact the events can be dissected in this way, is yet to be determined. Other mechanoreceptor organs systems studied include the apparatus of *Sepia* and several octopi (226). In these instances electron microscopic studies have indicated the intermingling in a plexus of dendritic branches of the encapsulated nerve cells, with the axons coming from the primary receptor organs. Many of the characteristics of the fine structure of the synapse are observed, including the close apposition of membranes and the presence of vesicles and of mitochondria. There is a considerable heterogeneity of structure in these invertebrate neurons, and, again, nothing is known of their chemistry.

HEARING

Because of the mechanical nature of the receptor structures for hearing, there is a close affinity in the fine structure subserving transduction to that observed in mechanoreceptors. That is, the cilia of the vestibular sensory cells of the labyrinth become the first focus of the study of the transduction process of hearing. While the cellular pattern is somewhat more developed in mammals and birds, two types of hair cells are observed, bottle-shaped cells and cylindrical cells. In the frog and fish labyrinth, only one type of sensory cell similar to the "Type II" cells in birds and mammals is observed (200). The sensory hairs of the organ of Corti represent the most highly specialized mechanoreceptor found in the inner ear. Two types of sensory cells are supported in a very regular delicate framework of supporting cells. Electron microscopic studies show contact between membranes surrounding sensory hair bundles with the membranes of nerve fibers innervating these sensory cells. Synapses occur between the hair cells and the nerve endings, so that the transition from mechanical to nerve cells is direct, membrane to membrane, with only the synaptic cleft between them. The presence of mitochondria and many vesicular structures in the synaptic zones give a hint that there are important chemical events occurring at the interphase of these two membranes, but little is known as yet of their nature (see Fig. 2).

Thus the transformation of mechanical energy of hair displacement into nerve impulses appears to have both electrophysiological and biochemical components, neither of which is as yet known. The molecular organization which is responsible for the transduction phenomena in the organ of Corti has been suggested to be in the centriole (180), or in the cuticle and the sensory hairs (554). The general notion that a conformational change in the receptor protein (467) might be the critical step in transduction has been discussed as a potential model for transduction phenomena in acoustic transmission (388).

OLFACTORY RECEPTORS

The differential sensitivity to taste and odor stimuli have been widely studied, but few workable molecular theories have been evolved. Some recent imaginative work on the stereochemical theory of odor has led to the suggestion that the psychophysical basis of odor is primarily the molecular size and shape of the stimulus substance (15). This approach suggests that the molecular size and shape outlines of stimulus molecules might fit stereochemically with a particular receptor of matching mirror-image configuration in the sensory receptor. The analogy of this mechanism to the lock and key hypotheses of immunology in terms of the molecular re-

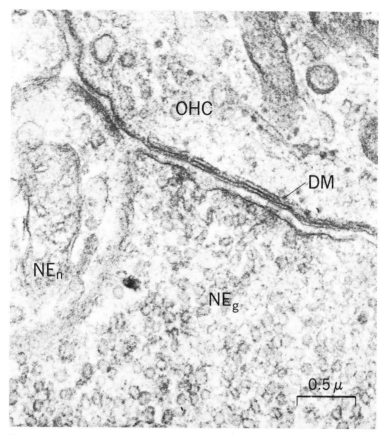

Figure 2. Synaptic area between an outer hair cell (OHC) and one non-granulated efferent (NE$_n$) and one granulated efferent (NE$_g$) nerve ending. DM = double membrane on the hair cell side of the synaptic membrane in the central area between the nerve and the hair cell in the process of hearing (554).

quirements for the fit of an antigen and an antibody in order that an antigen and antibody reaction occur, and to the same concept in enzymology, place this transduction formulation into a relevant position to the formulation of a possible molecular basis of memory which will be made in Chapter VII.

ELECTRICAL AND CHEMICAL RECEPTORS

There are a number of systems in which the receptor is sensitive to chemical or electrical stimuli. To the extent that the blood is a portion of the internal milieu in which mammalian cells live, the carotid body chemoreceptors, which have a regulatory role in respiratory and cardiovascular function, are of interest. Recent studies on the carotid body chemoreceptors, which are activated by low pO_2 and/or high pCO_2 of the surrounding blood medium, have suggested that a chemical substance is released from the carotid body during such stimulation, and that this chemical is capable of stimulating sensory nerve endings. The nature of the chemical is unknown (183). In the Elasmobranch fishes there are receptor mechanisms, devoid of sensory hairs and innervated by myelinated nerve fibers, which respond to thermomechanical, electrical, and salinity stimuli, but nothing is known of the transduction properties of these receptors as yet (386). Electric organs are not uncommon in fishes and have been the subject of considerable study, especially with reference to the acetylcholine hypothesis of neural transmission (387). Some of these organs produce sizable voltages with obvious defensive functions. Some progress has been made in the isolation of proteins and polysaccharides in the membranes of the electric organ which complex with quaternary ammonium salts, but a specific receptor-protein for acetylcholine has not been recognized uniformly (387). The function of weak electric organs that produce voltages too small to have any offensive or defensive value, such as those that occur in Mormyrids, may have certain functions in signalling to the outside world. The electroreceptors for these signals have been studied (43). The studies to date have defined some of the electrophysiological parameters in these receptors, but little is known of the transduction phenomena for them.

PHOTORECEPTORS

"Is not Vision performed chiefly by the Vibrations of this Medium, excited in the bottom of the Eye by the Rays of light, and propagated through the solid, pellucid and uniform Capillamenta of the optic Nerves into the place of Sensation?" (390a).

Two visual pigments, rhodopsin in the rods, and iodopsin in the cones, have been studied extensively in terms of photoreception. Rhodopsin has been shown to bleach under the influence of light through several intermediary compounds as follows: rhodopsin to pre-lumirhodopsin, to lumirhodopsin, to metarhodopsin I, to metarhodopsin II, and finally to all-trans retinal plus opsin. The all-trans retinal plus opsin is converted to 11-cis retinal plus opsin, yielding again the original product rhodopsin. This last reaction of regeneration occurs in the dark (351). The chromophore rhodopsin appears to be attached to the protein opsin by means of a Schiff base linkage (retinyl-opsin), and it is reduced with sodium borohydride to the much more stable N-retinyl-opsin ($C=N$ to $C-N$). This more stable form resists alkaline hydrolysis of the protein (97). Isolation of the retinyl amino acid derivative of alkaline hydrolysis of rhodopsin which had been reduced to a sodium borohydride gave evidence that the site of attachment may be lysine (96). By the difference spectrum of rhodopsin upon bleaching, and by optical rotatory dispersion evidence on rhodopsin, there was preliminary evidence that the α-helix structure of rhodopsin undergoes some alteration on bleaching (96). Previous less direct evidence showed that opsin is considerably more labile than rhodopsin (422); and that bleaching exposes new reactive groups, specifically sulfhydryl groups (538) and one proton-binding group with pK 6.6 (422). These changes apparently occur in consecutive stages in opsin, and all of them tend in the direction of a progressive loss of organization and a loosening of the protein fabric. A similar series of transformations have been demonstrated for iodopsin, resulting in all-trans retinal and opsin which are converted in the dark to 11-cis retinal and opsin and thence to the original iodopsin.

All reactions up to and including the formation of metarhodopsin II have been considered as possible sources of the transduction phenomena resulting in nervous transmission. The α-wave is the usual first impulse measured in monkey retina, but a still earlier potential, the early receptor potential (ERP), with latency of 25

microseconds or less, has been described (104, 103, 141). It has
been shown that the action spectrum of the ERP follows closely
the absorption spectrum of rhodopsin. It is not yet clear whether
the ERP lies on the main line of excitatory events, but if it does,
then the formation of metarhodopsin II is beyond the transduction
phenomenon (256). The exposure of charged groups, and the more
subtle changes in the electrical environment of the protein implicit
in conformational rearrangement, have been considered for the
molecular events underlying transduction in vision.

Concurrent developments in unrelated studies on the conformational changes in proteins with enzyme activity (346, 380) are of
interest. This type of effect, known as an allosteric transformation,
has also been invoked as being responsible for the Bohr effect in
hemoglobin, whereby hemoglobin becomes a stronger acid upon
combination with oxygen (564). The allosteric transition would
not necessarily involve a conformational alteration, but may simply
be restricted to redistribution of charges within the molecule. In
the case of vision, the electrical signal might be triggered by any
one of the chemical events referred to above.

In addition, it has been pointed out that considerable amplification is required for the conversion of the energy produced by one
photon of light to the electrical energy that results. The nature
of the amplification process is unknown, but possible mechanisms
have been discussed (537).

The molecular basis for the specificity which underlies such phenomena as color vision has been postulated to depend on three
groups of cones with various summing excitatory or inhibitory
effects. The human red and green sensitive pigments are both composed of the same chromophore, 11-cis retinaldehyde attached to
two different opsins. It is thought probable that the blue sensitive
pigment is also composed of 11-cis retinaldehyde, joined to a third
opsin (536).

The chemical detail that has been obtained in examination of
the photoreceptor transduction process exceeds that obtained for
any of the other sensory receptors, and is stimulating as a prototype
for the study of the chemical nature of initial-message-coding in the
nervous system.

Summary

Sensory transduction is the process by which the information from the environment, received by specialized peripheral sensory receptors appropriate to pressure, light, odor, etc., is converted to the (uniform?) language of the nerve cell for transmission, abstraction, storage, and other operations of the central nervous system. Since transduction represents the first coding of experiential information, it may be that it is the definitive coding which persists, perhaps with further modification, throughout the nervous system. Some biochemical changes thought to be related to learning, observed in deep brain nuclei, may be demonstrated in sensory organs as a result of receptor function only. Most of what is known about the chemistry of transduction derives from studies of vision, but in the conversion of the information contained in light to the message carried by the optic nerves, the definitive chemical processes responsible are still unknown.

Studies on nucleic acids in the nervous system in learning

One of the major stimuli to studies on the molecular basis of memory has been the tremendous advance made in the field of molecular genetics in recent years. The fact that the deoxyribonucleic acids (DNA) have been shown to be carriers of genetic information has given encouragement to the possibility that similar biochemical mechanisms underlie the handling of experiential information. There is no doubt that the genetic store of information has a great influence upon the development of the individual, and thereby upon all receptor and processing potentialities of the individual thereafter. This gives to the nucleic acids a pre-eminent role in the biochemistry of experiential memory right from the outset and without further evidence required. Also the ribonucleic acid

(RNA) mediation of protein synthesis appears to be a general phenomenon necessary at some level. But the theory that the nucleic
acids are totally sufficient for all coding functions, both genetic and
experiential, can be questioned, and will be discussed in Chapter
V. The data so far available on the actual chemical state of the
nucleic acids in the nervous system in learning situations now will
be reviewed briefly.

In contrast to the considerable volume of literature on the theoretical relationship of nucleic acids to learning, on the effect of
drugs that influence nucleic acid metabolism, and on the administration of nucleic acids to recipient organisms, there has been very
little actual quantitative and qualitative analysis of the state of the
nucleic acids themselves in the nervous system during learning.

a. Within the retina, the segment containing the photoreceptors
—the rods and cones—is followed by an external limiting membrane, then by an outer nuclear layer of cells, then by an external
synaptic layer, then by an inner nuclear layer of cells, then by an
inner synaptic layer, and finally by a group of ganglion cells. Em-
bryologically, the retina is an outgrowth of the nervous system, and
these various cells are generally regarded as actual or modified nervous system cells. Chemical studies on the ganglion cells of the
retina, must be recognized, however, as being several synaptic layers
away from the initial transduction processes which occur in the
photoreceptors. It may be, and indeed it seems likely, that in this
situation some of the chemical transactions which occur in the
outer and inner nuclear areas occur in the ganglion cells themselves. The so-called bipolar cells of the inner and outer zones have
been studied fairly intensively in terms of electrophysiological properties. Only recently, however, have attempts been made to study
such components as the ribonucleic acid content of these cell
groups. The ganglion cells of the frog showed changes in RNA
level when compared under three different conditions: in darkness,
in continuous light, and in flickering light. The RNA level was
found to rise only in flickering light (519). The RNA content of
the outer nuclear zone of the frog retina was shown to increase
under light flickering at a rate of 4 per second, although the RNA
level in the nuclei of the rods and cones had also been shown to

increase under conditions of 1 per second flickering light, and to increase further in 5 per second flickering light (519, 119).

These RNA changes, which occur at every cell level beginning with the photoreceptors, and which are experimentally detectable under the influence of flickering light, have been studied only by histochemical techniques.

b. It is entirely possible that much more subtle biochemical changes, both in quantity of RNA and, perhaps, in the base composition, would be observed if more micro techniques were applied. Thus, for example, recent studies have demonstrated a change in retinal RNA base ratios on photic stimulation (512). These findings are of marked importance for the evaluation of changes in RNA concentration at other deeper sites in the nervous system. Cervical sympathetic ganglia *in vitro* have also demonstrated rapid turnover of RNA (324). However, in isolated lobster stretch receptor neurons which had been discharging for many hours no significant changes in the quantity of RNA or in the base ratios were observed; and when RNA synthesis was inhibited, an adenine-rich RNA fraction disappeared without interfering with impulse activity or changing the membrane potential (173).

c. Analysis of the RNA of dissected cell bodies in the nervous system has shown RNA content to vary with the type of cell and in different loci between 20 and 2000 $\mu\mu$g. per nerve cell (263). Each nerve cell in the Deiters' nucleus of rabbit brain was shown to contain on the average 1500 $\mu\mu$g. of RNA. These figures did not differentiate between nuclear RNA and cytoplasmic RNA. Some of the smaller nerve cells had as little as 500 $\mu\mu$g. of RNA. Most of the RNA was ribosomal. The content of RNA in glia was much less, in the order of 125 $\mu\mu$g. Mauthner nerve cells in goldfish contain on the average 10,000 $\mu\mu$g. of RNA, with only 2000 $\mu\mu$g. in the cell body and 8000 μg. in the axon.

Postmortem measurements of the RNA content of anterior horn cells of human spinal cord in subjects that were from three to ninety years of age showed a steady increase from age three to about age fifty, going from approximately 400 $\mu\mu$g. per nerve cell to approximately 625 $\mu\mu$g. per nerve cell at its peak. Approximately the same slope of decline thereafter was observed, from fifty to ninety years of age, reaching the original minimum of approximately 400 $\mu\mu$g. again around age ninety. Motor activity has been shown to increase the amount of RNA in anterior horn cells of the barracuda. The curve for man, reaching its peak as it does around fifty years of age, certainly does not follow either the expected curve for physical activity or what is known of learning ability. The steady increase to around age fifty might possibly represent the accumulation of information on the basis of total experience, and the sharp decline after fifty might represent the entry of a second factor of degeneration superimposed upon the first experiential factor. However, in these studies it was concluded that, rather than correlating the total content of RNA to learning, the content might be an indicator of increased neural function, and that, at least as a single parameter, the total content of RNA cannot be used to correlate with learning itself. Another study has demonstrated that there exists a direct proportionality between the surface area of the spinal ganglion cell and the RNA content (174).

In further single cell studies, the RNA in the nucleus and the RNA in the "whole" cells were measured separately in learning experiments in rabbits, as were the molar proportions of the nucleic acid bases, adenine, guanine, cytosine, and uracil (176). Although it was claimed that no signs of stress were involved, these experiments involved quite marked rotary stimulation of the lateral vestibular nucleus. It was found that the nuclear RNA had a somewhat higher adenine concentration, but a little less guanine, and more cytosine, than the cytoplasmic RNA. In addition it was found that the RNA content of each nucleus was, on the average, 30 $\mu\mu$g., and of the whole cell, 680 $\mu\mu$g. In control stress experiments a 20 per cent increase of RNA per neuron was observed, but no significant change in base ratio occurred. On vestibular stimulation, there was no effect on the base ratios, although there was a significant increase in total RNA per cell. Food-seeking experiments were performed in rats, in which the rats had to learn to balance on a wire for training periods of 45 minutes per day. Analysis of cells of the vestibular nucleus in the learning rat showed a significant increase in the amount of RNA per Deiters' nerve cell (control 683 $\mu\mu$g.; learning 751 $\mu\mu$g.). It should be stated that the training experiments lasted four to five days, however, and those animals that failed to learn were not studied biochemically. Microelectrophoretic studies were performed on nuclear RNA. Each nucleus contained 30 $\mu\mu$g. of RNA. There was an increase of adenine, from 21.4 ($\pm$0.44) to 24.1 ($\pm$0.39) (molar proportions in per cent of the sum), and a decrease in uracil value from 20.5 ($\pm$1.01) to 18.2 ($\pm$.01), giving what was felt to be a significant increase in the ratio of adenine to uracil from 1.06 to 1.35. There was no change in the cytoplasmic RNA composition.

The composition of the RNA in glia surrounding the nerve cells was studied in control rats and in rats during the above learning situation which involved balance and stimulation of the vestibular nucleus. In learning rats the glial RNA changes were found to be similar to, but not identical with, the nuclear RNA changes in the neurons (264, 265). The adenine value was greatly increased but the uracil value remained unchanged, giving what was thought to be a significant rise in the ratio from 1.32 to 1.52, but no change in base ratios in glial RNA control experiments identical to those performed with the nerve cell analysis. The injection of actinomycin-D intracisternally into the animals, followed by the injection of tranylcypromine, inhibited the production of RNA fractions responsible for these changed base ratios. These investigators felt that it was not possible to differentiate between learning and performance on a chemical level (262).

Others have criticized the conclusions derived from these experiments from several points of view. First, the presence of adequate control situations from an experimental psychology standpoint has been doubted (334). Attempts to answer part of this criticism were made in further studies in which there were attempts to separate learning and function. Thus, right-handed rats were induced to use the left paw in retrieving food from a narrow glass tube, and cells were removed from the two sides of the cerebral cortex and compared (226, 267). The "learning side" of the cortex demonstrated a significant increase in the amount of RNA per cell. More difficult to negate, however, have been the criticisms having to do with the histological and chemical methods used in these studies. It has been questioned how individual cells can be said to have comparable size, weight and function, when they have been dissected from different pieces of brain (313, 316). It has been stated that in no case is it known what the previous functional state is of a given nerve cell which has been dissected, so that the over-all change in physiological activity of individual cells is not known. The fact that a stimulus usually activates the firing of some cells and suppresses the firing of others, makes for considerable uncertainty in the interpretation of the results of chemical changes in individual cells.

Also, there has been a question of whether the relationship can be clearly drawn between any particular cell and the general function under study. For example, the function of the Deiters' nucleus during rotation has been questioned, especially since the giant cells do not appear to have direct connections with the vestibular nerve. Another component of this criticism is that there is marked variability of local circulatory changes accompanying activity in brain.

If these criticisms are valid for nerve cells, they become even more valid in relation to glial tissue. It has been pointed out that when glia are dissected only parts of their cell bodies and processes are removed, and one ends up with "clumps of glia" (316). The examination of electron microscopic pictures of mammalian glia: nerve cell interrelations has shown a very impressive three-dimensional intertwining of these processes—so much so that it would be virtually impossible to dissect out an intact glial cell in mammalian brain. For this reason, it has been stated that the contamination of glia by only some 5 per cent of nerve processes is an overly optimistic estimate, and that the extent of mixing of neuronal and glial cell fragments is in effect unknown in the samples that have been measured.

Criticisms have also been offered of the basic assumption that learning and memory are functions of individual neurons and glia within a particular area of the brain, but as will be seen in Chapter V, there does not appear to be sufficient conceptual certainty to exclude any molecular approach on this basis alone.

d. It has been shown that brain cells, on the average, do not contain more DNA than somatic cells (459). If it is assumed that appreciably more DNA is required for the specialized function of information handling in the brain, these findings would not support such an assumption. A simple total average amount may not be the best test of this assumption, however, as may be surmised from the discussion in Chapter V.

e. The concentration of RNA in whole brain homogenates of chickens has been studied, both in the newly hatched chicks and at later periods that are associated with imprinting behavior. The newly hatched chicks were given the opportunity to follow a mother surrogate object when they were 16 hours of age and again 24 hours later, when they were 40 hours of age. There was a significant negative correlation between RNA and acetylcholinesterase and the distance the chicks followed the mother surrogate object. Chicks imprinted at either 16 or 40 hours of age as well as unimprinted controls showed no significant correlation with the two substances, nor was there a significant difference in absolute levels of RNA or acetylcholinesterase in any of the groups. In a test varying the interval between the time of first imprinting and testing it was found that only in that group with an inter-trial interval of 24 hours was there significant correlation between the imprinting score and the two biochemical substances (36).

f. The base composition of DNA in brain cortex, liver, and kidneys of dogs, and in brain cortex, whole cerebral hemispheres less the cortex, brain stem, cerebellum, liver, and kidneys of rats, showed no significant differences. It was concluded from the preliminary studies that the primary structure of DNA is not affected by experiential events, or that the technique used was not sufficiently sensitive to detect any changes that occurred (210). RNA/DNA ratio changes in cortex of learning rats was shown to be due to the effects of motor activity (211). Changes in the amount and in base ratios of nuclear RNA have been reported in the brains of catfish responding to different olfactory stimuli (430a).

g. In rats that were learning to navigate a swimming maze, the intracisternal injection of 8-azaguanine resulted in an impairment of memory function. The drug was presumed to have interfered with the synthesis of RNA, but the authors considered and did not reject the possibility that interference with some vital process other than RNA synthesis was the basis of the memory impairment (165). Subsequent attempts to interfere with both RNA synthesis

and with learning used actinomycin-D in mice which were taught
in a simple passive avoidance conditioning situation. In this study,
actinomycin-D produced 83 per cent inhibition of brain RNA
synthesis in mice, yet showed no interference with the ability of
these animals to learn and remember as well as the controls (33).
It should be noted that in this study the administration of actinomycin-D, in the doses used, produces diarrhea, illness, and death
within 24 to 48 hours. The authors state that, despite this, the
animals were able to learn, even though they were at all times
somewhat less active than normal. An experiment run with this
kind of debilitated animal nonetheless leaves one uneasy about
whether the processes occurring in that animal may be taken to
resemble normal learning. To this problem may be added the fact
that only 83 per cent inhibition of RNA synthesis was produced,
and that that portion of RNA synthesis left intact might well be
sufficient for the alleged functions with regard to learning. As a
partial resolution to these problems, an attempt was made to obtain a more complex set of tasks in learning, and a greater degree
of inhibition of RNA synthesis. Inhibition of 94 to 96 per cent was
achieved by multiple intracerebral injections of actinomycin-D.
Even under these conditions, the animals injected with actinomycin-D learned a one-choice Y-maze and a two-choice T-maze as
well as the controls, and retention by the two groups was indis-
tinguishable up to 4 hours later. Injections of the animals bitem-
porally with actinomycin-D, in other experiments, 1 day after acquisition, resulted in no interference with retention of the learned
skills (137). This is of interest when compared with the studies
done with temporal injections of puromycin, an inhibitor of protein synthesis, which, when given 1 day after acquisition markedly
impaired subsequent memory of the solution of a Y-maze (198).
Because of the debilitation and illness of the animals it was not
possible to draw conclusions about longer-term memory storage—
i.e., memory function more than 4 hours after learning. Thus, while
the possibility that RNA is needed for long-term maintenance of
memory was not taken by the authors to have received support
from these experiments, the possibility was still not excluded by
these studies that a small fraction of RNA, not inhibited, was

operating in memory processes in these experiments. In the nervous system, which is noted for its redundancy, 2 or 3 per cent may be enough for a given learning task. The central question of redundancy will be further noted in Chapter VII.

h. Ribonuclease (RNAse), injected intraventricularly in cats, has been reported to interfere with memory (281). RNAse injected into the surface of the cerebral hemisphere, or intraperitoneally, in mice, was reported not to alter the nature of unconditioned reflexes, but did cause the disappearance of conditioned reflexes (315). Further tests for the specificity of RNAse using serum albumin (8 to 16 μg.), trypsin (8 μg.), and deoxyribonuclease (DNAse) 8 to 24 μg.) as controls, all injected into animals after the formation and fixation of conditioned reflexes, showed no influence in any of the controls, but disappearance of the conditioned reflex in "100 per cent of the tests." When RNAse was injected before the conditioned reflex was formed, it retarded or totally prevented the development of the conditioned reflex. The injection of DNAse prior to the conditioned reflex formation lengthened the formation time several-fold, but the prior injection of trypsin before had no effect (314). Ribonuclease has also been reported to interfere temporarily with conditioned performance in pigeons (128), and with the development of conditioned responses in planaria (129). In evaluating the results with hydrolytic enzymes which are as destructive as are the nucleases, some reservation needs to be made for the possibility that alteration of structures, or secondary reactions, may be more directly related to the conditioning observations than are changes in the nucleic acids *per se*. Increased labeling of RNA during a training experience in mice has been localized to the diencephalon or closely related structures, but not to cortex or cerebellum (570), and not specifically related to learning.

Summary

Studies in which the nucleic acids, both DNA and RNA, are actually measured in the nervous system, are seen to be few in num-

ber, and they are often insufficient for or conflicting in their conclusions. The basic necessity for, and inherent difficulty in, defining
both learning and biochemical changes in as natural a system as
possible—without the influence of abnormally strong stimuli, stress,
or pharmacological agents, let alone those which produce sickness
and death within hours in the subject studied—taken together with
the fact that there is so little evidence as yet on the actual total
concentration of DNA and RNA, as well as on their concentrations
in their various subcellular instructional and subcellular transfer
situations, make it impossible to draw any firm positive conclusions at this time about the function of the nucleic acids in the
nervous system in learning and memory. Nor have any negative
conclusions been established as yet.

The evidence, however, with regard to the involvement of the
nucleic acids in the general function of nerve cells in several locations, taken together with the evidence of the effects of the nucleases on conditioned reflexes, and what is known about the nature
of nucleic acid influence on protein and carbohydrate synthesis in
general, make it imperative that more studies of the type reviewed
be undertaken, with greater refinements in both their biochemical
and experimental psychology aspects. The fact that the nucleic
acids are involved in the genetic programming of the nervous system for all of its future experiential involvements in itself reserves
an important place for further studies on the nucleic acids of the
nervous system to determine the precise mode and extent of this
influence on the experiential coding of memory.

Studies on acetylcholine and acetylcholinesterase in the nervous system in learning

a. Initial studies on the concentration of acetylcholine and acetylcholinesterase in brain in relation to learning suggested that these
substances might have a primary relationship to memory, but subsequent studies failed to substantiate the early findings (455, 454).
Further work on this subject suggested, however, that concentra-

tions of acetylcholinesterase in brain might be related to genetic lines of the rats studied. Maze-bright and maze-dull genetic strains of rats have been known for some time (444, 511). In addition, it was established that four of these genetic lines differ in the concentration of brain acetylcholine itself (40). The activity of acetylcholinesterase as a function of age and brain area was compared in two genetic lines, one developed to be maze-bright, the other maze-dull. The maze-bright line was shown to have higher acetylcholinesterase activity than the maze-dull line in both cortical and subcortical brain samples (42). Acetylcholine concentration was determined in six of the genetic lines referred to above, but significant differences were found only within two of the three pairs of strains (37). In comparing the differences in acetylcholinesterase activity between paired lines, no one cortical region of brain consistently showed the greatest difference across all paired lines. In pairs of lines of rats bred specifically for high or low cortical acetylcholinesterase activity, the largest relative differences were found in the cortex, but some subcortical areas also showed highly significant differences (39).

Littermates given enriched versus restricted experience from birth showed significant differences in the weight of the cerebral cortex, those with enriched environments being heavier and thicker (41). The increased weight did not reflect the over-all growth of the brain, nor did it reflect an increase in body weight as a whole. It did not occur equally throughout the cortex, but had a pronounced regional distribution, with the greatest differences occurring in the visual area and the least difference occurring in the somesthetic region of the cortex.

The total activity of acetylcholinesterase was also greater in those animals raised in the enriched environment, with the greatest changes again occurring in the visual region of the cortex (3.6 per cent) and the least in the somesthetic region. When enzymatic activity was measured per unit of tissue weight in the cerebral cortex, the enriched experience rats had lower values than the restricted animals, but higher values in the remainder of the brain. Since only 95 per cent of the activity measured in rat brain was ascribed with certainty to the brain as distinct from blood enzyme, it was assumed that at least 90 per cent of this total change was due to brain acetylcholinesterase. It was observed that the mean diameter of the capillaries is greater in the cortices of the enriched animals but it was calculated that even if the entire increase in cortical weight were to be attributed to increased blood volume, then the enzymes of the blood could not account for the observed change.

From control experiments it was concluded that the effects observed were not the result of handling or differences in locomotion. It was also claimed that the differences were not due to isolation stress, largely on the basis of the fact that the weight of the adrenals in some of the rats from the isolation experiments were not enlarged, and also that the housing of rats—three to a cage—did not bring the rats in this so-called "social control" into the same position as those which had been stimulated, except with regard to the weight of the subcortex. It was also concluded that these results were not related to age, since the differences could be observed in the adult rat as well as in the young when the same conditions were imposed. It was therefore concluded that the cerebral effects observed are residuals of experience itself, rather than being consequences of accelerated early development. The concurrent measurement of cholinesterase activity, as opposed to acetylcholinesterase activity, showed that the major differences were to be found between the isolated and "colony" rats, rather than between stimulated and "colony" groups. Hexokinase activity per unit of weight did not alter with differential experience in either cortex or subcortex, nor did the concentration of serotonin show differences between the two experimental groups. The proteins were shown to vary with the tissue weight, and tissue weight, as was previously observed, changed more than did the acetylcholinesterase with differential experience.

Differences were observed among brain acetylcholinesterase values of littermate rats between the stimulated and the nonstimulated colony groups. It was also observed that some genetic lines were more readily modified than others.

Further controls run in these studies included those for blindness and light deprivation. There was a 5 per cent loss in the weight of the visual cortex and an 8 per cent loss in the superior colliculi in the blinded animals compared with their sighted littermates kept in the same enriched condition. Surprisingly, however, total acetylcholinesterase activity increased by 4 per cent in the visual cortex of the blinded rats, although it decreased by 21 per cent in the superior colliculi. Deprivation of light in sighted animals produced anatomical and chemical effects similar in direction, but generally smaller in magnitude, to those following total blinding. In both blinded and light-deprived animals there was also an increase in weight and in total acetylcholinesterase activity in the somesthetic area of the cortex, suggesting that other areas of the cortex than that specifically subserving the function of vision may respond to environmental change.

It was noted as well that the differences which had been produced by selective breeding are several times greater than the authors could produce by differential experience.

These authors concluded that the coefficients of variance for acetylcholinesterase activity which they had observed are small, almost as small as those for the weight of the whole brain. They stated further that only by genetic selection or drastic treatments such as thyroidectomy or prolonged undernourishment can these parameters of brain weight and acetylcholinesterase activity be altered substantially. They emphasized that these changes in brain consequent to enriched experience were not proven to have any relationship to the storage of memory, but simply indicate that the brain is responsive to environmental pressure, a fact demanded by physiological theories of learning and memory (37). As noted in the next chapter, a general responsivity of brain in terms of growth through increased cell numbers or mass is not required by all physiological theories of learning and memory.

More recent work by these investigators has included more extensive depth measures, differential cell counts, and cell size measurements on the cortex of rats subjected to enriched environment. These studies confirmed the previously observed depth increase and found it to be greater in the more medial aspect of the visual cortex than in the lateral aspect. The glia/neuron ratio was found to be greater in the enriched brain than in the impoverished brain (16 per cent over-all), with oligodendrocytes and cells with mixed characteristics of both astrocytes and oligodendrocytes accounting for the increase in glial cells. No significant differences were found between the size of the perikarya or the size of the nuclei in the enriched versus impoverished animals in cortical cell layers II and IV (163).

b. An increase in glial cells subsequent to behavior or manipulation had previously been reported (11). The increase in glia/neuron ratio is in agreement with the relatively greater increase in cholinesterase, since glia apparently contain chiefly cholinesterase, and neurons chiefly acetylcholinesterase (453).

c. In another study of rats raised in enriched versus restricted environments, the difference in brain weight reported above was confirmed, but whole brain acetylcholinesterase activities of the rats were found not to differ. In addition, brain norepinephrine levels of animals in the isolated group were found to be significantly elevated, a finding which may have relevance to the question of stress as a crucial function in isolation studies. Tyrosine transaminase and tryptophane transaminase were also found to be significantly higher in the isolated animals, which again suggested the possibility of a chronic stress effect, as did the finding of increase in weights of the adrenals in the isolated animals (217). These findings on the adrenals are of particular importance in the attempt to distinguish non-specific effects due to arousal. The interchangeable use of the terms "arousal" and "stress" (9) is probably not indicated. From the discussion of electrical means of studying memory and learning, arousal and attention mechanisms are clearly early facets of learning. There is probably an appreciable difference between arousal effects and stress effects in learning, and, although their physiological correlates may well overlap, some effort should be made to distinguish between them.

d. The use of the drug diisopropyl fluorophosphate, injected into the hippocampus to produce amnesic effects, is of further interest in terms of the relevance of acetylcholine to memory function (160). These studies were not accompanied by measurements of acetylcholine or acetylcholinesterase, however. They are also considered in Chapter III (p. 36).

Summary

There is some reservation about the attempt to correlate with specific memory functions substances which have as general a distribution as the acetylcholine system. There is no doubt that these substances are somehow involved in the nature of nerve transmission, but it would be useful to distinguish this from more specific functions dealing with memory storage and retrieval. Acetylcholinesterase activity has not as yet been shown to be intimately related in a specific manner to learning. Brain cortical thickness and an increase in the number of glial cells occur in rats environmentally enriched. There is conflicting evidence that, under these conditions, acetylcholinesterase activity increases. Since brain norepinephrine and tyrosine and tryptophane transaminase activity have been shown to increase in isolated environments, the possibility of a chronic stress effect needs to be considered.

Studies on proteins of the nervous system in learning

As in the case of the brain nucleic acids, biochemical studies of proteins in the nervous system itself during learning situations have been quite infrequent. There have been an increasing number of studies attempting to define constituent brain proteins physicochemically, to assign them to histological sites, and even, in one or two studies, to investigate their state during the conduction of electrical impulses. But the bulk of the evidence to date deals with observations made with inhibitors of brain protein synthesis in learning situations, not with protein concentration itself.

a. Until recent years less than 20 per cent of the total proteins of brain had been solubilized and few of these had been characterized. Recent studies have permitted the more quantitative extraction of brain proteins, with approximately one-half of the total being solubilized in normal neutral buffers, and the remaining one-half requiring more vigorous methods of extraction, and the use of detergents such as Triton (71, 88, 420). The learning studies which have followed from these studies are discussed in Chapter VI.

An acidic protein (probably containing three to five constituent proteins (221a), called the S-100 fraction, has been described to be unique to brain (381, 382).

There is evidence that a specific brain protein fraction, named 10B, has a predominantly glial localization (see Chapter VI), and a mixed glial and neuronal nucleus location for S-100 protein has been reported (268). A number of brain proteins have been shown to have distinct properties as antigens (88, 289, 172, 425-429).

A group of proteins with high lipid content and soluble in organic solvents, termed proteolipids, have been described (204). The nerve growth factor is a substance capable of promoting growth of nerve processes and controlling differentiation of embryonic dorsal root ganglion cells and sympathetic ganglion cells (335).

A large group of phosphoproteins have been studied in terms of the possibility that they are involved in ion transport and excitability in nervous tissue (242). There is a sizable literature on the turnover of proteins in brain (321, 458). The proteins of squid axon have also been studied in relation to the action potential (465, 156, 257). The translocation of proteins and other substances in axoplasm, termed axoplasmic streaming, has been well demonstrated but is still poorly understood (341). Some structural changes in peripheral nerve during stimulation, suggestive of protein changes, have been reported (516).

Studies have been performed on RNA, DNA, and protein concentrations in different areas of the nervous system during development (212). In the rat nervous system, the protein:RNA ratio suggested that a given amount of RNA produces more protein at 50 days than at any earlier period. The kidney protein developmental pattern was similar to that in brain tissue, with the exceptions that in kidney, peaks of cellular activity occurred at both 50 and 75 days; kidney was richer in RNA, DNA, and protein per gram than most brain tissues; kidney had lower RNA:DNA ratios and lower protein:DNA ratios than all brain tissues except for cerebellum; and kidney had the lower protein:RNA ratio.

While none of the above studies have related proteins to memory and learning specifically, they provide a qualitative and, in some cases, a quantitative orientation to the studies of central nervous system proteins in memory and learning, which will now be reviewed.

b. In spinal cord neurones, increases in total proteins and phospholipids have been reported to be associated with transient increases in RNA (258, 399).

The use of the antibiotic actinomycin-D and of 8-azaguanine for interference with memory process has already been referred to in the discussion on studies of nucleic acids in the nervous system. It was not entirely clear whether these effects could be attributed to interference with nucleic acids *per se*, or with brain proteins. However, puromycin, which produced 83 per cent inhibition of brain protein synthesis, was shown to interfere with certain kinds of learning in mice (199). Puromycin is an antibiotic which suppresses protein synthesis *in vivo* (153); it exerts its action by being incorporated into growing polypeptide chains and released from polysomes as peptidyl-puromycin (389). These peptides are thus presumably deflected from forming the larger protein fragments. Puromycin has also been shown to interfere with the normal electrical recording obtained from the hippocampal region, so that the normal predominant activity of 4 to 6 cycles per second with amplitude greater than 50 μv. is replaced by recordings showing little activity that exceeds 10 μv., and almost total absence of activity at 4 to 6 cycles per second or other rhythmic activity (139). Puromycin in doses of 50 to 170 μg. injected intracranially in the goldfish was shown to inhibit the incorporation of radioactive leucine into a fraction of brain proteins (101). In this last study, actinomycin-D was also shown to inhibit the uptake of radioactive leucine, although the inhibitory action was slow in onset, reached a maximum at a later time, and persisted for a longer period of time than in the case of puromycin. Short-term memory was destroyed by bilateral temporal injections of puromycin into the brain substance of mice 3 to 6 days after a learning experience, while older memories could be interfered with as long as 6 weeks after learning by injections into bilateral cortical and ventricular sites as well (196, 198). The hypothesis has been offered (195) that the establishment of memory is dependent upon a change in the quantity of one or more species of messenger RNA, which then alters the synthetic rate of one or more proteins essential for memory. In the presence of an inhibitor of protein synthesis, the concentration of an esssential protein could fall to levels too low for the experimental demonstration that memory storage has occurred, but the apparent loss of memory would be temporary if the messenger RNA were conserved to direct protein synthesis when the inhibitor had disappeared.

The studies in mice have been supported by similar studies of learning in goldfish, in which it has been indicated that memory fixation becomes insusceptible to puromycin within an hour after training. In these studies, specific neuroanatomic sites were not differentiated for the injection of puromycin (4).

The time course of the effect of puromycin suggested to several investigators that memory is formed in three or more stages (154, 31). There appears to be an initial phase, uninfluenced by puromycin, which extends for a number of minutes after learning; a second phase, inhibited by temporal injections of puromycin, which may extend for several days; and a third phase, which can be interfered with only by more diffuse intracerebral injections of puromycin. On the other hand, the resistance of short-term memory to puromycin, and of long-term memory to puromycin in certain experimental preparations, has led some investigators to question whether brain proteins are in fact necessary for these two periods of memory function (154, 101, 32).

The use of another inhibitor of protein synthesis to disrupt memory, acetoxycycloheximide (AXM), has also been reported, although its action on memory in the goldfish may not be as marked as that of puromycin (101). Its effect on disrupting memory has also been studied in mice (32, 197). If AXM acts like its near relative cycloheximide, it can prevent the transfer of activated amino acids to polypeptides and their subsequent release from polysomes. Thus, the biochemical mode of action would differ from that of puromycin. The time course of action of AXM is somewhat similar biochemically to that of puromycin, in that when it is injected intracranially there is a rapid onset of inhibition of incorporation of labeled leucine which lasts for days in the goldfish (101). Comparison of puromycin and AXM chemically shows them to be two structually unrelated substances, both of which exert an inhibitory effect upon protein synthesis, perhaps by different mechanisms, and both of which affect memory. The effects on short-term memory are similar in goldfish and mice; however, in goldfish, long-term memory appears not to be susceptible to interference, in contrast to long-term memory in mice, which has been reported to be affected. It is interesting to note, however, that cycloheximide does not have the effect on electrical activity recorded from the hippocampal region which puromycin does. No distinction can be made between the tracings from animals under cycloheximide when compared with those injected with saline alone, or the normal uninjected mouse (139).

The interpretation of the results of these experiments on puromycin, cycloheximide, and AXM is made difficult for a number of reasons.

First, in any attempt to view learning in the reasonably normal state for the animal under study, debilitation, illness, and similar side effects of these drugs cannot be ignored.

Second, the time of the peak effect of the drug and the duration of its effect differ somewhat in terms of the biochemical effect, in terms of incorporation of radioactive precursors, and in the peak of the behavioral effect, as demonstrated by the interference with memory function.

Third, there are differences in the action of these drugs, depending on whether they are injected systemically, into a single area of brain, or into multiple areas of brain.

Fourth, the inhibition achieved is never complete, and the presence of a very small percentage of residual normal biosynthetic activity may be all that is required. There are two reasons for this: (1) the nervous system maintains the general principle of redundancy, i.e. a few per cent of active units may suffice for a limited task; and (2) the specific site of protein synthesis dealing with memory function may not in fact have been touched. There is considerable uncertainty about the extent to which the injected drug reaches all cells of the nervous system, and all submicroscopic portions of each cell. The order in which particular cell groups are reached would certainly be of interest in terms of the time sequence of events in the interference with memory function.

Fifth, the measures of the degree of inhibition of incorporation of radioactive precursors are different in the different experimental situations, both in terms of the specific precursors used—e.g. leucine, valine, tryptophane—and in terms of the methods employed for protein isolation. Because of the marked heterogeneity of nervous system proteins, the examination of total protein may well obscure marked changes in a quantitatively small but biosynthetically active subfraction.

Sixth, the total analysis of brain protein includes both soluble and insoluble residues, and where an insoluble "protein" fraction is studied, there is no guarantee that the radioactivity is actually in protein residues as opposed to other macromolecules. In fact, the simple demonstration of the incorporation of radioactivity into non-dialyzable macromolecules as opposed to dialyzable substances has seldom been made.

Seventh, the drugs used have different modes of action, and the mode of action biochemically is not completely understood in any case.

Eighth, the different species used have different nervous systems and may well have different learning characteristics both intrinsically and under the different learning conditions employed in different experiments. Thus, there may well be different time constants for both the patterns of learning and for the stages of learning.

Ninth, the whole concept of consolidation of memory usually rests on the definition of electroconvulsive-shock-induced amnesia, and it is not at all clear that this is a reliable indicator of what may be termed short-term consolidation.

Tenth, the degree of fixation of memory as a function of repetition of learning has been shown to be a factor in the effectiveness of a given pharmacological amnesic agent (138). In this case the prolonged repetition of the correct solution to a task may obscure the amnesic effect of the pharmacologic agent which, though highly potent, may not completely obliterate a chemical process by its action.

Eleventh, the amnesic effects of puromycin have been shown to be diminished by the addition of cycloheximide (32). This observation simply adds to the certainty that the mechanism of action of these two substances is far from well understood.

Twelfth, the rate of protein synthesis in the hippocampus following bilateral temporal injections of AXM has been shown to be inhibited up to 30 or 40 hours after injection, but to be increased over the normal in many animals between 30 and 60 hours after injection (197). This observation of increased incorporation into protein over the normal can also be made from the data of another study with puromycin, if the actual incorporation of leucine into protein itself is taken as the measure rather than the suggested ratio of incorporation into protein over incorporation into the TCA supernate fraction (101). The reason given for using the ratio value—i.e. to minimize error due to different conditions of the precursor pool in different animals—is valid, but the correction employed may not be justified; we lack knowledge of the state of labeling in multiple compartments of the nervous system (533), and in any case, the correction may blur the important fact of specific labeling of protein, which is what is being correlated with behavior. This observation of increased incorporation of precursor into protein after injection of inhibitor reinforces the conviction that there is much more to be learned about the mechanism of action of all three inhibitors.

Finally, it should be noted that the possible action of these inhibitors specifically on the incorporation of carbohydrate components of the macromolecular substances of brain has not been examined in the studies reviewed. This point is of interest to the discussions which follow on the possible function of the brain mucoids in memory and learning. Thus, a recent study has demonstrated that puromycin also inhibits the incorporation of carbohydrate moieties into brain gangliosides (284a).

It should be noted that these studies on protein metabolism in the nervous system in relation to memory and learning are all quite recent, that they involve complex interdisciplinary methodologies, and that they are being conducted with considerable awareness by the investigators of the problems raised above.

The first problem of stress mentioned above has received some careful study in terms of general function of nervous system in relation to stress factors, in a study of the utilization of radioactive leucine by brain proteins under different conditions of sensory input (9). This study suggests that considerable increases in protein metabolism are attributable to non-specific effects which have been characterized as those due to "arousal" or "stress," presumably produced by the experimental conditions. This interpretation attempts to explain the higher rate of incorporation of radioleucine into animals reared in an impoverished environment as compared to that in animals reared in an enriched environment, in that sudden exposure of the restricted animals to an unfamiliar environment in handling produces a stress reaction with concomitant facilitation of protein turnover. (See p. 60, however.) When a control was set for these stress effects, the biochemical changes were usually minimized. Thus, the presumed function of activation of the brain by a sensorimotor task did not lead to enhanced protein metabolism if the stress produced by forced exercise was reduced or eliminated by preadaptation to the task (12). In a study of the utilization of radioactive leucine by brain in visually deprived rats and in rats receiving prolonged training in a maze in a series of visual pattern-discrimination tasks, there was no significant difference in the utilization of the radiochemical by proteins of the brain in the two groups of animals. However, there was a trend of increased uptake in several visual and non-visual structures in the visually deprived animals. The result was taken to support the previous conclusion that the presumed functional activation of the brain by behavioral engagement need not necessarily lead to an increased protein metabolism. The slight increase in the utilization of radioleucine in the visually deprived animals was attributed to the greater stress produced by the injection procedure in these previously unhandled animals (13).

Summary

The study of the relationship of the biosynthesis of brain proteins to learning is seen only to have just begun, and to require much further study before any positive or negative conclusions can be reached. The evidence at hand suggests a role of protein in long-term storage. Little can be said from the studies reported above, especially with regard to the possibility that specific brain proteins, which may only represent a small percentage of the total, are involved in memory and learning (see also Chapter VI, pp. 185-208). Almost all of the evidence for the relationship of total brain protein to learning derives from studies of inhibitors of protein synthesis. There is a possibility that much of this data will need to be reinterpreted when the exact nature of action of these inhibitors is better understood. Thus puromycin has recently been shown also to inhibit the incorporation of carbohydrate moieties into brain gangliosides, a finding of considerable interest to the mucoid-memory hypothesis.

2. Attempts to achieve "passive" biochemical transfer of information

STUDIES IN PLANARIA

The observation that ribonuclease may interfere with a conditioned response in regenerated planarians has already been referred to in the discussion on nucleic acids in the nervous system (147). Two groups of workers subsequently reported that cannibal worms which had ingested classically conditioned worms subsequently performed better than did cannibals which had ingested untrained worms (352, 281). Further work indicated that classical conditioning effects could be distinguished from pseudo-conditioning effects in planarians, and an enhanced response was produced by injection of RNA from classically conditioned but not from pseudo-conditioned or non-conditioned planarians (270, 272, 271, 205, 571). It was further observed that the loss (or extinction) of a conditioned response could not be transferred with the injection of extracted RNA from trained planaria. Instead of the extinguished response, the original response appeared to be transferred (271). The transfer of training by cannibalism was confirmed for classically conditioned worms by other investigators (477, 523, 471), and confirmed for habituation to light (555). In one instance, while a significant transfer effect was obtained with classical conditioning, conditioning as a result of maze-learning failed to transfer (552).

While there apparently have not been many negative reports, the general use of planaria in learning experiments has been challenged (270). The partially related problem of the ability of planaria to regenerate cutoff sections, and to show the retention of a conditioned response in the regenerated portion, has also been both positively and negatively discussed (521, 102).

The considerable controversy with regard to whether learning in planaria actually can be demonstrated has been recently reviewed (354). Elsewhere, many of the variables which need to be considered in the experimental design of studies on learning in planaria have been discussed (355). Some of these variables include the ambient temperature; the time of day or night; the season; the lunar month; whether it is a "good day" or "bad day" for the planarian; the chemical composition of the water in which the animals are kept; whether all the animals are trained at the same time or not; the species used; behavioral differences within members of a species; whether the tail or head is worked with in regeneration studies; the amount, type, and frequency of food given to the animals both prior to the onset of the experiment and during the training itself; the type of apparatus used; the experimental paradigm followed; the quality and quantity of the stimuli used; the type and intensity of shock used; the sensitivity of planarians to light; the fatigue state of the animal; whether a clean trough (or troughs) in which slime trails left by the planarians is used; and last but certainly not least, the "viewpoint" of the investigator. When these variables are considered, it is not difficult to understand why there is still some uncertainty about whether worms learn in a quantitative and definable form, and, therefore, whether the transfer of learning can occur by cannibalism, the injection of nucleic acids, or other means. The need, frequently mentioned in this book, for the use of experimental systems for which a maximum amount of quantified experimental data on behavior is available, is nowhere more urgent than in the evaluation of studies in learning and the transfer of information chemically in planaria. Finally, it should be noted again that the nervous system in planaria is of a very rudimentary form, with chemical barrier functions poorly if at all studied. Such questions as whether certain chemical substances can reach a particular neuroanatomical site thought to be important to learning still needs to be answered in the case of planaria.

Summary

It would be most welcome indeed if relatively simple nervous systems, such as those observed in planaria, could be shown quantitatively—and reliably—to perform in learning experiments in a manner which would make the correlation with chemical data on memory feasible. Once again, neither the positive nor the negative case appears to have been proven, and much more work is needed in this fascinating area.

STUDIES IN RATS

The results reported for the chemical transfer of information to planaria led several investigators to undertake to produce similar effects in higher forms such as the rat, with mixed results. Positive results have been reported by independent laboratories in several countries (23, 24, 117, 129, 5, 181, 193, 274, 273, 435, 436, 451,

450, 514, 517). The material which was injected in the successful cases reported for transfer of learning was either whole brain homogenate, or an extract designed to contain the nucleic acids, carried to various degrees of purification. In some cases the extract was given intracranially, and in some intraperitoneally. The experimental psychology conditions included a wide range of situations of both classical conditioning and instrumental learning types. Control injections usually were saline, but sometimes included the injection of homogenates of other organs of the same animal, such as the liver. The material actually injected was almost never thoroughly analyzed from a chemical point of view, although in several instances qualitative determinations were made for carbohydrates, proteins, and nucleic acids. Within the group of positive results, the conclusions ranged from the notion that specific chemicals which actually carry information were transferred from one brain to the other, to the notion that some agent stimulated general performance or attention in the recipient rats.

One group of investigators has presented evidence to support the notion that the transfer of information is stimulus-specific. Thus it was first shown that naïve mice ("naïve" being a euphemism for "untrained in the laboratory") that were injected with extracts of brain taken from rats habituated to sound showed a significant loss of their startle response when submitted to the same stimulus (517). Subsequently these investigators presented evidence that the transfer of habituation was stimulus-specific, the recipients given sound-habituated-rat-brain extracts were habituated only to sound, and responded normally to air puff; whereas those injected with extract of air-puff-habituated donors had significantly decreased responses to air puff but not to sound (513, 515). These investigators have also considered the possibility that the increased rate of learning was not an entirely satisfactory criterion for an actual transfer of information, and that the brains of trained animals may contain factors which could stimulate learning without conveying any specific information to the recipients.

In contrast to the above positive findings, a number of laboratories have been uable to produce clear evidence of transfer of learning by injection of chemical materials (223, 229, 292). A further negative report employed several different training schedules (344). In this last report the investigators, attempting to trace the fate of ^{32}P-labeled RNA injected in rats, showed that negligible amounts of RNA injected intraperitoneally actually reached the brain. Further negative reports have been published by seven other laboratories, which reached the conclusion that the reported transfer of training due to transfer of RNA was not a demonstrable phenomenon. All seven laboratories used the phenol extraction procedure described in the publications of some of the investigators who had achieved positive results, although there were some minor procedural variations on this method in different experiments. The extract of the brain of a single donor was used in some experiments, while pooled brains were used in others. The injections were intraperitoneal except in a few instances in which the intracisternal route was used. Training included the acquisition of an approach response with several variations, including learning of brightness discrimination in a T-maze with food reward, learning of a complex maze problem with food reward, conditioning of an emotional response, and learning of other discrimination problems. A total of eighteen experiments were performed and in none was there clear evidence of transfer. Nonetheless, these investigators concluded that "it would be unfortunate if these negative findings were to be taken as a signal for abandoning the pursuit of a result of enormous potential significance," especially since the methods employed did not cover all of the experimental conditions utilized in all of the positive studies (118, 535, 44, 148, 134, 130, 327).

More attention recently has been paid to the standardization of methodologies involved in these complex experiments. Thus, some of the experimental psychology variables have been defined as follows; the amount of preinjection handling the recipients received, the length of time the recipients were in the laboratory before being injected, the approximate age of the recipients at the time of injection, the range of weights of recipients at time of injection, the general state of excitement of the animals, the state of deprivation at time of injection, and the broad range of learning tasks employed (356). The biochemical methods require similar standardization. Thus, the actual chemical analysis of injected material has rarely been performed in a quantitative manner, and when performed on a qualitative basis, has been shown to include substances of protein, carbohydrate, and lipid nature, as well as nucleic acids. In addition, the methods of extraction and purification have varied greatly in the various experiments. Recent seminars have been held by the investigators interested in this area in order to attempt to develop and standardize methods.

STUDIES IN HUMANS

There have been relatively few studies in humans of the chemical transfer of information. RNA has been given intravenously and orally to patients suffering arteriosclerotic or senile memory defects (120, 122, 123), with some reported positive effects and evidence of increased retention in memory as indicated by a counting test, Wechsler test, and conditioned reflex parameters. Negative reports have also been published (121a). All of the objections to the experimental methodology employed in such studies in rats are even more relevant in regard to studies in humans, since the subject is so much more complex and the methodology required to demonstrate changes in memory or learning have not been completely worked out quantitatively.

Summary

Once again, it is impossible to reach positive or negative conclusions with regard to the passive biochemical transfer of information in mammals from the conflicting evidence at hand. From a biochemical point of view, there are precedents for influencing genetically determined characteristics, for example, by the recombination of DNA strands from disparate sources. However, the ability of molecules that carry information to influence a fully developed organism has less clearly defined experimental precedents, and takes one into problem areas such as latent virus and cancer. That informational molecules on injection, might pass through the blood-brain barrier, seems unlikely. However, if they could pass into the brain, it does not seem completely impossible that they might, by chemical specificities, find their way and become attached to the correct sites in the nervous system so that their informational content was incorporated into the "knowledge" of the recipient brain. The implications of a reproducible experimental demonstration of this type are of such great importance that much further effort is clearly indicated.

V

Some current non-molecular and molecular theories of memory

Introduction

There is no paucity of theoretical formulations on the nature of memory and learning. However, as befits the complexity of the nervous system itself, the problem of experimentally verifying such theories is formidable. That man sees what he knows is nowhere more apparent than when he looks at the nervous system. The more comprehensive the attempt to explain memory, the more the story comes to mind of the blindfolded wise men who were required to define an elephant, which they had never seen. With the aid of only tactile sensations of that part of the body at which each was stationed, each defined "an elephant." As the elephant is more than each of these separate descriptions, doubtless the nervous system and memory are more than the best individual theories which we have at present can encompass.

Nonetheless, in recent years the problem has come to appear more finite than it previously did, and the appreciable advances which have been made in various areas of science provide somewhat more confidence than was available only fifty years ago.

Non-molecular theories

"Non-molecular theories" is probably a misnomer, since, as pointed out in Chapter II, Section 4, even those theories which derive their inspiration from computer sciences recognize that their knowledge is being applied to a living, growing, and decaying organism with tremendous plastic functions. Thus, most non-molecular theories of memory assume that it is a fact that a living organism has produced a stable circuitry and that there are therefore molecular components to the structure of the circuitry, but that the molecular nature of the machine is a trivial fact when compared to the essence of the circuitry as it relates to memory and learning. Perhaps the most generous statement with regard to the importance of molecules in the nervous system in such theories is the following:

> . . . The essential features of physiological memory are its various abilities to manipulate symbols, first, inductively, by computing generalities from particulars, and then deductively, to reconstruct the particular from the structure of the generalities. It seems also to be plausible that during "learning," that is when these specific abilities are developed, changes will take place in the functional or structural make-up of these systems predisposed to such changes. However, such changes, which must also manifest themselves on the microscopic level, cannot be interpreted to be "traces" or "engrams" of events in the exact sense of these words. They should be understood as changes in the structure of distributed computers that facilitate inductive operations (532).

Thus, one is dealing with "Living Models for Lively Artifacts" (357).

Having accepted the premise that there are individual units which form networks in the brain, memory is seen to function as an adaptive inductive inference computer (532). Networks are defined as collections of arbitrarily branching, unidirectional transmission lines which interact with each other at certain discrete, localized regions in space. That which is transmitted over these lines is referred to as a "signal," and that which takes place at these localized regions is referred to as "information processing." The regions at which this infomation is processed are reduced by engineers to functional boxes with inputs and outputs. However,

Neurophysiologists find it more difficult to identify these localized regions of interaction, for they find them crammed with structural and functional details as e.g., the neuron's, perikaryon with all its dendritic ramifications and with all the interstices and interfaces that are produced by the transition or termination of axons arising from other neurons.

Even more difficulties are encountered if effects of interaction are to be specified (501).

Here the situation is so complex, the possible responses so numerous, and the measurements so difficult that, in spite of the tremendous knowledge gained in the last decade, neurons are still very enigmatic. Nevertheless, concepts as, e.g., "facilitation," "inhibition," "temporal integration," etc., appear to be generally applicable to these regions (531).

The operational modalities of neural networks close to the sensory layer of the frog's eye have recently been clarified (331). It appears that these nets process information in parallel by performing distributed operations on their inputs so as to extract certain invariants from a given set of stimulus configurations. The theoretical foundations for these abstracting operations were laid down some twenty years ago (358, 359).

Neurophysiologists, however, have objected that the current activities employed in these theories or the transfer of function suggested for the elements have little if anything in common with the physiological entities, and that their complexities are insufficiently represented in the naïve theoretical models.

Some of the ways in which these objections are being met are illustrated by the following list of postulates relevant to memory for which there is now thought to be considerable justification (532):

(i) There are parallel networks without loops that are known to compute invariants (abstracts) in a set of stimulus configurations.

(ii) Cascades of such parallel networks are known to compute abstracts of ascending order of generality.

(iii) It is known that nets with loops, once excited, may continue their activity around these loops and, under certain conditions, may maintain reference to the past for an indefinite period of time.

(iv) It is known that nets with loops are equivalently represented by indefinite temporal cascades of virtual parallel networks without loops.

(v) From points (ii) and (iv) it is clear that networks with loops may in time compute abstracts of ascending order of generality.

(vi) It is known that linear networks with loops, once excited, will continue their activity around these loops, however, eventually without reference to the past whatsoever, save for the fact of having once been excited.

(vii) No such decay occurs, if linear superpositions are replaced by superpositions defined in nonlinear algebraic systems.

(viii) Reference to algebra only, without specification of function, suffices to show the possible decomposition of present activity into representations of elements belonging to the remote past.

Some of the properties of network assemblies have been further discussed in terms of dynamic stability, logical stability, and information storage (531).

The computer analogy may run into difficulty with reference to the nature of the living nervous system, which is held to be unimportant by some computer theorists. In addition, the best present computers contain 10^6 units; projections for future computers extend to 10^9 units, although these are not yet operational. The number of nerve cells in the cortex alone is known to be in the order of 10^{10} units. Both this and the nature of the organization of the units may account for the fact that there are many functions performed by the brain which cannot as yet be performed by computers. Miniaturization of components in the brain is also impressive; thus, 10^{10} units occupy less than one-half of a cubic foot. From a practical point of view, there is considerable attention being paid at present by the computer industry to the problem of fatigue and breakdown in computer units and the difficulty in repairing them. It is possible that a better examination of the living computer, the brain, will provide indications of how facilities for repair processes are built in. The great turnover in the chemical constituents of the nervous system throughout the lifetime of the individual has obvious reference to this point. We are as yet quite unaware of the full degree of plasticity of the nervous system in the mature state. While a cell may remain the same in gross appearance, all of its chemical constituents may turn over, i.e. be replaced by new ones, over a period of time. Whether regular and complete renewal of cell constituents is required for day-to-day alterations in the living circuitry is unknown. (See also Chapter VII).

The computer models have had numerous practical applications to examinations of how the nervous system works in terms of receptor and effector pathways. Thus, the organization of the neocortex into columns, or "vertical internuncial chains," has been described (338). Evidence has also been obtained for feedback loops which operate in "lateral" or "surround" inhibition, as in the retina, and in the olfactory bulb (567) and in the skin and somatosensory cortex (384, 385). The possibility that certain central subsystems may be those chiefly concerned with learning has also been developed (187).

There seems little question that the computer sciences have at once enriched the understanding of how the nervous system operates and presented a whole vista of complexities which require future resolution. From the point of view of memory and learning, the integration of computer science with other biological theories about the handling of experiential input still needs to be accomplished (see also Chapter VII).

Molecular theories of memory

There are a number of relatively discrete hypotheses which have been proposed with regard to the molecular basis of memory. Some of these will now be briefly enumerated.

There are two comments which might be made before these hypotheses are listed. First, in common with the early development of many other scientific areas, it is frequently difficult to trace the precise origin and subsequent course of an idea on memory. The scientific community concerned with this problem over the past seventy years has been relatively small, and communication between its members has been sufficient to cause incorporation and modification of ideas into several experimental and conceptual settings. Second, perhaps in no other scientific endeavor have so many propositions managed to appear so lacking in conflict with each other. That is, although certain concepts are preferred by one or another theoretician, there is remarkably little conflictual debate suggesting that any two propositions are mutually exclusive. There are several possible reasons for this. The first one is trivial; that is, the theoreticians in this field are more accurate than in most other areas. The second is that each hypothesis is a reasonably accurate representation of one particular aspect of nervous system function; they are all correct, but the entire problem is so great that there is more, much more, which needs to be known. Thus, the potential space in which these several "molecules" of theory operate is so large that it is rare for two ever to collide. This is a somewhat distressing thought, since it would suggest that the number of further correct statements or propositions which need to be made is very large when compared to the number already made. Finally, it is of course possible that, in addition to some postulates being incorrect, all of the propositions stated to date are incorrect and have no relationship whatsoever to the essence of memory. This last possibility seems unlikely since there is considerable experimental support for some of the propositions so far conceived. Since there is a good deal of agreement, either tacit or explicit, by almost all of the contributors on theory for all of the propositions of others, those references will be given in which either the author prefers a particular proposition, or in which the statement is made with some degree of clarity.

1. *Memory is mediated by certain distinct brain regions (lobes, nuclei, tracts).*
As previously discussed, there is evidence that certain brain regions have different memory functions. Partly because investigators in the last fifty years have been noted for moving away from thinking in

terms of the nervous system as a group of centers and regions with different functions, partly due to the discouraging interpretations by early searchers for engrams (326), and partly due to the absorption with circuitry in the nervous system, much of the data on localization briefly summarized in Chapter III has been ignored in the formulation of molecular theories of memory. An exception to this has been found in the work that illustrates differences in the effectiveness of inhibitors of protein synthesis injected in different brain regions at different times after learning (194). Thus, puromycin injected into the temporal lobe may interfere with consolidation of memory if injected within the first hour, but several days later, injections must be made at multiple sites throughout the cerebral cortex to effect interference. This experimental approach suggests the postulate that memory functions are subserved by series of regions or organ subsystems of the central nervous system at different times.

2. *Memory traces are contained in neurons.*
While almost all theories of memory have either taken for granted or stated explicitly that nerve cells are the repositories of the chemical processes subserving memory (282), the recent work on the changes in base structure of nucleic acids of neurons and glia tend to deal with the neuron-glia unit in terms of the chemistry of memory (262). While the glia and the neuron are thereby thought to constitute the functional unit of the nervous system, some neurophysiologists doubt that this theoretical unit is in harmony with the known facts about impulse generation (171).

3. *Memory traces are contained in one specific population of neurons.*
While there is no chemical evidence which has been presented to support the concept of two different sets of neuron population, one dealing with memory and one not, there might be chemical characteristics distinguishing two such neuronal types. It is interesting to observe the recurrence of this idea:

> A main characteristic of nervous tissues is memory: that is, quite generally, a capacity for being permanently altered by

single occurrences. . . . A psychological theory deserving any
consideration must furnish an explanation of "memory." Now
any such explanation comes up against the difficulty that it
must assume on the one hand that neurons are permanently
different after an excitation from what they were before, while
nevertheless, it cannot be disputed that, in general, fresh excitations meet with the same conditions of reception as did
the earlier ones. It would seem therefore, that neurons must
be both influenced and also unaltered, unprejudiced. We
cannot offhand imagine an apparatus capable of such complicated functioning. . . . By attributing the characteristic of
being permanently influenced by excitation to one class of
neurons, and, on the other hand, the unalterability—the characteristic of being fresh for new excitations—to another class
. . . has arisen the current distinction between "perceptual
cells" and "mnemic cells"—a distinction, however, which fits
into no other context and cannot itself appeal to anything in
its support (207).

. . . responses in striate cortex in the mature animal may
be "wired in" or resistant to change through experience, . . .
in central systems in which storage does occur, a certain fraction only of the neuronal population may be involved (186).

In the vertebrate CNS there may be two major neuronal
populations. The first is composed of units in which memory
formation either may not occur at all because of restriction of
input, or may occur, but reversibly. Such units may predominate at the sensory periphery and in subsystems a few
synapses from the latter may be found chiefly on the receptor
or input side. . . . The second population consisting of
units in which lasting memory formation may occur, may then
have approximately the converse distribution, both in the
CNS as a whole and in those subsystems in which they are
found at all (185).

This postulate has not yet been stated in precise molecular terms,
but it follows that there may be chemical specificities to such separate neuronal systems. Certainly the well-recognized notion that
neurones may be cholinergic or adrenergic, i.e. possessed of specificity with regard to their transmitter substances, is of interest in

this regard. Although this has been proved to be the case in the peripheral nervous system, this point is not yet clearly established in the central nervous system, where it would be relevant to memory (see Chapter VII).

4. *Memory is mediated by axonal changes.*

As an alternative to what is being termed the "labile synapse," the hypothesis has been put forward that: "1) from one synapse to another continuously firing neurons can transmit information in only one way, and that is by means of impulse frequency; 2) each nerve cell has an exclusively precise mechanism available to it for changing and controlling this impulse frequency" (2). The molecular changes which subserve these properties are referred to in terms of the ionic equilibria and possibly the proteins in axoplasm. Thus the ionic membrane conductances are seen to depend on the electric field, and it is suggested that it is imperative to study the behavior of interfacial macromolecular systems in the presence of high intensity electric fields in order to determine the basis for selectivity of neuronal function that may subserve memory (2).

5. *Memory is subserved by new growth of nerve cell processes.*

Although the nerve cells of the brain are thought not to divide in the adult, there is evidence that they are able to grow new branches. The growth of new processes has formed the basis of several theories of memory (244, 218, 529, 416). While there have been in the past no clear chemical correlates of this nerve cell process growth, the identification of certain brain proteins (Groups 1-3) whose developmental accumulation correlates temporally with the growth of nerve cell processes is of interest in this regard (see Chapter VI).

6. *Memory is a property of the formation of new cells.*

The new cells which have been invoked in this regard have included both neurons and glia. The evidence of facilitation of glia multiplication in the cerebral cortex of animals whose environment has been enriched is relevant to this theory (453, 8).

It has also been proposed that new synaptic connections are

established among invariant input-output elements of the nervous system through the interposition of internuncial short-axoned neurons or granular cells. The postnatal origin of these cell types, their slow postnatal development, and an increase in their relative number as the phylogenetic scale is ascended, have resulted in consideration of the possibility that these cell types are the plastic elements of the central nervous system, and that their development is dependent on their organism's experiential input (8, 19, 461).

7. *Memory is a product of events occurring at synapses.*
The idea that learning involves the establishment of new "connections" between nerve cells where they meet, i.e. at the synapse, includes not only the idea of formation of new contacts, as with growth of new processes, but also involves theories about almost all of the substances which interact at synaptic regions, whether in aqueous or membranous media.

One of the earliest, perhaps the earliest, hypothesis in this regard follows:

> We can therefore say still more correctly that memory is represented by the differences in the facilitations between the . . . neurons. . . . Every . . . neuron must in general be presumed to have several powers of connection with other neurons —i.e., several contact-barriers. On this, indeed, depends the possibility of the choice that is determined by facilitation. It now becomes quite clear that the state of facilitation of one contact-barrier must be independent of that of all the other contact-barriers of the same . . . neuron (206).

Here is a more recent statement with regard to the relationship of synapses to memory:

> The . . . [structural] theory of memory postulates a structural change and does not require continuing circulation of impulses . . . some enduring changes built into the fine structure of the nervous system, making some particular path-

ways more favorable for impulse transmission than others. This is the kind of memory trace that may persist throughout the whole of life, and is effective as long as we have a method of recall. I am going to concentrate on the structural or trace theory of memory, not the dynamical. I am assuming that the structural change is essentially synaptic, . . . (171).

This hypothesis considers several phenomena occurring at synapses, such as rapid repetitive activation, inhibitory phenomena, and the immense dendritic structures and special types of synapses on dendrites. These considerations tie in, in certain instances, with those of computer models discussed previously, and in fact some of the best demonstrations of feedback control, and information loops, are provided by studies of this sort (171).

Further elaboration has also been presented of the synaptic model for memory as it correlates with the synapse as a biochemical self-organizing micro-cybernetic unit (438). In this consideration, the physiological state of the synapse when inactive, the state of presynaptic excitation, the state of postsynaptic excitation, and negative feedback are all considered in one theoretical formulation which includes the possible function of gamma aminobutyric acid (438).

The importance of the synapse is also stressed by theoreticians who predominantly employ the computer model, and who seek no specific chemical basis for its function (530).

Other examples of possible synaptic bases of memory include activity either presynaptically, such as increased synthesis of transmitter or release of transmitter; or postsynaptically, such as increased synthesis of receptor, increased sensitivity of receptor, increased permeability to transmitter, or decreased degradation of transmitter (30).

The attempt to integrate what is known to occur chemically at the junction between neurons also is a crucial concept in other understandings of memory functions (464, 483).

It should be noted that of all the theories of memory, those which deal with synaptic function are the most devoid of direct experimental support or contradiction from a biochemical point of view, since methods have not yet been evolved for the chemical study of pre- and post-synaptic as well as synaptic cleft regions in learning situations.

8. *Memory is a function of glial cells.*

A number of suggestions (213a) have been made about the possible role of glia and memory: First since glial cells form the matrix in which nerve cells are embedded, the environment and hence the properties of neurons may be radically altered by glial proliferation (8). Second, increased glial multiplication, through the role of glia cells in myelination, may be associated with recruitment of more conducting elements into newly formed neuronal circuits (8). Third, the neuron-glia unit contains the molecular bases for memory (462). Finally, glial RNA is the substrate for short-term memory, whereas neuronal RNA is the substrate for long-term memory (265).

9. *Memory is coded in deoxyribonucleic acids and/or in ribonucleic acids.*

The suggestion that the actual coding of information occurs in the nucleic acids has come through a variety of theoretical transformations in the last ten years. At first, qualitative changes were proposed in the actual base-ratio structure of RNA (258, 259). In more recent publications, a quantitative change in RNA or a combination of qualitative and quantitative changes have been suggested as the molecular basis of memory. Thus, for example, the following statement summarizes some recent thoughts:

> What happens when an animal is placed in an acute learning situation which has no precedence in its life? I would suggest that the time pattern of frequencies set up in the neurons involved leads to a release of repressed regions of chromosomal DNA. This leads to a production of highly specific DNA-copied RNA. In its turn, the RNA synthesis occurring on the demand of the situation gives, as an end product in the neuronal soma, specific proteins. The presence of these proteins or, at later stages, their rate of production, leads to an activation of the transmitter substance. The next time the same modulated frequencies enter, these specific proteins answer

with a rapid reaction leading to an activation of the transmitter substance. (261).

In other formulations of this theory, either the electrical phenomena influence directly the RNA or work first as in the above, to derepress the chromosomal DNA. Variants of this theory also include the possibility of a stable RNA which does not change with time, or a transitory RNA which is present only during the synthesis of the new protein.

Favoring the derepression concept and less inclined to non-DNA-dependent RNA synthesis, one theory suggests that the RNA made during the learning process should be a gene product and therefore hybridizable with genomal DNA (93). Thus, the learning-induced RNA synthesis, since it is made by transcription of genes previously repressed, should be different from the RNA made in the same cell in the absence of learning. In conformity with this hypothesis, one is led to the impression that all learning must consist of "recollection" of knowledge already present in some form (280). This "selective theory" for the nucleic acid-mediated coding of memory can be contrasted with the "instructional theory," in which it is possible to synthesize macromolecules *de novo* rather than just "select" them from genetically stored chemically coded information. It is interesting to note that these considerations bring the theories on nucleic acids and memory directly in line with current theoretical problems in immunology, where there is a similar theoretical choice between the synthesis of antibodies according to a selection theory or an instruction theory (114). Further theoretical parallels have been proposed between the induction of genetic capability in the normal developmental processes of embryogenesis as compared with induction of the reinforcement type as studied in behavioral conditioning situations (417). Thus, embryological inductors evoke and organize the genetic potential of the organism, behavioral reinforcers evoke and organize the behavioral capacities, and so on. Since the biochemical mechanisms of induction in embryogenesis are far from fully understood, all of the biochemical aspects of this comparison cannot be examined. However, the fact that RNA appears to be involved in embryogenic induction, and is thought to be involved in the induction of experiential memory recording, is the essential chemical basis of such theoretical comparisons.

It should be noted that almost all statements on the coding functions of the nucleic acid in memory assume that a macromolecular product, usually stated to be a protein, results. The protein is the specific macromolecule which is involved in specific transactions either within the neuron or between neurons. Thus in the nucleic acid theories of memory, another macromolecule, usually a protein, constitutes the storage molecule of memory, the actual engram.

The nucleic acid theory, however, stated in these terms, approaches a level of generality which excludes it as a specific molecular coding theory. Thus, specific memory molecules might not be required at all, and "the biochemistry of learning would become the biochemistry of the hypertrophy and atrophy of synapses, of the concomitant repression and derepression of the genetic potentialities in the various cellular components in the CNS" (437). Utilizing the same criticism, however, one might simply redirect one's attention to the products of synthesis (e.g. proteins) and their specificities, and away from the mechanisms of synthesis of these specific products which theoretically contain the actual memory code.

10. *Memory is coded in proteins.*
Almost all of the foregoing molecular theories of memory suppose that the final molecular product bearing memory specificity in its code is a protein; they differ only in their concept of how the proteins are involved. The specificity of protein might be changed simply by a conformational change (464). On the other hand, there are those who believe that entirely new protein species would be synthesized as specified by the nucleic acids (260). Still others propose that the specificity of the protein is dependent upon its combination with certain small molecules, biogenic amines, which are themselves the alphabet of the code (245). Some believe that the specification through proteins may be independent of the an-

atomical location of these protein molecules; i.e. these are specifically coded molecules "without geography" (3).

11. *Brain mucoids and memory.*
The particular contribution to the theoretical basis of the molecular coding of memory made by this book is the suggestion that the mucoids of the nervous system are involved in the actual encoding of experiential information (68, 69). This thesis will be more fully developed in Chapter VII.

Summary

The large number of theories on the non-molecular and molecular basis of memory currently available is one indication of the attention which the field is receiving. Even non-molecular theoreticians must, though sometimes begrudgingly, agree that the organic substratum of the brain's circuitry is after all formed by living cells; but this fact may be trivial to the essence of the function. Molecular theories of memory include the idea that distinct brain regions mediate memory; that memory traces are contained in neurones; that they are contained in one specific population of neurones; that memory is mediated by axonal changes; by new growth of nerve cell processes; by growth of new cells; that it is a product of synaptic events; a function of glial cells; that it is coded in deoxyribonucleic acids; coded in ribonucleic acids; coded in proteins; and now, coded in brain mucoids. The fact that there is little conflict between these theories whereby any two of them become mutually exclusive is here regarded as a curious and perhaps relevant phenomenon.

VI

Central nervous system mucoids in learning and memory

Some requirements for prospective coding molecules

From the evidence just reviewed on current concepts of the nature of the memory process in the nervous system, the molecular requirements for coding functions are generally considered to be such that a number of molecular species do not appear to be likely candidates. Those molecules which might qualify would have the following characteristics:

1. *Heterogeneity.*
The need for sufficient heterogeneity in structure is based partly on the massive number of bits of information which must be handled. For this reason alone, most small molecules out of a macromolecular matrix, appear to be ruled out, and most macromolecules qualify. (See dissenting opinions in Chapter V, however.)

2. *Location.*
The anatomic location of the eligible macromolecules should conform to the cellular and fiber collections known from anatomical and electrophysiological studies to have relevance to memory. The histologic location of the memory macromolecules would seem to be favored in structures which have geometric order of some permanence. Thus, cytoplasmic components diffusing freely in random association would be less favored, and those in fixed membranous locations more favored.

3. *Development.*
A macromolecule which was at its maximum concentration in the
senescent period and at its lowest concentration during the years
of greatest learning for the organism would not appear to be a
likely candidate, whereas one whose developmental curve conformed to the learning curve might be more likely.

4. *Pathology.*
Impairment in the concentration of or conformation of the memory molecule, or its specific components, or impairment of its function, should be correlated with impairment of memory processes.

5. *Recognition functions.*
The most likely macromolecules would be those which displayed
"recognition" functions, such that the specificity of their interaction with other molecules was of a high order. It might be possible
to demonstrate properties which they possess as antigens, as receptors, and possibly also as stimuli.

6. *Biosynthesis.*
The generative and regenerative properties of the macromolecules
are of interest because of the need for a full range of permanence,
from temporary conformations, whose half-life is measured in seconds or minutes, to those whose stability is measured by the lifetime of the organism. In addition, inhibition of the synthesis of the
memory macromolecule should have negative effects on memory
function.

7. *Change with behavior.*
The memory macromolecules might show changes in total structure or in the structure of key constituents accompanying behavioral changes. This may be easier to demonstrate than is the
next requirement.

8. *Change with learning.*
More specifically, changes in the total or component concentration

should occur in direct relationship to specific learning, rather than just to activity or total behavioral performance.

The knowledge currently available for a role for CNS mucoids in memory functions is reviewed in this chapter. The evidence, although still only sparsely available, is discussed under each of the above requirements, and has been judged to be sufficiently consistent with these requirements that a role for the brain mucoids in actual encoding functions has been proposed (68, 69).

Most of the evidence to date, while sufficient for hypothesis formulation, will require much more experimental amplification and specification before a state can be reached which resembles certainty.

Nomenclature for the CNS mucoids

"Mucoid" is an old term for substances with carbohydrate and protein, and/or lipid characteristics. The recently recommended nomenclature (28) of different mucoids is italicized in the following discussion. The common groupings isolated are the carbohydrate-amino substances (aminopolysaccharide, *glycosaminoglycan*), the carbohydrate protein (*glycoprotein*), and carbohydrate-lipid (aminoglycolipid, *glycosaminolipid*). The chemistry of the aminopolysaccharides, of the glycoproteins, and of the aminoglycolipids have been until recently three relatively separate specialized fields of investigation.

While little is known of the native state of these substances, it is likely that in the three-dimensional structure of living tissues, carbohydrates, lipids, and proteins are covalently or ionically linked in forms which would permit the isolation of glyco-lipo-proteins, were the appropriate methods available. Obtaining a glycolipid or a glycoprotein fraction would therefore be dependent upon the method of isolation employed, i.e. upon the bonds that are ruptured in the process. It follows that the molecular size of the fragment could also vary from small dialyzable peptides and oligosaccharides through huge non-dialyzable complexes. The molecular weight of the fragment could vary with the solvent used when bonds looser than the covalent type prevail in holding the fragment together.

In fact, the conditions which now obtain in the laboratory isolation of these substances yield just such a mixture of fragments. It
would appear likely that it will become increasingly possible to
extract and isolate specific parts of the *in situ* three-dimensional
lattice formed by the mucoids, which is the postulated structural
basis of intracellular membranes in this hypothesis.

The constituents of the CNS mucoids

The glycoproteins were first recognized and described in the mucin-
ous secretions of the body (28). Their physical characteristics
were studied and their constituent sugar and amino acid components analyzed before the turn of the century. The historical
milestones have been summarized (225) in the definition of the
various amino acids, the hexosamines (galactosamine and glucosamine), the hexoses (galactose, mannose and glucose), neuraminic
acid and its derivatives, and fucose as the carbohydrate constituents in the glycoproteins. Xylose has more recently been recognized as a constituent of some glycoproteins.

The simpler *glycolipids* were first characterized at the beginning
of this century (452, 509) and then further studied in the past
fifty years. The simplest glycolipids, called cerebrosides, contain:
(1) sphingosine, or one of its derivatives; (2) a fatty acid, linked
through its carboxyl group to the amino group of sphingosine; and
(3) hexose, usually glucose or galactose, linked glycosidically to
the terminal hydroxyl group of sphingosine.

Variations in each of these three constituents of the cerebrosides
provide a series of distinct compounds separable by their physical properties and by the hydrolytic identification of their constituents. The galactocerebrosides contain galactosidosphingosine
(psychosine) and a fatty acid which varies. Thus, the cerebroside
cerasine contains lignoceric acid, while the cerebroside phrenosine
contains cerebronic acid. A galactocerebroside which has been isolated from human brain contains dihydrosphingosine, galactose,
and hydroxylignoceric. A glucocerebroside (gangliocerebroside) has

been crystalized as a split product of bovine brain gangliosides and from spleen.

The addition by glycosidic linkage of further carbohydrate residues to a cerebroside molecule produces a series of compounds of increasingly larger size and structural complexity which have been given the group name of aminoglycolipids (76). The presence of only one further hexose attached to a cerebroside yields a cytoside such as that isolated from spleen (299) and from epidermoid carcinoma (431). The term aminoglycolipid is applicable to a wide range of substances of plant, bacterial, and animal source, including substances whose basic constituents are glycolipid in nature, and whose additional constituents include some amino-carrying components, such as hexosamines and other amino sugars, muramic and neuraminic acids and their derivatives, amino acids, or any combination of these types of substances.

When the amino acids are covalently linked to the other constituents of an aminoglycolipid by means of a sufficient number of consecutive peptide bonds so that a protein results, the entire covalently linked substance then can be termed a *glycolipoprotein*. For compounds of large molecular weight which contain amino acid and carbohydrate, but no lipid residues, the term *aminopolysaccharide* is used.

The manner in which lipid constituents are covalently linked to the carbohydrate constituents in the aminoglycolipids has been largely determined. The manner of linkage of the amino acids in the aminoglycolipids is still unknown, although some progress has been made in understanding the manner of linkage of amino acids to carbohydrates in the glycoproteins.

For each substance, the structural studies have generally taken the following course: first, isolation; second, identification of constituents; third, physicochemical properties; fourth demonstration of order of assembly, with preliminary evidence for the type of linkage between constituents; and finally, the exact determination of orientation of atoms about each asymmetric center, and the precise characteristics of the bonds between constituents. For some of the members of each class of small physical size, such as neuraminlactose and phrenosine, many of these properties are known.

However, for none of the aminoglycolipids larger than the cytoside class, nor for the glycoproteins, is anything but preliminary information available on even the first four of the above categories. For an exhaustive survey of the chemistry of these substances a number of recent reviews and symposia are available (486, 550, 28, 225).

Aminopolysaccharides

GLYCOGEN

Glycogen is a macromolecular carbohydrate composed of polymerized glucose. It contains no amino groups, and should not therefore be classed as an aminopolysaccharide, but because it is a major storage form of glucose, and hence undoubtedly is involved indirectly in the anabolic and catabolic balance of the sugar constituents of the mucoids, it is of some relevance. Furthermore, much of what has been learned about its straight-chain and branching characteristics, and of its mode of synthesis, has proved relevant to structural studies of the mucoids. Experience gained with the rapid autolytic degradation of brain glycogen between death of the animal and extraction of the material had drawn attention to the possible need to control for this variable in the isolation of the mucoids, yet there is as yet little data available on the comparison of the structure of brain mucoids extracted from living and postmortem tissues. The molecular weight studies of glycogen show the isolated material from liver to be polydisperse with two major ranges of sedimentation constants, 60-100S and 150-300S (413). Methylation studies (240), periodate oxidation studies (250, 236), and acid hydrolysis studies (563, 557) have revealed straight chains of α-1:4 linkage glycopyranose residues, with one chain linked to another by an α-1:6 linkage at branching points. The synthesis of straight chains is accomplished via the mediation of the phosphorylases (144). These occur in less and more soluble form, "a" and "b," respectively, and require the presence of "primer" glycogen units for activity (238). Pyridoxal 5-phosphate is a firmly bound cofactor for the reaction (523, 33a). The synthesis of branch points is mediated by amylo-

(1:4-1:6)-transglucosidase (143). An alternate mechanism for the synthesis of glycogen is mediated by uridine diphosphoglucose-glycogen transferase (330). Glycogen synthesis and glycogenolysis are under the regulation of the hormones insulin, glucagon, and adrenocorticotropic hormone (430, 241), and are implicated in the glycogen storage diseases that affect the nervous system and other tissues (p. 150).

RHAMNOSE- AND XYLOSE-CONTAINING AMINOPOLYSACCHARIDES OF BRAIN

In protease-digested brain extracts, xylose and arabinose have been shown to be present as constituents of acidic mucopolysaccharide peptides which can be precipitated by cetylpyridinium bromide (CPBr). An electrophoretically homogeneous mucopolysaccharide peptide was extracted from the CPBr precipitate with dilute acetic acid. It contained xylose, galactose, galactosamine, hexuronic acid, sulfate, and nonhexosamine N in the molar ratio 1:2:7:9:8:2. Another arabinose-containing fraction has also been partially purified (545).

Aminoglycolipids

An examination of the various types of brain aminoglycolipids demonstrates a series of increasingly complex structures which, in contrast to many other substances in brain that show relatively little individual variation (41), are characterized by marked heterogeneity and individual variation.

CERAMIDE-DIHEXOSIDES

A compound composed of a cerebroside with one extra mole of hexose attached was reported from ox spleen (305), the molar ratios being fatty acid:sphingosine:hexose (1:1:2). A similar compound, called *cytolipin H*, has been isolated from human epidermal carcinoma.

The term cytosides also has been used for these ceramide-dihexo-sides (431). Cytolipin H was later compared with spleen ceramide-dihexoside and Cytolipin H was found by its iodine number to contain a greater number of unsaturated double bonds (432). The complement fixation test, however, failed to distinguish be-tween the antisera produced against the two substances. A cera-mide-dihexoside from horse red blood cell stroma has also been described (306) and one such compound from Tay-Sachs' brain has been isolated (45).

CERAMIDE-DIHEXOSIDE-HEXOSAMINE COMPOUNDS (ASIALOGANGLIOSIDES)

The next substances in order of increasing number or type of con-stituents are the ceramide-dihexoside-hexosamine types of com-pounds. This type of aminoglycolipid, called *globoside*, has been isolated from stroma of human red blood cells (566, 299, 300). The same type of compound has been expected to be present, because of the demonstration of an increase in hexosamine over neuraminic acid, in brain aminoglycolipids (76), and one such sub-stance has been isolated from Tay-Sachs' brain (45). The latter authors expressed some reservations that this compound may have resulted from degradation of a brain ganglioside during isolation, but considered this unlikely since they were unable to demonstrate the compound in normal brain. Nonetheless, the failure to recover quantitatively all the aminoglycolipid-neuraminic acid placed on silica gel in chromatography raises some questions as to the *in situ* existence of these isolated asialo-relatives of the gangliosides (419, 507, 510). The susceptibility of the brain gangliosides to degrada-tion by *in vivo* enzyme systems is also relevant in this regard.

SIALIC ACID-CONTAINING AMINOGLYCOLIPIDS (GANGLIOSIDES, SIALO-AMINOGLYCOLIPIDS)

These substances are of two types: the first, ceramide-dihexoside-neuraminic acid compounds, which do not contain hexosamine;

the second, ceramide-dihexoside-hexosamine-neuraminic acid compounds, which contain both hexosamine and neuraminic acid.

An ahexosamino-ganglioside fraction has been separated into two components by thin-layer chromatography (296). The detection of the sialo-aminoglycolipids in brain dates back to the observations of a glycolipid fraction which gave a colored reaction with Ehrlich's reagent (322, 323). Several similar fractions were also isolated (544, 293, 294, 50) before the term "ganglioside" was applied. The demonstration that the constituent responsible for the color reactions of these substances was neuraminic acid (295) also preceded the use of the term ganglioside.

The first use of the term ganglioside (296) was for a water-soluble non-dialyzable glycolipid preparation, from human Tay-Sach's brain, described as containing fatty acids, sphingosine, hexoses, and neuraminic acid. The presence of hexosamine in this preparation was only noted later (51). The manner in which these constituents were combined was unknown.

Starting with a preparation of "crude brain ganglioside," prepared by hot methanol extraction of bovine brain (203), and subjecting this material to six successive partitions between chloroform methanol and water, a highly purified preparation of brain ganglioside was obtained (59). By repeated partitions the percentage of the ganglioside constituents increased and the phosphorus contamination decreased. It is also clear from later data (76) that with each successive partition, several classes of aminoglycolipid are separated from the brain ganglioside persisting as upper phase material. Included among those removed are both hexose- and hexosamine-rich aminoglycolipids, and those which contain amino acids bound by covalent or ionic linkages. The repeated acidification and dialysis at 0 to 4°C. to reduce ash content from 11 per cent to 1.1 per cent also probably helped to remove other loosely bound dialyzable contaminants. These investigations have made it quite likely that the use of at least six purification repartitions were responsible for the chemical differences observed between these and some other preparations of brain ganglioside.

One final preparation of brain ganglioside (59) was completely water-soluble, free of phospholipids (P, 0.7 per cent) and free of dialyzable contaminants. It contained N 2.9 per cent, hexose 24 per cent (as galactose), neuraminic acid 30.3 per cent (N-acetyl-neuraminic acid), and free amino N 0.5 per cent. It was homogeneous by electrophoresis, and over 95 per cent homogeneous in the ultracentrifuge. It had a minimal aqueous molecular weight of 250,000.

A stepwise hydrolytic procedure was employed to investigate the structure of this ganglioside. Using quantitative dialysis to separate dialyzable constituents freed and non-dialyzable constituents remaining at each step, it was possible to isolate and identify monosaccharides and oligosaccharides in each fraction by column and paper chromatography, and to follow quantitatively the fate of each constituent through each hydrolytic step. This latter point is of considerable importance in such studies, since it permits the detection of the destruction or loss of constituents during isolation and hydrolysis procedures. Clearly, if all of one constituent cannot be accounted for at the end of a particular hydrolytic or separation procedure it is not possible to deduce the structure of all of the original compound from only the fragments remaining. Few studies have been reported to date in which quantitative recovery data are actually reported for the ganglioside constituents through all phases of isolation and hydrolysis (59). The immediate practical importance of this point is illustrated by the studies which utilize silicic acid column chromatography or thin-layer silica gel for the separation of what are concluded to be several distinct species of ganglioside (549, 152). However, it was noted (510) that in none of the separation methods, including thin-layer chromatography, could all of the ganglioside constituents be accounted for quantitatively, and that there was a marked loss of neuraminic and in aminoglycolipid fractions purified on silica gel column chromatography (419, 507).

The diffusible and non-diffusible fractions thus obtained have been analyzed in terms of dry weight, nitrogen, neuraminic acid, hexosamine, hexose, and reducing sugar, partitioned by paper-chromatographic and ion-exchange procedures, and the subfractions further hydrolyzed and analyzed. The mode of linkage of the neuraminic acid component was demonstrated. Oligosaccharide

GANGLIOCEREBROSIDE

Glucose

Sphingosine

Stearic acid

$C_{42}H_{81}O_8N(H_2O)$

Melting point, 172 to 174° C.

Iodine number 23.2

$[\alpha]_D^{20}$ −2.08

X-ray diffraction spacings at
2.41, 4.10, 9.1, 10.4, 15.6, 21.1,
30.6, 49.2, 55.5, and 63.5 Å

	% C	% H	% N	% Hexose (as glucose)
Found	67.13	10.95	1.86	21.8
Calculated	67.65	11.14	1.88	22.0

Figure 3. Structure and analytic data on gangliocerebroside (59).

fragments were isolated, the hexoses shown to be exclusively galactose and glucose, and the hexosamine, galactosamine. The galactosamine content was found to be 10 per cent, and a reaction of
galactosamine on heating with concentrated acid was observed.
The constant order of release of constituents, together with the
evidence regarding the structure of isolated fragments, was used
to formulate the structure of the repeating unit of the molecule. A
glucocerebroside was cleaved from the intact ganglioside, characterized, and named gangliocerebroside (Figure 3). A hexodicerebroside also was isolated. Observations were made relevant to the
over-all structure and orientation of the macromolecular glycolipid.

The determination of structure of brain ganglioside (59) by the
quantitative stepwise hydrolytic procedure suggested that what was
being studied was an organized arrangement of constituents bound
together in firm covalent linkage. This was indicated by the stoi-
chiometric appearance of reducing groups as constituents were successively cloven from glycosidic binding, and by the constant order
of release of diffusible constituents. This constant order of release
of constituents observed in repeated stepwise hydrolyses, i.e. neuraminic acid, galactosamine, galactose, glucose, sphingosine, and
fatty acids, was suggestive of a structural sequence. Furthermore,
the data from the analysis of the fractions presented evidence for

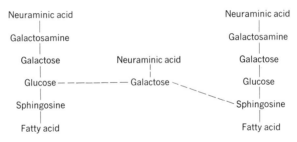

Mol. wt. of repeating unit: 3,314

Figure 4. Suggested repeating unit for the structure of brain ganglioside (59).

the existence of the following groupings: neuraminic acid-galactosamine; galactosamine-galactose-glucose; glucose-sphingosine; glucose-sphingosine-fatty acid; sphingosine-fatty acid, and hexodicerebroside. These data, considered with the percentage composition of the constituents of the intact ganglioside, suggested the repeating unit shown in Figure 4 (found: N, 2.9; neuraminic acid, 30.3; hexose, 24; galactosamine, 10. Calculated for the structure: N, 2.96; neuraminic acid, 30.5; hexose, 24.4; and galactosamine, 10.8 per cent).

In Figure 4 the linkages which were not positively identified are shown by interrupted lines. Since there would be a shortage of reducing groups required to unite all of the members of the repeating unit in the manner suggested by the hydrolytic studies, the evidence suggesting a sphingosine molecule modified in that it possesses a reducing group, was considered pertinent. The empirical observation that about 60 per cent of the total neuraminic acid can be removed by autohydrolysis, but that freeing the remainder requires more vigorous acidic hydrolysis, was in agreement with the more peripheral localization of two of the three moles of neuraminic acid/unit.

A repeating unit of this molecular size would appear to be unique, and it presents interesting problems with regard to the spatial organization of the macromolecular polymer. By simply arranging the repeating units linearly, a fibrous structure would be realized. The physical properties, however, suggested a globular molecule.

Thus, in aqueous solution flow birefringence is not marked and, on autohydrolysis, the initial fall in viscosity followed by a later increase suggests the uncoiling of a globular unit, followed by the aggregation of linear fragments. A further empirical point requiring some attention was the fact that whereas brain ganglioside is remarkably soluble in water (despite its high lipid content), it is also soluble in organic solvents. The sequence indicated by this study would permit the coiling of the polymerized units into, for example, a helix, in such a way that lipid-soluble constituents could be enfolded by water-soluble constituents in aqueous solution. In organic solvents, the coiling might occur in the opposite direction, such that the lipid-soluble constituents "faced" the solvent. It was also noted that the extended linear form of the brain ganglioside could function admirably in transport phenomena at the nerve cell surface, where it would be useful to present water-soluble constituents in one direction and lipid-soluble constituents in the other. The relation of neuraminic acid to the surface receptor substance of cells for the attachment of viruses (299, 297), and the demonstration that this preparation of brain ganglioside was an inhibitor of the hemagglutination reaction of influenza virus (55, 86) were of interest in relation to the suggestions made for the over-all structure.

The isolation of the glucocerebroside, "gangliocerebroside," in addition to solving the first portion of the over-all ganglioside structure, gave structural evidence of the relationship of the basic smaller cerebroside structure to the larger aminoglycolipid ganglioside, and provided suggestions for both the synthesis and catabolic pathways which may be followed by the gangliosides.

Subsequent work (184) with silicic acid chromatography permitted the isolation of an aminoglycolipid whose analysis conformed to one chain of the "double unit" structure, as shown in Figure 5. The problems of degradation on silica gel chromatography, referred to above, make it necessary to reserve judgment at this stage as to whether both "single" and "double unit" structures exist as such *in vivo*, or whether one or both of these are split from some larger polymerized unit during isolation. The isolation of the single unit, however, does confirm a part of the structure of Figure

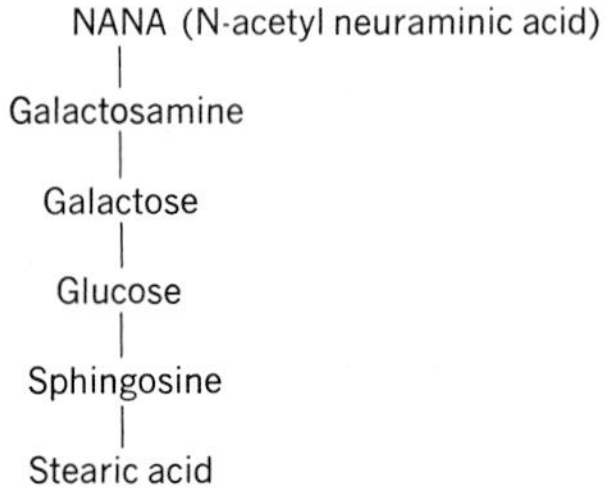

NANA (N-acetyl neuraminic acid)
Galactosamine
Galactose
Glucose
Sphingosine
Stearic acid

Figure 5. This single chain unit (184) of brain ganglioside is identical to part of the structure of Figure 4 and to compounds isolated by different methods (298).

5, and, in addition, is in complete agreement with one of the structures for another preparation for brain ganglioside ("Ganglioside I") (298) and with the "G_2" ganglioside preparation (318). For this straight single chain structure, therefore, there is agreement among four laboratories.

Isolation of a second type of chain from human brain, "Ganglioside II," has also been reported, in which galactosamine was totally absent and in which there was instead an extra mole of hexose (298). It may be seen, as shown in Figure 6, that a sub-

NANA
Galactosamine
(b)
Galactose
Glucose
Sphingosine
Stearic acid
NANA
Galactose
(a)
NANA
Galactosamine
Galactose
Glucose
Sphingosine
Stearic acid

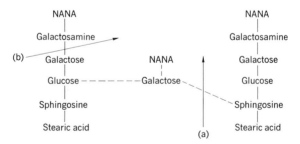

Figure 6. An illustration of how, by hydrolysis at (a), a disialoganglioside $G_{GN.T.r\,II^{2}}$ (550) could be split from the "double unit" structure, and by hydrolysis at (a) and (b), a galactosamine-free aminoglycolipid-like "Ganglioside II" (298) could be split from the "double unit" structure (59).

stance free of galactosamine can be split from the "double unit" structure of Figure 4; this substance would contain the extra mole of galactose in place of galactosamine. The evidence of several laboratories (317), that both neuraminidase (522) and "gangliosidase" activities (312) are present in brain, make it quite possible that the "Ganglioside II" substance (298) could indeed be split from the "double unit" ganglioside structure (59).

Additional structures of human brain ganglioside (496, 497) containing more than one mole of neuraminic acid per mole of ceramide also have been described (see Figure 7).

It must of course still be considered possible that there is a whole range of independent ganglioside structures, unpolymerized *in vivo*, which differ in man and other species. Furthermore, a remarkable uniformity has been demonstrated in the total amounts of ganglioside constituents in a large number of species (510).

While the "monosialoganglioside" structures (496, 317) agree with the "single unit" structure (59, 184) and with "Ganglioside I" (298), several hydrolytic fragments have been obtained which cannot readily be reconciled with the "single unit" or with the "double unit" structure in Figure 4 (550). Some of these structures are

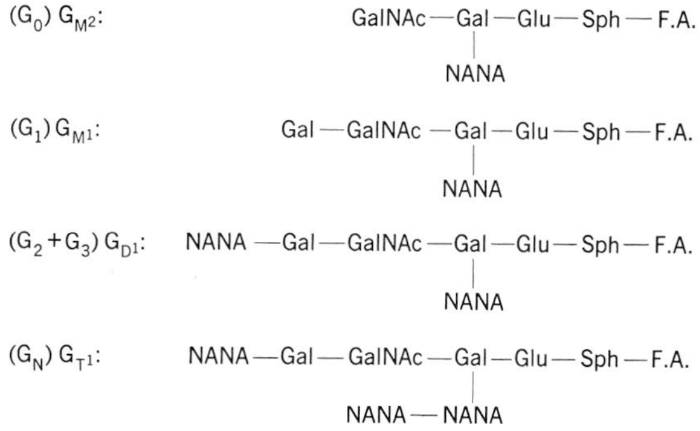

$(G_0) G_{M2}$: GalNAc —Gal —Glu —Sph — F.A.
|
NANA

$(G_1) G_{M1}$: Gal —GalNAc —Gal —Glu —Sph —F.A.
|
NANA

$(G_2 + G_3) G_{D1}$: NANA —Gal —GalNAc —Gal —Glu —Sph —F.A.
|
NANA

$(G_N) G_{T1}$: NANA —Gal — GalNAc —Gal —Glu — Sph — F.A.
|
NANA — NANA

Figure 7. Some additional types of brain ganglioside recently described (550). Key: F.A. = Fatty Acid; Sph = sphingosine; Glu = glucose; Gal = galactose; GalNAc = N-acetyl galactosamine; NANA = N-acetyl neuraminic acid. First row, (G_0) etc., and second row, (G_{M2}) etc., are equivalent designations for the same structure.

shown in Figure 7. The attachment of extra moles of neuraminic acid to the monosialoganglioside might possibly occur enzymatically during isolation. Certainly the reverse occurs, since several investigators have shown that the di- and tri-sialogangliosides are readily converted with neuraminidase to the monosialo-form (317, 46, 495, 312).

The "double unit" structure (59) has a "branch point," and the reducing power of the isolated gangliodicerebroside structure supported this structure. Evidence for branching of the carbohydrate chains in gangliosides was also obtained through periodate studies (449) and by time course hydrolysis studies (510). On the other hand, evidence has been offered from reduction studies followed by hydrolysis that there is an unbranched carbohydrate chain in the gangliosides. Several ganglioside preparations are of large molecular weight in aqueous media (59, 449), and polymerized structures are suggested in which branch points would be appropriate. Those ganglioside structures islated under harsher conditions, are monomeric, as is the "single chain" unit, and these would have no evident branching. The differences with regard to branching may therefore, prove to be related to the monomeric or polymeric form of the ganglioside material isolated.

Opposing the notion of a polymerized ganglioside are the data (510) showing that, by flourescence polarization, the preparation gave a molecular weight of 217,000 in aqueous solution, but a value of less than 2,000 in 50 per cent methanol. The earlier data (298, 175) gave molecular weights ranging from 1500 to less than 5000 in dimethylformamide, although in these cases both substances were prepared under harsher conditions.

However, unless a polymerized unit can be isolated in which covalent linkages between single units can be demonstrated, it will have to be assumed that the high molecular weight data obtained in the past are caused by the ionic association of monomeric gangliosides. Until such evidence is forthcoming, the criteria of homogeneity by ultracentrifugation and electrophoresis cannot be considered to be adequate indicators of purity of the gangliosides (522).

The existence *in situ* of aminoglycolipids containing, in addition to ganglioside constituents, covalently bound amino acides (201,

446, 448, 202, 76, 419) must also be reconsidered in view of the following findings: first, while gangliosides extracted from fresh brain contain accompanying amino acids, gangliosides extracted from acetone dehydrated brain were free of amino acids (46); second, in a study of Tay-Sachs' disease brain, large numbers of amino acids adsorbed to membranous granules rich in ganglioside have been observed (460). The matter of whether amino acids or peptides are actually linked *in situ* to gangliosides could be resolved if covalent bonds between amino acid and carbohydrate or lipid components were demonstrated in these preparations.

GLYCOPROTEINS

It has been only recently observed that a large number of protein species in the nervous system have appreciable quantities of covalently linked carbohydrates, and thus are glycoproteins (88, 75). The chemistry of the CNS glycoproteins will be discussed throughout the sections of this book which follow.

Summary

Some aspects of the structure of the brain mucoids have been briefly discussed. Glycolipids, aminopolysaccharides, aminoglycolipids, glycoproteins, and glycolipoproteins are some of the molecular types recognized to date. Studies on the structure of brain gangliosides, a type of aminoglycolipid, are one example of the progress achieved to date in understanding the structural complexity of these substances.

1. Heterogeneity of CNS mucoids

HETEROGENEITY OF HUMAN BRAIN AMINOGLYCOLIPIDS

The methods used for the extraction of bovine brain ganglioside have also been applied to human brain specimens obtained at autopsy in forty-six general hospital and mental hospital cases, whose age ranged from the fifth to the ninth decade (76). Quantitative results were obtained for the yield of "crude brain ganglioside," neuraminic acid, hexose, hexosamine, nitrogen, and amino acids, per gram of whole fresh tissue.

Aliquots of this "crude brain ganglioside" were hydrolyzed with varying concentrations of acid and varying time to determine the maximum yield of hexosamine. This was found to be obtained maximally by 15 hours of hydrolysis with N hydrochloric acid in a sealed tube at 100° C. in hydrolysis curves (½, 1, 3, 4, 7, 9, 12, 15, 24, 36, and 48 hours) on five different brains. Another aliquot of "crude brain ganglioside" was hydrolyzed with 6 N hydrochloric acid in sealed tubes at 100°C. for 1, 3, 6, 12, 24, and 36 hours, and the hydrolysate was tested quantitatively for free amino nitrogen and examined by paper chromatography. Semiquantitative paper chromatography of amino acids present in this dialyzed material after 36 hours of hydrolysis demonstrated the presence of serine, glycine, glutamic acid, aspartic acid, cysteic acid, arginine, alanine, isoleucine, leucine, lysine, and one as yet unidentified amino acid; these were quantitatively present in approximately the order named. These findings are similar in some respects but quite different in others from those described for a similar preparation from ox brain (446). Thus, threonine, phenylalanine, histidine, and valine were absent in our preparation, and serine was present in excess of glutamic acid. With short-term (1 and 3 hours) hydrolyses, some indication was obtained of the order of release of these amino acids. Glycine and serine were almost completely released in 1 hour, arginine, glutamic acid, and aspartic acid were present in approximately one-half their total, together with only traces of the other amino acids mentioned here.

Table II shows some of the characteristic values for the carbohydrate constituents obtained to date. It may be noted that the crude brain ganglioside in different brains differed in each case, not only with regard to the absolute amounts of neuraminic acid, hexose, and hexosamine obtained per gram of whole tissue, but also with regard to their relative ratios. There is a higher content of hexosamine with reference to neuraminic acid in human brain and usually still higher content of hexose. It is therefore clear that this "crude brain ganglioside fraction" derived from human brain by hot alcoholic extraction contains related non-dialyzable aminoglycolipids other than bovine brain ganglioside as classically defined (296). Thus, bovine brain ganglioside contains in salt form approximately 26, 20.8, and 8.7 per cent, respectively, of neuraminic acid, hexose, and hexosamine. In no case so far analyzed did these ratios hold for the human brain material examined. It was concluded that there must therefore be either a different type of ganglioside in the human brain, or that a ganglioside similar to that found in bovine brain is present but considerably contaminated by substances richer in hexose and hexosamine which are non-dialyzable and partitioned to this point along with the hypothetical human brain ganglioside.

In the purification of bovine brain ganglioside, the crude material was repartitioned four or five times between chloroform-methanol and water. When crude brain ganglioside material, after isolation from five different brains was combined and further repartitioned four times, the lower phase contained some 9 or 10 per cent of the dry weight of the fraction at each stage and the material in the lower phase contained increasing amounts of both neuraminic acid and hexose. Thus, the lower phase from the second, third, and fourth repartitions contained, respectively, 6.7, 8.9, 12.4 per cent hexose and 4.6, 10.8, and 13.0 per cent neuraminic acid. The upper-phase material remaining after the fourth repartition contained 16 per cent hexose and 22.3 per cent neuraminic acid, thus approaching the theoretical concentrations and molar ratios of these substances observed in purified brain ganglioside.

It was clear from these results that the classical brain ganglioside is only one of a group of non-dialyzable aminoglyclopids which can be extracted from human brain gray matter by means of the hot-methanol method described; that the other substances so extracted are quite rich in hexose, hexosamine, and neuraminic acid; and that these substances can be separated from each other. It would therefore appear that a large family of related substances exists in human brain with varying amounts of the structural constituents described here, in macromolecular association, which might be grouped under the term "aminoglycolipids." In addition to the heterogeneity of these materials isolated with alcoholic solvents, the yield in terms of both neuraminic acid and hexosamine was only one-third to one-fifth of the total that can be demonstrated by the aqueous emulsion-fractionation procedure subsequently developed (66).

Table II. Heterogeneity of brain aminoglycolipids and constituent neuraminic acid, hexosamine, and hexose in forty-six individual human brain specimens (66)

SOURCE	CRUDE AMINOGLY-COLIPIDS, (mg./g. WET WT.)	NEURAMINIC ACID (μg./g. WET WT.)	HEXOS-AMINE, (μg./g. WET WT.)	HEXOSE (μg./g. WET WT.)	% N
Gray Matter					
Mean	2.37	285.2	163.3	320.0	1.58
Range	(0.44-7.76)	(105-445)	(29-304)	(54-976)	(0.48-2.82)
White Matter					
Mean	1.86	66.0	44.1	164.3	2.16
Range	(0.13-7.30)	(6.7-191)	(3.2-124)	(31-419)	(1.1-5.0)

HETEROGENEITY OF HUMAN CEREBROSPINAL FLUID GLYCOPROTEINS

The work on the structure of brain ganglioside suggested that a search for related carbohydrate groupings in the cerebrospinal fluid (CSF) would be of interest. The CSF is at present the only part of the nervous system which can be repeatedly sampled in both man and animals without unphysiological effects. Methods were developed for the systematic study of the carbohydrate and protein constituents of small individual samples of CSF, the quantitative partition of these substances, and the demonstration of the potential for chemical individuality in the nervous system (63).

The great individual variation encountered both in the absolute quantities and in the relative ratios of particular carbohydrate constituents of CSF glycoproteins was noted (see Table III). Whether this potential for individual variation reflects genetically determined normal characteristics, or specific chemical patterns of particular functional or disease processes, or both, is yet to be determined. Similar heterogeneity has been observed in glycoproteins of other body fluids as well (165a). Since the potential demonstrated for individuation of the chemistry here described is a property of this compartment of the nervous system, the possibility exists that, by means of similar studies on other compartments of the nervous system, the chemical bases of individuality may be defined. The heterogeneity in brain aminoglycolipids (Table II) is therefore paralleled by the heterogeneity in CSF glycoproteins, and heterogeneity will be seen in the next section to be the case for brain glycoproteins as well.

HEREROGENEITY OF BRAIN GLYCOPROTEINS

Extraction of brain proteins by standard techniques previously available yielded usually less than 20 per cent of the total protein content of brain, and only up to fourteen components were demonstrable by electrophoresis (321, 285, 252, 439, 164, 286, 320, 328, 35, 36, 158, 288, 125, 473, 25, 26, 47, 398, 34, 415, 414, 201, 520, 488, 505, 442, 290, 350). Recent work in this laboratory was directed to the definition of more quantitative methods for the extraction of brain proteins and for their more adequate separation, physicochemical characterization, and histological localization by immunochemical methods. The following procedures, used in sequence, have been found by us to be useful for the definition of discrete protein fractions:

1. Solubility characteristics.
2. Column chromatography on purified DEAE cellulose (Cellex D) as supporting medium.
3. Tube-by-tube quantitative analyses of the protein, hexose, hexosamine, and neuraminic acid content.
4. Electrophoretic analysis, with acrylamide gels as supporting media, of fractions indicated to be discrete by the above three methods.

Table III. Heterogeneity of cerebrospinal fluid glycoproteins: molar quantities and ratios of hexose, hexosamine, and neuraminic acid in glycoproteins of individual specimens of CSF (63)

TOTAL SOLIDS IN GLYCOPROTEIN FRACTION	MOLAR RATIOS			
	HEXOSE (AS GLUCOSE) :	HEXOSAMINE AS GALACTOSAMINE :	NEURAMINIC ACID	MOLAR RATIO HEXOSE : HEXOSAMINE
mg./cc. CSF				
0.338	1.4	5.6	1	0.25
0.331	1.8	2.8	1	0.65
0.490	3.5	5.2	1	0.69
0.530	1.3	1.8	1	0.72
0.616	2.9	3.8	1	0.76
0.320	3.8	4.8	1	0.79
0.658	2.7	3.0	1	0.90
0.450	3.2	3.6	1	0.91
0.314	2.2	2.2	1	1.00 (1:1)
0.734	2.7	2.7	1	1.00
0.292	3.7	3.5	1	1.06
0.323	3.4	3.1	1	1.10
0.275	4.7	4.1	1	1.15
0.335	3.8	3.2	1	1.19
0.159	4.6	3.9	1	1.18
0.371	3.6	3.0	1	1.20
0.499	4.2	3.4	1	1.24
0.150	4.5	3.6	1	1.25
0.274	5.0	3.8	1	1.32
0.178	2.9	2.0	1	1.45
0.278	7.4	4.2	1	1.76
0.428	6.9	3.9	1	1.76
0.403	5.4	2.8	1	1.93 (2:1)
0.192	5.0	2.3	1	2.17
0.308	5.7	2.6	1	2.19
0.424	6.2	2.8	1	2.22
0.179	3.2	1.4	1	2.28
0.345	4.3	1.9	1	2.30
0.354	14.4	6.2	1	2.32
0.434	6.1	2.6	1	2.34
0.403	6.6	2.7	1	2.44
0.374	10.3	3.6	1	2.80
0.187	5.0	1.7	1	2.94

Table III. (Cont.)

TOTAL SOLIDS IN GLYCOPROTEIN FRACTION	HEXOSE (AS GLUCOSE)	HEXOSAMINE AS GALACTOSAMINE	: NEURAMINIC ACID	MOLAR RATIO HEXOSE : HEXOSAMINE
mg./cc. CSF				
0.425	9.9	3.3	1	3.00 (3:1)
0.534	7.7	2.4	1	3.20
0.296	3.3	1.0	1	3.30
0.278	34.4	9.9	1	3.48
0.538	5.3	1.3	1	4.07 (4:1)
0.142	8.7	2.1	1	4.20
0.480	6.1	1.1	1	5.55
0.276	6.7	1.1	1	6.09 (6:1)
0.428	13.6	2.2	1	6.18
0.594	6.7	0.7	1	9.58 (10:1)

(The header above the data: MOLAR RATIOS spans HEXOSE, HEXOSAMINE : NEURAMINIC ACID columns.)

Results Obtained with Only Two Homogenizations of Brain (88)

The application of these sequential analyses to date has given evidence for the presence of not less than fifty major chromatographic fractions and over one hundred electrophoretically separated fractions in human gray matter alone. The total yield of protein in these experiments is 6.1 g. per 100 g. wet weight of gray matter, a figure in range for previous figures for total unfractionated brain protein (457). The previously known partially characterized protein fractions of brain (34, 415, 414, 201, 329, 520, 488, 505, 442, 290), together with the small contribution by serum proteins from blood remaining in small vessels and capillaries of gray matter, are not likely to account for more than 10 per cent of this total yield. Thus, the bulk of the proteins here demonstrated apparently have not been separated or studied previously as physico-chemical entities, although the enzymatic properties of some have permitted these to be studied functionally.

In preliminary experiments, 70 grams of human gray matter, carefully dissected from autopsy specimens which had been stored at —20°C. until extraction, were homogenized either in a Potter-Elvejham homogenizer (0—5°C.) or in a precooled Waring Blendor for 3 minutes in the cold room, with 100 cc. of 0.005M phosphate buffer, pH 7, then centrifuged at 80,000 g. for 30 minutes in a Beckman Model L-2 Ultracentrifuge for clarification. The insoluble residue is rehomogenized with a further 100 cc. of phosphate buffer and centrifuged, and the second soluble extract combined with the first. The soluble proteins thus obtained (Extract A) account for 42 per cent of the total protein recovered. Extraction of the residue with 0.5M sodium chloride in 0.005 phosphate buffer, pH 7, yields another 6.9 per cent of the total protein recovered (Extract B). The residue remaining after this extraction is then extracted with 0.3 per cent Triton X-100 (106) in 0.005M phosphate buffer, pH 7, yielding a further 15.8 per cent of the total recovered (Extract C). The remaining residue has been separated into four distinct residues (Residues 1 through 4) accounting for the remaining 35.9 per cent of the total recovered. It should be noted that the proteins of Extract A are obtained under very mild conditions of extraction, while those of Extracts B and C and the Residues have been exposed to more harsh conditions of extraction. All of the detailed column, chemical, and electrophoretic analyses to be reported in this section apply to Extract A alone.

Extract A is dialyzed for 4 hours at 4°C. against 4 liters of 0.005M phosphate buffer with constant magnetic stirring of the dialyzate, then concentrated approximately tenfold against Carbowax (88) for approximately 4 hours in the cold to a final volume of dialysand between 15 and 20 cc. This concentrate is then dialyzed once more against 4 liters of phosphate buffer at 4°C. with stirring. On completion, the volume of the dialysand is noted, an aliquot is taken for total protein analysis, and 15 cc. is placed for fractionation in the cold room (4°C.) on a DEAE cellulose column 2.5 × 11.0 cm., which has been equilibrated with 0.005M sodium phosphate buffer (478). By the use of a mixing chamber containing a constant 150 cc. of solution, the solvent changes are made according to the schedule given in the legend for Figure 8. Three cc. aliquots of effluent are collected by means of an automatic fraction collector. Each tube is quantitatively analyzed for protein (340), hexose (479), hexosamine (179), and neuraminic acid (547). Where inadequate quantities are present in a single tube, from two to five tubes are combined, lyophilized, made up to suitable volume and analyzed for the carbohydrate constituents. Amino acid analysis was performed by means of an automatic amino acid analyzer. Disc electrophoresis was performed with acrylamide gel techniques at pH 9.4 (155).

Figure 8 shows the chromatographic pattern obtained in terms of tube-to-tube protein content. The distribution suggests several relatively discrete peaks, but the presence of frequent subpeaks makes it difficult to assess by this method alone how many protein fractions are actually represented. Table IV shows the detailed tube-to-tube analysis for hexose, hexosamine, and neuraminic acid. It may be seen that what appears to be a single large peak on column chromatography, e.g., the first peak that appears, as shown in Figure 8 (tubes 1 through 25 or 30), is actually separable into at least six areas, on the basis of the chemical data shown in Table IV. Indeed, disc gel electrophoresis of the contents of individual tubes of this peak show the presence of a minimum of six electrophoretic bands with the frequent expected overlap of these bands between adjacent fractions (Figure 8). Examination of the chemical data (Table IV) for each of the other peak areas obtained by column chromatography also indicates that most of these are further fractionable. On the other hand, examination of the carbohydrate content of tubes 86 through 92 (cerebroprotein fraction XXVI), or of tubes 102 through 109 (cerebroprotein fraction XXX), suggest that these are chemically relatively discrete peaks when compared with the peak for tubes 1 through 30 (cerebroprotein fractions 1 through VI). The carbohydrate content of these protein fractions is therefore used as one index of discreteness or nondiscreteness of what appears to be a homogeneous peak on column chromatography, and sections or "cuts" of the plotted protein values are made where gross changes in tube-to-tube carbohydrate content appear. On the basis of this combination of column chromatography and quantitative carbohydrate analysis, at least fifty discrete cerebroprotein fractions may be discerned, which are here denoted by Roman numerals I through L.

Recovery of protein from the column is 92 to 96 per cent. The peaks and the fractions are highly reproducible (within 2 tubes) from brain to brain, but show variation in relative amounts in

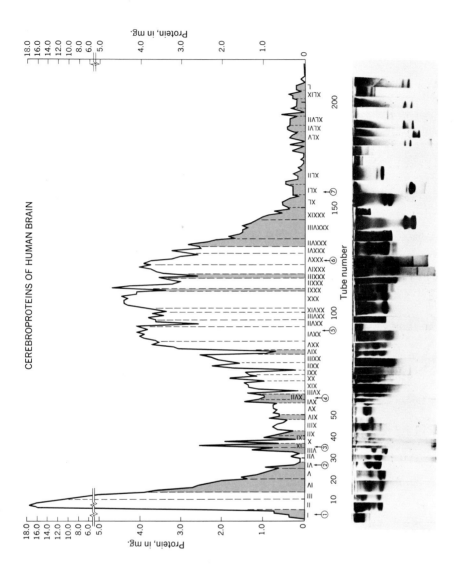

CEREBROPROTEINS OF HUMAN BRAIN

Figure 8. Column chromatography of cerebroproteins of Extract A only of human brain gray matter on DEAE cellulose.

Tube number and volume of effluent are shown on abscissa. Cerebroprotein fractions are designated by Roman numerals I through L. Shaded areas represent cerebroprotein fractions with hexose content of 2.5 per cent or greater. Numbered arrows on abscissa indicate points at which new solvents were introduced into automatic mixing chamber: (1) 75 cc. of 0.005 M sodium phosphate buffer, pH 7; (2) mixture of 12.5 cc. of 0.005 M sodium phosphate buffer, pH 7, and 12.5 cc. of 0.05 M sodium phosphate buffer, ph 4.7; (3) 75 cc. of 0.05 M sodium phosphate buffer, pH 4.7; (4) mixture of 50 cc. of 0.05 M sodium phosphate buffer, pH 4.7, and 50 cc. of 0.3 M sodium phosphate buffer, pH 4.3; (5) 100 cc. of 0.3 M sodium phosphate buffer, pH 4.3: (6) 100 cc. of 1.0 M sodium phosphate buffer, pH 4.1; (7) 100 cc. of 1.0 M phosphoric acid, pH 1.0. Electrophoretic pattern for each major cerebroprotein fraction is shown under the respective column fraction (88).

The method used to obtain the above data differs from that used to obtain the data given in Figures 9, 11, 12, 16, and all later figures depicting human and pigeon brain protein separations. The data in those figures were obtained by the use of a modified method. The two methods differ in the following ways:

1. Two homogenizations only were employed in the extraction of Figure 8; exhaustive homogenization (4 to 13 times) was used later.
2. Extract was concentrated against Carbowax in Figure 8, rather than by prevaporation, as later.
3. Purified preparation of DEAE (Cellex D) was used in all later separations.
4. The same eluting solvents, (1) through (7) above, also were employed later, but the spacing between these was increased in order to permit more complete elution with each solvent (see p. 123). Total number of tubes was later increased to 259 for the first seven eluting solvents.
5. Triton X-100, not used in the above elution, was routinely employed later, following solvent (7), that is, beginning with tube 260 and ending with tube 350.

different brains. The cerebroprotein fractions in different brains also appear to date to be consistent in terms of high and low carbohydrate content, respectively, as shown by the respective shaded and non-shaded areas of Figure 8, but the absolute amount of carbohydrate in each fraction varies. These variations may be due to age, pathological changes, postmortem change, functional states at death, or individual variability, and these, as well as other possibilities, must be explored in future studies.

Examination of each of the fifty cerebroprotein fractions by means of disc gel electrophoresis reveals that each contains between two and eleven electrophoretically clearly separated protein zones or subfractions. While it is evident that two neighboring effluent tubes from column chromatography will have at least some proteins with identical electrophoretic mobilities, it is not possible without further data to come to any conclusions regarding their identity of structure. For example, the comparison of the electrophoretic pattern of cerebroprotein fractions I and II shows a marked change in the zone where the carbohydrate content changes from 6.8 per cent to 0.2 per cent. Thus the several new protein species which appear for the first time in tube 7 and continue through 11, and which are apparently low in carbohydrate content, are demonstrable both by chemical analysis and by electrophoresis. Counting only those bands which appear *de novo* in succeeding cerebroprotein fractions, cerebroproteins 1 through 100 can be distinguished; whether some of these differ only in molecular size, in only a few amino acid residues, in only a few attached carbohydrates groups, or in some other minor structural way cannot be ascertained at this point, but they differ sufficiently that they are separable by means of electrophoresis.

It may be noted that the carbohydrate content frequently, although not invariably, tends to increase as one passes from the first to the last tube of a given chromatographic peak. For example, if one compares cerebroprotein fractions II through VI, the hexose increases from 0.2 per cent to 6.6 percent. Are cerebroprotein fractions II through VI composed mostly of proteins with similar or identical amino acid sequences but with more or less carbohydrate units attached? The answer to this question requires detailed quantitative amino acid analysis of each of the cerebroprotein fractions. This has not as yet been completed, but the initial results are of some interest. With regard to this first chromatographic peak, two areas were analyzed for constituent amino acids in hydrolyzed samples. The residues of amino acids per thousand for almost all of the amino acids were similar or identical, with two marked exceptions: serine and glutamic acid. Thus comparison of the two cerebroprotein fractions showed one to have twice as many serine residues per thousand (123.3 compared with 62.9), and 50 per cent more glutamic acid residues per thousand (75.1 compared with 50.7) as the other. Since there is considerable evidence in other glycoproteins that these two amino acids are involved in the linkage of carbohydrates to proteins, and since there are marked differences in the carbohydrate content of fractions I to VI of this peak, this variability in only carbohydrate content and a few amino acid residues is of considerable interest and will be further examined.

In addition to specific isolation and characterization studies of these human cerebroproteins, specific antisera to these cerebroproteins are being prepared (425-429) both for immunological tests of homogeneity, and for the demonstration of the histological localization of as many of these proteins as possible in cell types (e.g. neurons or glia), and in different architectonic layers of the cerebral cortex. The use of histochemical methods for the assessment of enzyme activities in each of these protein fractions has also begun. It has been shown by us to be applicable to the esterases, and will be carried out with other enzymes such as proteinases (321) as well.

The comparison of these proteins in human brain specimens with regard to their presence or absence as isoantigens, and the examination of their development through embryonic and postnatal periods has been initiated (see p. 134). Also, these methods permit a more thorough examination of the biosynthesis of brain proteins (see p. 201) (534), and offer an opportunity not previously available for the investigation of a broad range of neurologic and psychiatric disorders with regard to the possible implication of some of these proteins in pathological processes (see pages 139-155).

Table IV. Carbohydrate content of cerebroprotein fractions I through L of human brain cerebral cortex

CEREBRO-PROTEIN FRACTION	% HEXOSE	% NEURAMINIC ACID	% HEXOSAMINE
I	6.8	—	o
II	0.2	—	—
III	0.5, 0.6	0.04, 0.09	0.6
IV	2.1, 3.1, 1.5	o	1.7, 2.0
V	4.2, 5.4, 5.7, 2.4	o, o, o, o	—
VI	6.6, 10.1	o, o	—
VII	12.0, 17.6	o, o, o	—
VIII	8.0, 4.2	o	—
IX	7.6, 5.0	o, o	0.2
X	1.6	o	—
XI	4.6	o	—
XII	8.4	o	—
XIII	2.1, 4.5	o	o
XIV	4.0	o	—
XV	2.0, 1.5, 3.2	o, o	—
XVI	0.5	—	—
XVII	2.4, 6.5, 1.5	o, o	—
XVIII	o	—	—
XIX	o, o	—	—
XX	1.4, 1.2, 2.1	o	o
XXI	11.2	o	o
XXII	0.2	—	—
XXIII	0.6, 1.2, 0.6	o, 0.3, o	o
XXIV	2.8, 4.9	—	—
XXV	1.2, 1.6	o, 0.3	o, o
XXVI	1.0, 1.0, 1.0, 0.9	0.1, 0.1, 0.1	o, 0.9, o
XXVII	0.8, 1.3	0.04, 0.1	o, 1.5
XXVIII	1.0, 1.1	0.1, 0.2	o
XXIX	0.8	0.2	—
XXX	1.1, 1.6, 1.5, 1.4	0.1, o, 0.2, 0.1	o, 0.6, o
XXXI	2.7	0.1	1.4
XXXII	1.0, 1.6, 1.9	0.3, 0.3	0.8, 2.3
XXXIII	o, 2.5	o, 0.3	0.8, 1.9
XXXIV	1.0, 1.2, 0.8	0.4, —, 0.2	o, o
XXXV	o, 1.3	0.2	—
XXXVI	0.5, 1.1	0.2	—
XXXVII	3.6, 2.1, 2.8	0.1	o
XXXVIII	4.3, 2.8, 3.6, 3.6, 3.7	1.5, 1.6	2.3
XXXIX	6.0, 5.9	1.9, 0.6, 2.0, 0.6, 1.4	o

Table IV. (Cont.)

CEREBRO-PROTEIN FRACTION	% HEXOSE	% NEURAMINIC ACID	% HEXOSAMINE
XL	3.9, 5.8	1.5, 0.6	—
XLI	8.8	0.7, 0.9	—
XLII	5.7	—	7.2
XLIII	—	—	0
XLIV	12.5	0	0
XLV	18.8, 12.0	0.0	—
XLVI	6.1	0.7	0
XLVII	8.8, 10.2	1.0	3.5, 0
XLVIII	18.2	0.1	0
XLIX	14.5	—	0
L	11.4	0	0

As % of protein; successive numbers left to right represent successive tube determinations from beginning to end of fraction; 33 year old male; anoxic death.

All of the data in Figure 8 and in Table IV pertain to Extract A only. These discernible and separable proteins represent only 42 per cent of the total prepared by us from gray matter alone. It is clear that years of work lie ahead for many laboratories in terms of the further physical and chemical definition of species of proteins in human and other mammalian brain. The findings here presented suggest that this task will involve the study of large numbers of individual proteins. This may not seem unreasonable when the complex functional requirements of the brain, such as those pertaining to the specificity of interneuronal transmission and the need for specificity in such functions as memory, are taken into account. The specificity of coding in the amino acid chains of proteins elsewhere has been shown to be fundamental to specificity of function, as in the case of hormones, and in antigen-antibody reactions. The addition of eight or more individual carbohydrate residues (see p. 200) to such amino acid chains adds many more, perhaps n^8 or higher power orders of variation to the macromolecules of the CNS, a fact of considerable interest in the consideration of these substances for molecular coding functions.

Results Obtained by Increasing the Number of Homogenizations
The extraction of the dissected gray matter later was carried out according to a more exhaustive procedure (420).

Table V. Extractability of human and rat cerebroproteins with 0.005 M phosphate buffer, pH 7.0

STARTING MATERIAL	NUMBER OF HOMOGENIZATIONS	ORIGINAL BRAIN YIELD mg./g.
Human gray matter	2	7.7
	9-14*	19.3 (12.6-25.8)
Separated subcellular fractions:		
Human gray	2	32.0
Rat whole brain	2	34.4

* Rehomogenization of residue continued until protein less than 100 μg./ml. in supernate (420).

Table V shows the quantitative extractable yields obtained on the basis of mg. of protein per gram original brain material in all of the subcellular fractions added together, compared with those obtained in morphologically unseparated gray matter and whole brain. The yields are increased by three factors: (1) the number of homogenizations; (2) the preliminary separation of subcellular particles prior to homogenization; and (3) the more adequate resuspension of separated particles with Teflon-glass homogenizer prior to homogenization in a Waring Blendor. All these factors, taken together with the data that follow on the fraction of protein which is difficult to elute from DEAE cellulose without Triton, suggest that one crucial factor in the low recoveries of protein in brain extracts is the failure to pay attention to the highly membranous nature of the starting material and the need to rupture those membranes by mechanical means.

Modified Procedure
The concentration of the combined extract was accomplished by

perevaporation rather than by Carbowax. This change in procedure was established because it was found that dialysis does not free the extract completely of the remaining Carbowax, which interferes with the carbohydrate analysis of the protein fractions. The chromatography of the concentrated extract was accomplished as previously described, with the exception that a purified form of DEAE cellulose, Cellex-D, was employed routinely. The elution scheme utilized the same seven solvents previously described (88), but the spacing of these was changed in order to provide more complete elution with each solvent. Thus solution 1 began with tube 1, solution 2 with tube 88, solution 3 with tube 98, solution 4 with tube 114, solution 5 with tube 155, solution 6 with tube 187, solution 7 with tube 212, and 0.3 per cent Triton X-100 with tube 260.

In all, 350 tubes of 3 cc. each were utilized for complete fractionation. The collection of the effluents was performed by means of a Beckman automatic fraction collector. This, as all other preceding operations, was carried out in a cold room 0-4°C. Each effluent tube was analyzed for its content of protein (Folin-Lowry) the early studies being done manually, later studies being done with a Technicon Autoanalyzer. The effluents were combined into thirteen groups in the present studies, and groups 8, 10, and 11 were each later divided into two subgroups, A and B. The groups were lyophilized, dissolved, and dialyzed exhaustively against distilled water.

The protein content was repeated, and 500 μg. of protein concentrated for each run on gel electrophoresis. The remainder was used for carbohydrate analysis (59).

The column chromatographic results obtained with autopsy specimens (i.e. No. 218 and No. 219) and biopsy specimens (i.e. No. 3 and No. 9c) are comparable (72). This step in the analysis provides only a preliminary separation of major groups, the heterogeneity of which, as pointed out in earlier publications, is clearly established by the carbohydrate analysis tube-to-tube, and disc gel electrophoresis of separated groups. Figure 9 shows the comparison on column chromatography of brain proteins of normal and tumor tissue (see also p. 150).

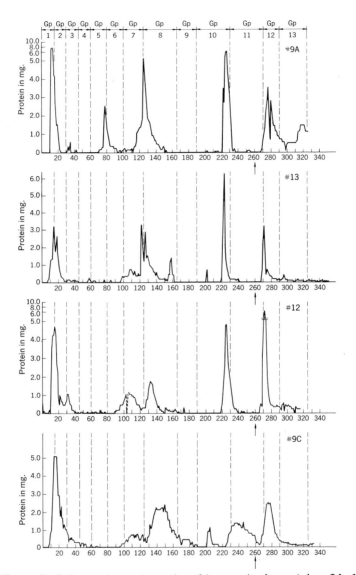

Figure 9. Column chromatography of human brain proteins. 9A, 13, and 12 are human glial brain tumors; 9C is normal human gray matter.

Summary

Marked heterogeneity is found to be the rule for the brain amino-glycolipids, for the cerebrospinal fluid glycoproteins, and for the brain glycoproteins. The vast range of molecular species available in the brain mucoids would therefore be consistent with their postulated function in memory processes.

2. Location of CNS mucoids

BRAIN GANGLIOSIDES

The brain gangliosides are in their highest concentration in gray matter areas, cerebral and cerebellar cortex, and deep nuclei, as well as in dorsal root ganglia. This nerve cell localization of gangliosides is confirmed by the fact that in Tay-Sachs' disease, in which the concentration of ganglioside is markedly increased, the cellular accumulation of this material swells the nerve cells. Immunofluorescent studies with anti-ganglioside serum confirms the nerve cell localization of ganglioside (91). As will be seen in the section on Pathology, gangliosides account for up to 50 per cent by weight of the membranous intracellular accumulations in nerve cells in Tay-Sachs' disease. The nerve cell body localization of these mucoids would conform with the hypothesis that the storage of experiential information involves chemical constituents of nerve cell body. However, the presence of high ganglioside concentration in synaptic regions in association with acetylcholine has been reported (115), and gangliosides have been shown to be concentrated in the external synaptosome membrane (558a). The essential absence of gangliosides from pure fiber tract white matter is also in agreement with the findings above. Several investigators have shown "lipid-soluble neuraminic acid" to be predominantly associated with the microsome fraction of brain cells, but the characterization of this neuraminic acid as gangliosides cannot be made with certainty since the other constituents of gangliosides have not been determined and protein-bound neuraminic acid not distinguished. This is the problem attending the attempt to localize gangliosides to membranes in serial section studies as well (561a, 561b, 248a).

SUBCELLULAR FRACTIONATION OF GLYCOPROTEINS AND OTHER MUCOIDS OF HUMAN, RAT, AND GUINEA PIG BRAIN

Human gray matter, rat gray matter, and rat whole brain were homogenized for exactly 2 minutes in a Potter-Elvejham glass homogenizer with glass or Teflon plunger in an ice-water bath, with 10 volumes of 0.32 M sucrose containing 10^{-5} M $CaCl_2$ ("sucrose solution") to each gram wet weight of tissue (419). The homogenate was centrifuged (Spinco L_2 ultracentrifuge at 3000 rev./min. for 10 min., supernate ("post-nuclear") removed, and the pellet three times resuspended in "sucrose solution" (by a few gentle strokes in the Teflon-glass homogenizer), and recentrifuged (at 3100 rev./min. for 10 min., 3500 rev./min. for 12 min. and 4000 rev./min. for 12 min.). The final pellet ("nuclear fraction") was dialyzed twice for 4 hours each against 2 l. aliquots of sodium phosphate buffer (Figure 8, solution I). The "post-nuclear" supernate plus three washings combined were centrifuged at 15,100 rev./min. for 10 min., the post-mitochondrial supernate decanted, the pellet twice resuspended in "sucrose solution" and recentrifuged (at 15,300 rev./min. for 12 min.; then at 15,600 rev./min. for 14 min.). The final pellet ("mitochondrial fraction") was dialyzed as above. The "microsomal fraction" (centrifuged at 40,000 rev./min.) was dialyzed as were the other two. The post-microsomal "supernate" was also dialyzed, as were the three pellets.

Each subcellular fraction after dialysis was brought to 90 ml. volume with solution I and homogenized twice for 3 min. periods in a Waring Blendor, and the homogenate centrifuged each time for 20 min. at the appropriate speed: 15,000 rev./min. for the nuclear fraction; 16,000 rev./min. for the mitochondrial fraction; and 40,000 rev./min. for the microsomal fraction. The two supernates combined from each and the postmicrosomal supernate ("super-

nate") were concentrated, then chromatographed on purified
DEAE cellulose (Cellex-D) as previously described, except that 4
ml. aliquots of effluent were collected, the original spacing of solvents was employed (88), and Triton X-100 was used at the end of
the run to remove any remaining material from the column.

Figure 10 shows the column chromatographic patterns obtained with the subcellular fractions in human gray matter and rat
whole brain studied to date. First, despite the over-all similarity,
the quantity of individual peaks within each species indicate that
certain organelle-specific or organelle-rich proteins are characteristic. Thus, for example, compare the peaks between 400 and 500 ml.
effluent in the four fractions. This suggests that further separation
of these peaks and full electrophoretic examination will yield
higher discrimination between organelles. Second, human gray
matter and rat whole brain show an inverse relationship in the
relative amount of protein solubilized readily, i.e. in the supernate
fraction, and the amount that is in the nuclear fraction. Thus human gray matter yields a greater proportion in the nuclear fraction,
and rat whole brain a greater proportion in the supernate (see
Table VI). Third, in human gray matter, the relative and absolute

Table VI. Subcellular distribution of cerebroproteins of human gray
matter and rat whole brain

SUBCELLULAR FRACTION	HUMAN GRAY MATTER		RAT WHOLE BRAIN	
	mg./g. WET WT. GRAY MATTER	% OF TOTAL EXTRACTED	mg./g. WET WT. WHOLE BRAIN	% OF TOTAL EXTRACTED
Nuclear	14.74	45.9	8.77	25.5
Mitochondrial	9.30	29.0	11.43	33.2
Microsomal	1.77	5.5	3.96	11.5
Post-microsomal supernate	6.27	19.6	10.25	29.8
Total	32.08	100.0	34.41	100.0

amounts of protein which need Triton X-100 in order to be eluted
from DEAE cellulose increases in amount passing from microsomes through mitochondria to nuclei. This appears to be the rela-

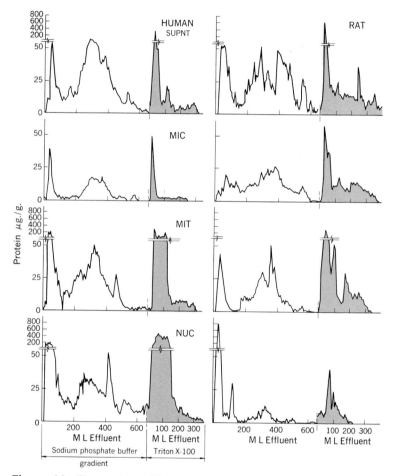

Figure 10. Chromatographic patterns obtained with 0.005 M sodium phosphate buffer extracts of separated subcellular fractions. "Human" refers to human gray matter; "Rat" to rat whole brain.

tionship in rat whole brain between microsomes and mitochondria, but the consistently low over-all DEAE cellulose recovery of the rat nuclear fraction does not allow for any conclusions in the case of the rat at this time. Fourth, the advantage of using aqueous buffers as long as possible is clearly illustrated here since this allows for a differentiation of the proteins more difficult to elute from the bulk. In addition, the bulk of the brain proteins never have to come in contact with a detergent with its attendant disadvantages of confusing microanalytic studies in the future, and its denaturing effects.

In human gray matter at least, where the recoveries are good, it may be that the Triton-elutable material represents more firmly membrane-bound or membrane-enclosed proteins, possibly with higher lipid content. (See p. 130 and Figure 11.)

Table VII. Quantitative recovery of cerebroproteins of human gray matter and rat whole brain on DEAE cellulose chromatography

SUBCELLULAR FRACTION	% RECOVERY HUMAN GRAY MATTER			% RECOVERY RAT WHOLE BRAIN		
	WITHOUT TRITON X-100	WITH TRITON X-100	TOTAL % RECOVERY	WITHOUT TRITON X-100	WITH TRITON X-100	TOTAL % RECOVERY
Nuclear	36.7	58.8	95.5	48.4	6.7	55.1
Mitochondrial	43.0	30.8	73.8	16.0	24.3	40.3
	81.5	18.8	100.3*			
Microsomal	73.7	24.6	98.3	47.1	35.0	82.1
Post-microsomal supernate	65.2	18.3	85.5	39.3	25.0	64.3

* Method modified in that three homogenizations employed, extract was centrifuged at 30,000 r.p.m. for 90 minutes, and supernates concentrated by perevaporation. Note improved recoveries on p. 122 and p. 194.

Table VII shows the quantitative data for these recoveries from DEAE cellulose and illustrates quantitatively the transition from microsomes through nuclei for presence of Triton-elutable proteins. It may be seen that for the human gray matter quantitative recoveries usually are achieved. The over-all recovery from DEAE cellulose in the case of rat whole brain is poor even with Triton, presumably because of the presence of white matter components. It must be emphasized that these do not interfere with extractability from the tissues, but with elutability from DEAE cellulose.

Table VIII. Ammonium sulphate fractionation of mucoids of human gray matter mitochondrial fraction A (GMA) (See Figure 10)

FRACTION PRECIPITATED	% AMMONIUM SULPHATE USED	% HEXOSE*	% SIALIC ACID* (AS NANA**)
GMA I	0	46.8	7.0
GMA II	30	25.5	8.7
GMA III	50	28.5	12.3
GMA IV	70	30.0	16.8
GMA V	90	217.7	143.8
Recovery of hexose and sialic acid from GMA		91%	86%

* As % of protein in precipitate   ** N-Acetylneuraminic acid

Table VIII shows the concentration of hexose and neuraminic acid in the further fractionated zone A (see Fig. 10) of the mitochondrial fraction. The data suggest a range of species of glycoproteins and mucoids with varying proportions of protein to carbohydrate constituents. The complexity of the molecular forms apparent here makes it clear that the immunological data which we have to date obtained by producing antisera to some of these fractions in rabbits (see Section 5 of this chapter) needs to be interpreted conservatively, and that future work in this complex field will require that we give attention to a multiplicity of molecular forms.

This multiplicity once more points to the potential range for informational coding and biochemical individuality now available in the glycoproteins and mucoids of the nervous system.

PROTEINS OF SUBCELLULAR FRACTIONS OF GUINEA-PIG BRAIN
GRAY MATTER

With the improvement in column chromatography achieved by

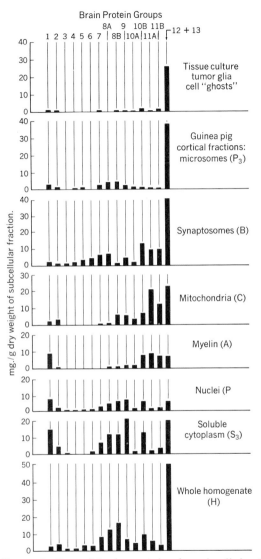

Figure 11. Concentration of brain proteins in subcellular fractions of glial tumor cells grown in tissue culture (75) and of normal guinea pig cortex (92).

the spacing of eluting solvents (72), and the more thorough separation of subcellular components by sucrose gradient centrifugation, the distribution of prain proteins was once more examined (92).

Figure 11 shows the concentration of proteins of each group in mg./g. of dry weight of subcellular fraction. These data are far from definitive for two reasons: first, the subcellular fractions were still morphologically heterogeneous, and second, poor extractability was observed, possibly due to the dialysis of isolated subcellular fractions against distilled water rather than phosphate buffer as above.

Membrane Proteins

The impression in previous work (419) that the Triton-elutable protein (groups 11B, 12, and 13) has its source in membranes was again supported in the present work. The simplest protein pattern was seen in the *microsomes*, where almost all groups are absent with the exception of group 12. Microsomes are pure membranous forms without aqueous enclosures.

The lowest relative concentration of groups 11B, 12, and 13 combined was in the soluble cytoplasmic fraction, and in nuclei when compared to myelin, and to mitochondria. The highest relative concentration was in microsomes and synaptosomes which contained little of the cytoplasmic proteins (see also the discussion of glial tumor cell "ghost" proteins, Figure 20).

Non-membrane Proteins

The proteins of apparently non-membranous origin, in contrast, are seen to predominate in the soluble cytoplasmic fraction, i.e. groups 7, 8A, 8B, and 9. In those organelles in which aqueous media are enclosed by membranes, these proteins of groups 7, 8A, 8B, and 9 are present in amounts consistent with the electron microscopic impression of the amount of aqueous substance enclosed; thus, they are relatively least in myelin and synaptosomes, and enriched in nuclei.

Protein of groups 1 and 2 are almost absent from microsomes, mitochondria, and synaptosomes, but present in myelin, soluble cytoplasmic fractions, and nuclear fractions (see also Figure 12 and p. 134).

Proteins of Less Certain Source

Group 10B proteins are present in mitochondria, synaptosomes, and myelin. Other evidence has suggested that 10B is a glial component; i.e. 10B is elevated six- to ten-fold in glial tumors (75), elevated seven-fold in gliosis with loss of nerve cells (72), and can be extracted from glial tumor cells grown in tissue culture (75). The presence of 10B in higher concentration in synaptosomes, which are composed of nerve terminals, i.e. the continuation of the outer nerve cell membranes together with vesicles, but no nuclei, suggests that 10B is a component of both nerve and glial outer membranes, or alternately suggests the presence of glial membranes in nerve ending preparations. This would be compatible with the electron microscopic finding of the intimate three-dimensional intertwining of glial processes with nerve cell processes near synapses.

Group 11A proteins are present in high concentration in *mitochondria* and in *myelin*. They are absent from microsomes, and present in only trace amounts in soluble cytoplasm and in nuclei. The presence of 11A proteins in appreciable amounts in synaptosomes would correlate with the electron microscopic evidence of the presence of small mitochondria in this synaptosomal preparation, but also with recent electron microscopic evidence of glycoproteins at synapses (430a, 430b).

Summary

The evidence at present on the subcellular location of brain mucoids suggests that gangliosides occur predominantly in nerve membranes; group 2 proteins originate in myelin, cytoplasm, and nuclei; group 10B in membranes of glia and possibly nerve cells; and 11A in mitochondria and synaptosomes. It should be emphasized that these data represent only a first approximation. The quantitative changes in these three protein groups which have been observed in learning in pigeons will be discussed later in this chapter. Electron microscopic evidence of glycoproteins at synapses is especially relevant to the mucoid-memory hypothesis.

3. Prenatal and postnatal development of human brain proteins

Data on the correlation of brain protein concentrations with experiential learning during what is perhaps the most important period of the human lifespan, that between two and forty-five years of age, are not yet available. In addition, the number of specimens studied to date in each developmental period is too small to permit conclusions.

Some of the data available are of interest, however (71). Thus, there is a suggestion of a "critical period" between 15 and 20 gestational weeks, in which the protein of groups 1 and 2 increases markedly. In contrast, the stability of other groups during this period is noteworthy (see Figures 12-15). The change in groups 1 and 2 correlated in time with the appearance of new dendritic cell processes, and with the rapid growth of the cortical gray mantle, beginning in the insular area and spreading over both occipital and frontal poles (565). Discrete specimens from the insular region as distinct from the poles, in a 20-week-old human brain, showed the insular area to contain 1.3 mg./g. of groups 1 and 2, while the poles contained only 0.1 mg./g. This temporal relationship to nerve cell process growth has led to the use of the term dendritic proliferation protein for the relevant proteins of groups 1 and 2 (71).

Figure 12 shows the protein patterns on column chromatography of human fetal brain proteins (cerebral hemispheres). From top to bottom, the specimens are 14-week, 15-week, 16-week, and 22-week prenatal gestational age, followed by a 36-day-old postnatal specimen. The sudden appearance of groups 1 and 2 in appreciable amounts can be seen.

In the adult, and depending on the amount of brain specimen homogenized, the first effluent peak occupies group 3 as well as 1 and 2. Figure 13 compares these groups in prenatal, postnatal, and adult brain specimens. Solid symbols represent whole cerebral hemisphere specimens, whereas open symbols represent dissected gray matter only.

In groups 1-3, and in group 11A, there is a greater amount of

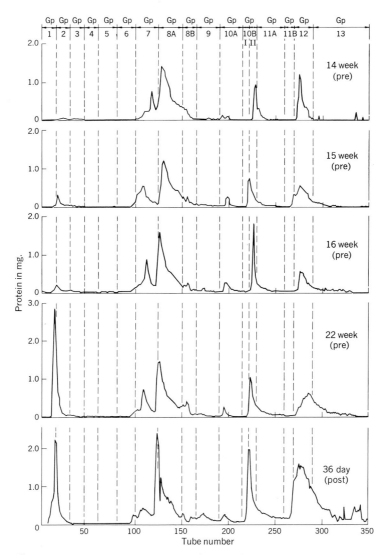

Figure 12. Embryonic human brain proteins: 14th, 15th, 16th, and 22nd gestational weeks and 36-day postnatal. Note change in groups 1-3.

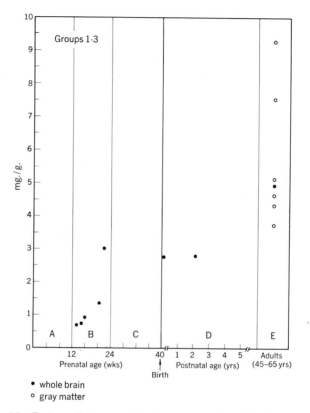

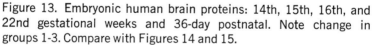

- • whole brain
- ° gray matter

Figure 13. Embryonic human brain proteins: 14th, 15th, 16th, and 22nd gestational weeks and 36-day postnatal. Note change in groups 1-3. Compare with Figures 14 and 15.

protein in adults, but in several other groups no such gradient is apparent. The changes in pigeon brain groups 2 and 11A with learning are of interest in this regard.

Maturational differences can also be observed on disc gel electrophoresis of the individual protein groups.

The analysis of each group by disc gel electrophoresis yields mobilities (Rd) for each protein band relative to the front-running dye marker (72). The proteins are denoted according to their chromatographic group first, and then their Rd; thus, the protein from group 1 which has an Rd of 0.42 is designated 1:0.42. There are certain general differences between the normal child specimens and the normal adult specimens. Thus in group 1, four protein bands are visible in the normal child which are not present in the adult. Protein bands 1:0.42 through 1:0.44, 1:0.69, 1:0.89, and

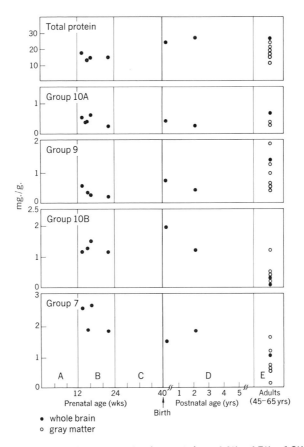

Figure 14. Embryonic human brain proteins: 14th, 15th, 16th, and 22nd gestational weeks and 36-day postnatal. Compare with Figures 13 and 15.

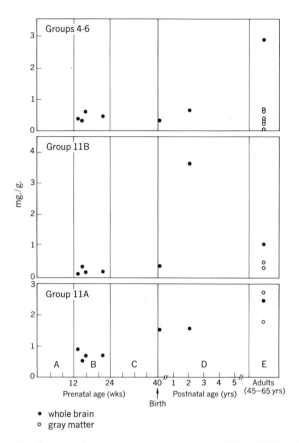

Figure 15. Embryonic human brain proteins: 14th, 15th, 16th, and 22nd gestational weeks and 36-day postnatal. Compare with Figures 13 and 14.

1:0.96 have not been seen in the adults, nor are these bands seen in group 2 or group 3.

Group 8B lacks the heterogeneity in the normal child that it exhibits in the adult specimens, whereas groups 9 and 10B show more heterogeneity in the child than they do in the adult.

Summary

Preliminary data on the maturation of brain proteins known to contain carbohydrate groups are, in certain instances, notably groups 2 and 11A, consistent with the requirements for memory function, but the data are still meager, and much more work needs to be done in this important area.

4. Pathology of the CNS mucoids

TAY-SACHS' DISEASE

Tay-Sachs' disease is an inborn disorder of aminoglycolipid metabolism characterized by the accumulation in brain of excessive amounts of brain ganglioside (295). The hypothesis (59) that brain ganglioside is a membrane constituent received strong support from the isolation in Tay-Sachs' disease of curious membranous formations which accumulate intracellularly, and which have been shown to contain up to 50 per cent of their weight as ganglioside by analysis of isolated membranes (312). While the common method followed in previous years for the determination of brain ganglioside in cases of Tay-Sachs' disease involved the determination of neuraminic acid, hexosamine, or both in an unpurified or only partially purified lipid extract of brain, the results from this laboratory and others indicated that neither of these constituents, alone, or together, accurately reflects the presence of brain ganglioside, because of the presence in brain of a large family of related aminoglycolipids. The presence of these related aminoglycolipids most probably explains the high hexose content, high galactose: glucose ratio, low neuraminic acid content, and marked heterogeneity on countercurrent distribution of the material previously isolated from human brain (447). Later studies have shown these aminoglycolipids to be generally involved in Tay-Sachs' disease

(66) and that non-dialyzable carbohydrates of protein fractions are similarly elevated in this disorder (72).

One fraction of brain in Tay-Sachs' disease obtained by the emulsion-fractionation method (66) contained markedly elevated concentrations of hexosamine, hexose, and neuraminic acid per gram of gray matter. Several other fractions were markedly diminished in concentration of non-dialyzable phosphorus. In gray matter there was an abnormal accumulation of aminoglycolipids which did not have the molar ratios neuraminic acid-hexose-hexosamine (3:2.4:1) of the classic ganglioside, but rather had their greatest increase in non-dialyzable hexosamine. This increase occurred entirely in one of the nine fractions isolated, fraction IX, the others being essentially normal with regard to their content of non-dialyzable carbohydrates (Tables IX and X).

The evidence of decrease in non-dialyzable phosphorus in some of the complexes, together with the fact that the greatest total increase of the three carbohydrates was in hexosamine, raised the possibility of some disturbance in the synthesis and utilization of hexosamine. That this disturbance may be related to a failure of normal maturation of biosynthetic functions with regard to these

Table IX. Total concentrations of solids, phosphorus, hexosamine, hexose, and neuraminic acid (The last four represent non-dialyzable quantities) in Tay-Sachs', normal child, and adult brains; emulsion-fractionation method (66).

CONSTITUENT IN GRAY MATTER, WET WT. (MG./G.)	TAY-SACHS' (4 YEARS)	NORMAL (8 MONTHS)	NORMAL (5½ YEARS)[a]	NORMAL ADULT[b]
Total solids	129.6	128.0	212.0	180.0
Total non-dialyzable solids	95.5	113.0	149.0	130.0
Total phosphorus	0.81	1.15	1.27	1.24
Total hexosamine	4.84	0.84	1.07	1.58
Total hexose	6.30	2.57	2.90	3.20
Total neuraminic acid	2.75	1.47	1.99	1.40

a. Congenital heart disease, death due to post-operative complications.
b. Mean values for 6 postmortem specimens from subjects 45 to 83 years of age.

Table X. Distribution of non-dialyzable phosphorus, hexosamine, hexose, and neuraminic acid in emulsion-fractionation method; fractions I to IX in Tay-Sachs', normal child, and adult brain. (Concentrations as μg./g. gray matter, wet weight)

CONSTITUENT IN GRAY MATTER, WET WT. (μg./g.)	E.F. FRACTION	TAY-SACHS' 4 YEARS	NORMAL 8 MONTHS	NORMAL 5½ YEARS[a]	NORMAL ADULT[b]
Phosphorus					
	I-VII	321	410	886	883
	VIII	15	0	0	0
	IX	474	739	378	406
Hexosamine					
	I-VII	1356	717	923	1203
	VIII	49	77	0	16
	IX	3433	173	144	360
Hexose					
	I-VII	2517	1408	2326	2151
	VIII	177	269	136	157
	IX	3605	897	440	696
Neuraminic acid					
	I-VII	1329	843	1587	1003
	VIII	102	135	90	61
	IX	1320	492	312	301

a. Congenital heart disease, death due to post-operative complications.
b. Mean values for 6 postmortem specimens from subjects 45 to 83 years of age.

substances was suggested by the chemical similarity of the 4-year-old Tay-Sachs' brain to the 8-month-old normal brain. If it were assumed that hexosamine might be synthetically incorporated in two different ways into nondialyzable complexes, that is, with or without molar equivalents of phosphate, the pathological state here found might be defined chemically as one in which the incorporation into non-dialyzable compounds of hexosamine plus phosphate together is diminished, whereas that of hexosamine alone is favored. The results in this case, in fact, showed that for each mole of phosphorus in deficit in non-dialyzable gray matter complexes, there were 1.08 moles of hexosamine present in excess in non-dialyzable complexes. Since these molar comparisons are based on only eight non-Tay-Sachs' brain specimens, the conclusions which may be derived therefrom are tentative. This chemical lesion might be the result of some disturbance in the uridine-diphosphohexosamine trasferase system whereby hexosamine rather than hexosamine phosphate is exchanged. The presence of hexosamine unbound by phosphate in higher concentrations than normal might favor the synthesis of excessive neuraminic acid via the N-acetyl neuraminic acid aldolase synthetic reaction or in some other way may induce increased formation (or decreased destruction) of the aminoglycolipids found in excess in Tay-Sachs' disease.

The relative concentration of different brain ganglioside subtypes have been studied, and one (G_{M2}) shown to predominate (496). Whether this is due to increased gangliosidase activity or due to preferential synthesis of this one subtype has not been established.

From the evidence above indicating an increase in asialo-aminoglycolipids, and the evidence which follows indicating that protein-associated non-dialyzable hexoses are also generally elevated, the definition of Tay-Sachs' disease as a purely ganglioside disorder does not appear to be indicated. Instead, Tay-Sachs' disease should be viewed as a disorder in mucoid metabolism involving many types of non-dialyzable carbohydrate substances.

FURTHER STUDIES ON TAY-SACHS' DISEASE: TAY-SACHS' PROTEIN

The progress which has been made in understanding the molecular basis of the sphingolipidoses has naturally followed the methodological advances for the study of particular tissue constituents. Thus, during the past thirty years, most biochemical studies in the sphingolipidoses have centered upon the lipids and glycolipids, while little or nothing is known about the structure of metabolism of proteins in sphingolipidoses. Our ignorance with regard to the brain proteins has been a function of the inability quantitatively to extract, separate, and define these constituents of brain. Up until less than four years ago the methods available permitted the definition of only some fourteen protein species. The studies in our lab-

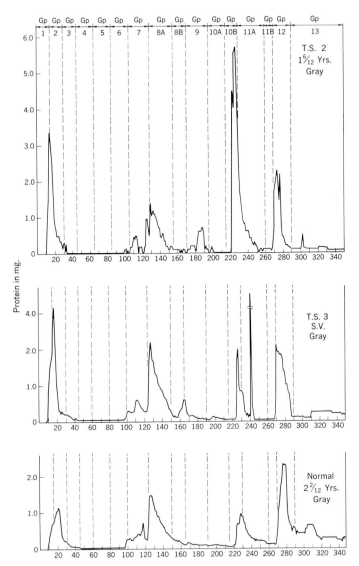

Figure 16. Column chromatography of case of Tay-Sachs' disease, age $1^{6}/_{12}$ years (upper), case of Spielmeyer-Vogt disease, age $20^{1}/_{12}$ years (middle), and normal child of $2^{2}/_{12}$ years (lower).

oratory described earlier which developed a three-dimensional approach to the extraction and characterization of the brain proteins by means of column chromatography, tube-to-tube carbohydrate analysis of the effluents, disc gel electrophoresis of fractions, and more quantitative extraction by exhaustive homogenization have permitted quantitative comparisons to be undertaken of the protein constituents of brain in the sphingolipidoses. Both biopsy and autopsy specimens were examined in these studies (72).

Figure 16 shows the column chromatographic patterns obtained in the case of a child, aged $1\frac{6}{12}$ years, who had Tay-Sachs' disease, as compared with the pattern obtained in the normal child, aged $2\frac{2}{12}$ years. The striking difference in group 10B proteins in the case of Tay-Sachs' disease is apparent when compared to the normal child, and when compared to adult specimens as well. When the contribution of each of these groups is calculated on the basis of mg./g. of original gray matter, it is seen that group 10B in the case of Tay-Sachs' disease (7.0 mg./g.) contains greater than five times the protein of 10B in the normal child specimen (1.24 mg./g.) and greater than ten times that in the normal adult gray matter specimens (0.53 ± 0.25 mg./g.). Groups 1 and 2 together, and group 9, are also somewhat elevated in the Tay-Sachs' case, while groups 10A, 11B, 12 and 13 appear to be depressed (72).

In the Spielmeyer-Vogt case, groups 6 and 7 appear slightly elevated when compared to the normal, but otherwise there is no large difference discernible in the total quantity of protein and its distribution on column chromatography, with the possible exception of a single sharp peak in group 11A (Fig. 16).

Electrophoresis and Carbohydrate Analysis: Sphingolipidoses
The Tay-Sachs' specimen and the Spielmeyer-Vogt specimen (with the exception of groups 1, 2, and 6) showed a greater number of discrete protein bands in each of groups 1 through 9 (Figures 17 and 18). The major difference shown on column chromatography was in group 10B. On disc gel electrophoresis, the major component in 10B was the front-running protein band, i.e. in 10B:1.00. A definite band was also present at 10B:1.00 in the Spielmeyer-Vogt case. Because it is not possible to prove identity by column chro-

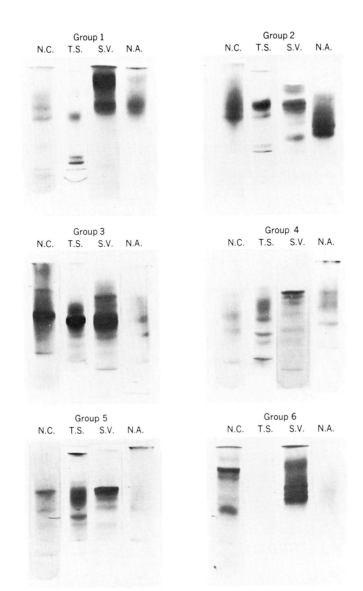

Figure 17. Disc gel electrophoresis of human brain proteins. N.C. = Normal child, 1½ years; T.S. = Tay-Sachs' disease; S.V. = Spielmeyer-Vogt disease; N.A. = Normal adult. (See Figure 16.)

Group 7
N.C   T.S.   S.V.   N.A.

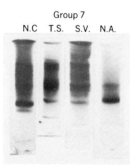

Group 8A
N.C.   T.S.   S.V.   N.A.

Group 8A, N.A.
Further Fractionated

Group 8B
N.C.   T.S.   S.V.   N.A.

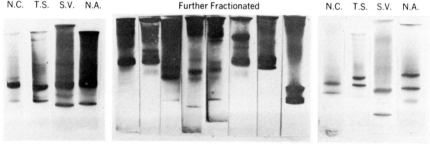

Group 9
N.C.   T.S.   S.V.   N.A.

Group 10A
N.C.   T.S.   S.V.   N.A.

Group 10B
N.C.   T.S.   S.V.   N.A.

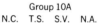
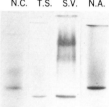

Figure 18. Disc gel electrophoresis of human brain proteins. N.C. = Normal child, 1½ years; T.S. = Tay-Sachs' disease; S.V. = Spielmeyer-Vogt disease; N.A. = Normal adult. (See Figure 16.)

matographic and electrophoretic mobility alone, it is not yet determined whether the quantitative increase in 10B proteins represents the presence of a novel protein or the marked increase in a normal protein.

Table XI. Non-dialyzable carbohydrate content of cerebroprotein fractions in Tay-Sachs' disease and Spielmeyer-Vogt disease

PROTEIN GROUP	% HEXOSE (AS % OF PROTEIN)		% SIALIC ACID (AS % OF PROTEIN)	
	SPIELMEYER-VOGT	TAY-SACHS'	SPIELMEYER-VOGT	TAY-SACHS'
1	45.0	35.6	5.5	7.9
2	16.4	27.6	6.4	6.7
3	—	—	2.7	2.5
4	—	—	—	—
5	23.8	—	—	—
6	41.5	—	—	—
7	6.4	6.2	2.3	1.3
8A	4.0	3.1	1.6	1.0
8B	6.8	7.4	3.3	2.3
9	—	13.0	2.3	5.0
10A	—	10.0	2.8	5.0
10B	19.1	3.9	7.5	1.6
11A	9.7	6.3	14.5	3.4
11B	13.2	11.2	2.6	6.5
12	19.8	25.0	4.0	4.2
13	—	66.5	—	8.0

The non-dialyzable carbohydrate content of the two sphingolipidosis cases were compared with normal data given in the first section of this chapter (see Table IV). Despite extra dialysis, both cases show several groups in which the non-dialyzable carbohydrate is moderately to markedly elevated (Table XI) (72).

From the analysis of the sialic acid content of the various groups it appears unlikely that the protein responsible for the marked protein increase in 10B in the Tay-Sachs' case is rich in sialic acid or hexose, since the over-all concentration is only 1.6 per cent and 3.9 per cent, respectively, based on protein, as compared to a content of 7.5 per cent and 19.1 per cent in the Spielmeyer-Vogt case.

The Spielmeyer-Vogt case shows two very strong bands, 10B:0.34 and 10B:0.56, which have not been seen in normal adults. While the total quantity of protein in 10B in this case is on the high side of the adult range, the degree of increase is not comparable to that seen in the Tay-Sachs' case.

Because these new methods have been applied to only two cases of the sphingolipidoses to date, no conclusions can be drawn with regard to the sphingolipidoses as such. On the other hand, it is clear that the methods are applicable to the fine resolution of proteins in the sphingolipidoses and other diseases of the nervous system, and that the results obtained with the one case of Tay-Sachs' disease require examination in a large number of cases by the same methods.

There are several methodological problems which remain. First, as seen in Figure 18, Group 8A requires further resolution. Second, from previous work (420) it is clear that the increased number of homogenizations yield proteins which, although quite soluble, are difficult to elute from DEAE cellulose, and require Triton X-100 for elution. These very proteins (groups 11B, 12, and 13) then cannot be followed well on gel electrophoresis, possibly because they denature more readily, although it may be the combination with Triton which makes them in some other way unsuitable for this procedure.

There is a fair degree of agreement between various brain specimens with regard to the amount of protein in a given group (72) (see also p. 195). This provides some assurance as to the nature of the fractionation. However, it is not possible at this time to state whether the small variations between the same group of different brains which occur are a function of the error of the method or represent individual small differences between brains. Both possibilities need to be considered, especially in those brain specimens in which the recovery from the column is less than complete. In this case of Tay-Sachs' disease the recovery was essentially quantitative, so that this, taken in combination with the very marked change in group 10B, suggests strongly that this result needs to be considered further. The fact that the electrophoretic findings also show differences in group 10B in Tay-Sachs' disease as compared with the normal, although more qualitative than quantitative, is further evidence of an abnormality, but it points to the possibility that this is the abnormal accumulation of a normal constituent. The low sialic acid content of this fraction suggests that we have not isolated the protein-ganglioside complex, although it does not preclude the possibility that this is the protein of that complex which has been split from the ganglioside during the isolation procedure. It seems possible that this protein, 10B, is a constituent of the membranes which are known from the work of others (460) to be increased in Tay-Sachs' disease. We are in the process of testing this hypothesis by several means, including the extraction of the isolated membranes, and the immunological examination of the membranes and other cell constituents with antisera prepared to the Tay-Sachs' disease protein.

The definitive enzymatic disturbance which lies at the basis of Tay-Sachs' disease is as yet unknown, so that it must be considered as a possibility that the Tay-Sachs' disease protein (10B) represents the enzyme, or the enzymes, responsible for the disorder in Tay-Sachs' disease. It is possible that this abnormal accumulation of protein is a trivial finding in relation to the essence of Tay-Sachs' disease, and that it is related to the secondary pathological changes (e.g. if a glial constituent, it may reflect the marked gliosis) which are consequent to the degenerative changes in this disorder. Finally, it is as yet not known whether the Tay-Sachs' disease protein is structurally identical with the normal constituent(s) of similar mobility, or whether it will be found to be specific to this disorder. Further work is needed to distinguish between these possibilities.

It should be noted that these proteins of brain are quite rich in carbohydrate constituents (72). Which, if any, of these non-dialyzable carbohydrates that appear in this protein isolation, and are at least in part glycoprotein in nature, are extracted by the organic solvent preparations of brain ganglioside is not known at present. This intriguing problem is at the center of the search for chemically and geometrically accurate reconstructions of membranes of the nervous system. The marked heterogeneity of the brain proteins, partly conferred by amino acid coding and additionally by carbohydrate sequence coding in the glycoproteins, is apparent. As previously stated (68), this provides a possible molecular basis for experiential and learning phenomena in the nervous system.

Summary

That a severe dementia accompanies the gross disturbance in the chemistry of the brain mucoids in Tay-Sachs' disease is at least consistent with the hypothesis that the mucoids are somehow involved in memory function in the nervous system, but the marked loss of nerve cells as a whole at the end stage of this process makes the disorder too gross to permit specific correlation with memory functions to be made. The chemical studies to date in Tay-Sachs' disease are therefore most useful in terms of the information provided on heterogeneity of brain mucoids and on the membranous location of brain mucoids.

OTHER GENETIC DISORDERS

Other disturbances in nervous system mucoids are also accompanied by mental defect. Among the "mucopolysaccharidoses" are gargoylism and its variants, Hunter's syndrome, and Hurler's syndrome (415a). Some cases of Gaucher's disease, in which cerebrosides accumulate, affect the brain. In galactosemia, in which there is a defect in the conversion of galactose-1-phosphate to glucose-1-phosphate, mental deficiency is prominent. In some glycogen storage diseases the brain may be damaged by the resultant hypoglycemia, as in von Gierke's disease, or by excessive accumulation of glycogen in neurones and glia, as in Pompe's disease (415a).

In all of these disorders, as in Tay-Sachs' disease, however, the extensive gross pathology frequently precludes the definitive correlation of disturbed mucoid metabolism *per se* with defective mentation.

HUMAN BRAIN TUMOR PROTEIN FRACTION 10B

Recent methods employing a quantitative approach to brain protein fractionation (72) have indicated that the fraction classified as Group 10B (72) is one of three which are quantitatively increased in human brain glial tumors when compared with normal gray matter or whole brain (67). These findings are of interest in the attempt to isolate constituent brain tumor when compared to normal brain proteins. Thus, antisera prepared against the tumor protein, when injected, might localize preferentially in tumor cells, leaving normal brain cells completely or relatively unaffected. If the human brain protein had an accessible location, this type of immuno-specific "labeling" might permit the concentration in tumor cells of chemical or neutron-capture antitumor agents complexed to the injected antibody.

Evidence is now available indicating that group 10B protein can be extracted and isolated from three glial tumor cell sources: first, from *in situ* glial human brain tumor tissue removed at surgery; second, from mouse brain glial tumor transplanted to and grown in subcutaneous sites in the mouse; and third, from the membranous "ghosts" remaining after lysis of human glial tumor cells directly transplanted to and grown in tissue culture. Preliminary evidence is also available which suggests that the concentration of Group 10B protein in human brain glial tumors resembles its concentration in normal human fetal brain more than it does its lower concentration in normal adult brain.

Glial tumors *in situ in* human brain, histologically classified as malignant gliomas of various types, were removed from brain at surgery, placed in dry ice, and extracted within two hours with 0.005 M phosphate buffer for brain proteins according to methods previously described (88, 72). Human glial tumors grown subcutaneously in the mouse were surgically removed, frozen, and extracted as above.

Glioblastoma multiforme tumor cells removed at surgery were grown in tissue culture media (348). The resultant preparation of cell "ghosts" shows the presence of cellular membranes and the marked absence of cellular nuclei. The morphological, immunological, and electro-immunological properties of these cultures are being studied (418).

The tissues were carefully minced into 1 mm. fragments and placed in glass bottles with 25 cc. of a medium of 20 per cent fetal calf serum, 80 per cent F-10 medium with 1 per cent glutamine and penicillin (100 units/ml.), and streptomycin (100 μg./ml.). At the present time 61 such tumors have been consecutively successfully grown for varying periods in monolayer cultures.

The tumors are of varied types, but interest has been focused primarily on the glioma group, astrocytoma, and glioblastoma multiforme.

In the specimens used for this study of protein isolation it was felt important to have well-established morphologically consistent lines for study. This required multiple subcultures by trypsinization with 10 cc. of 0.25 per cent trypsin in Earle's solution at 37°C. followed by centrifugation at 300 r.p.m. for 5 minutes. When the lines were kept from 3 to 6 months in monolayer and were seen on stained preparations to be uniform in appearance, they were then prepared for this study (418).

Approximately 16 to 24 bottles of tumor were harvested by the trypsinization technique, and the cellular material was pooled. Then "ghost cells" were prepared (239) and washed with Earle's balanced salt solution and then stored at minus 70°C. until ready for use. The "ghost cell" preparation was considered a means of minimizing nuclear material and providing a primarily cell membrane material.

Human embryonic whole brain of normal fetuses from the 14th to the 24th gestational week were obtained following therapeutic interruptions of pregnancy. Children's brains (age 30 days and $2\frac{2}{12}$ years) were obtained at autopsy in two cases in which the nervous system was grossly unaffected. Normal adult whole brain and gray matter of individuals aged 45 to 65 was obtained both at autopsy and at biopsy. The extracts from all of these sources were treated in exactly the same way for the isolation of 10B, i.e. concentrated, dialyzed, and chromatographed on purified DEAE cellulose (Cellex D) columns, with a stepwise elution by methods previously described.

The recovery on column chromatography using these methods has been previously demonstrated to be quite quantitative, 95 per cent $\pm$ 5 per cent (72), and was again of the same order for the tissue and cell materials studied here (see also Figure 9, p. 124).

It was found that the concentration of tumor 10B proteins was

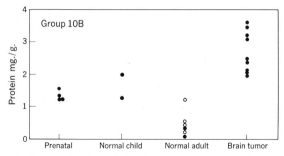

Figure 19. Group 10B protein in prenatal, normal child, normal adult, and brain tumor specimens. Solid circles, whole brain or tumor; open circles, gray matter only.

several-fold greater than that of normal adult brain, and that it resembles that of prenatal and normal child brain more than it does that of the normal adult (Figure 19).

In subcutaneously grown glial tumor, the concentration of 10B was found to be 2 to 4 mg./g., consonant with its concentration in the *in situ* tumor.

The chromatographic patterns of normal brain, *in situ* glial tumor, tissue culture whole glial tumor cells, and tissue culture glial tumor cell "ghosts" were compared. The tissue culture glial tumor cell membranous "ghosts" showed the absence of most of groups 1, 2, and 3, and the absence of almost all of groups 7, 8A, and 8B; however, groups 10B, 12, and 13 are present in appreciable amounts (see Figure 20). The membranous localization of 10B is further supported by previous studies on subcellular fractions of both human and rat brain proteins (420) and by recent studies on normal purified subcellular myelin, mitochondria, microsome, and synaptosome fractions (92) described earlier in this chapter (p. 131).

The glial localization of 10B is now suggested, but not yet established, by several different types of evidence. First, 10B occurs in both gray and white matter in approximately equivalent amounts. Second, 10B shows a six- to ten-fold quantitative increase in glial tumors over its concentration in normal adult brain. Third, glial tumor cells grown subcutaneously in the mouse contain 10B in

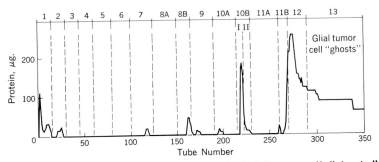

Figure 20. Cellex-D chromatography of glial tumor cell "ghosts."
Human glial tumor cells were grown in tissue culture, harvested,
and lysed. Outer membranes were centrifuged, washed, and extracted for proteins. Compared with the intact tumor (Figure 9,
cases 9A, 13, and 12), there is in this figure a relative absence of
protein groups 1-3, 7, and 8, but presence of 10B, 12, and 13.

amounts consistent with that in the *in situ* brain tumor. Fourth, a
sevenfold quantitative increase of 10B was demonstrated in a case
of Tay-Sachs' disease, in which a marked absolute increase of glial
cells, amounting to gliosis, is accompanied by a concurrent destruction and loss of nerve cells (72). Fifth, anti-10B antisera have been
prepared in rabbits against Tay-Sachs' fraction 10B, which on immuno-diffusion against the tumor 10B antigen and Tay-Sachs' 10B
antigen show similar lines of reaction, at least one of which is a
line of identity (75).

While it is considered that these preliminary results on 10B proteins are encouraging, many problems including those of immunological specificity and the delivery of adequate concentration of
antibody to tumor cells *in situ* remain to be resolved by future work
before any therapeutic application of these findings can be established.

The possible assignment of 10B to glial membranes is of interest,
in that 10B shows quantitative changes in learning situations in
pigeon brain. This will be discussed later in this chapter. Further,
while 10B normally contains 2 to 5 per cent hexose, brain tumor
10B was found to contain less than 0.1 per cent hexose (560a).

Summary

The increase of brain protein group 10B in human glial tumors is of interest to the cellular localization of one of the protein groups which change quantitatively in learning. The fact that 10B is also increased in Tay-Sachs' disease, and that anti-Tay-Sachs'-10B antiserum reacts with 10B of tumor origin requires further study with purified 10B from both sources. It is possible, but not yet proven, that 10B is a glial constituent.

5. "Chemistry of recognition" and CNS mucoids

CNS MUCOIDS HAVE SUFFICIENT CHEMICAL SPECIFICITY TO ACT AS ANTIGENS IN THE CLASSICAL IMMUNOLOGICAL SENSE

Little work has been done on the immunology of the mucoids of the nervous system. Structurally, they relate to the glycoprotein and glycolipoprotein antigens of the bacterial world (472). Since it has been shown (556) that the specific antigenic portion of the bacterial antigens resides in the polysaccharide moieties, which contain a variety of sugars and amino sugars, the obvious relation in structure of these bacterial antigens to the brain mucoids should raise considerable interest in the possibility that similar functions are subserved by both groups of substances. In bacteria, these substances are associated with contact properties, as in agglutination, and with motility and virulence (391a). In addition, human blood group antigens of the ABO system have been much clarified in recent years in terms of the chemical basis of their antigenicity (548). The highly specific antigens in this system have been shown to relate to the sequence of a very few glycosidically linked sugars, again similar in structure to the brain mucoids. While reasoning through structural anology has its pitfalls, the chemical resemblance of the brain mucoids to both the bacterial and ABO-specific antigens is intriguing.

Up until 1960 most of the experimental work on the immunology of brain constituents ignored the mucoids and centered upon an experimental disease produced in laboratory animals, experimental allergic encephalitis (EAE). While a considerable literature has grown with reference to this disorder, it was not until recent years that much progress has been made in the chemical identification of the actual encephalomyelitogenic agent. It has been shown that, upon purification of defatted guinea pig white matter, the encephalitogenic activity is found in the protein fraction (289, 291). There are a series of conflicting reports as to whether the EAE-inducing material is actually a complete antigen in itself or just a hapten, but this evidence will not be reviewed here. Further progress has been made in the fractionation of the basic protein antigens responsible for EAE induction and passive cutaneous anaphylactic sensitization (22, 289).

Immunology of the Gangliosides
Whether brain gangliosides can act either as haptens or as complete antigens has been explored (65).

Since the preparation of brain ganglioside used did not contain amino acid or protein components, adjuvants might have been used in initial immunization attempts. However, it was decided to attempt to obtain an antibody response to the pure substance. Rabbits were injected at weekly and monthly intervals with 0.5 mg. of bovine brain ganglioside salt in physiological saline, the first injections being made in the toe pads of the animal, and subsequent injections being made intravenously. The presence of antibody in rabbit serum was determined by collecting blood by free drip from the marginal vein of the ear, separating the serum, and determining the precipitin by means of the quantitative precipitin test (283). The nitrogen in the precipitate was quantitatively determined by means of a Nessler's method (59). Figure 21 shows the results of a representative quantitative precipitin determination. In approximately one-half of the rabbits studied there was present a small amount of precipitin prior to immunization. The amount of precipitin in the serum could be increased by means of repeated injections of brain ganglioside. It may be noted that the peak of the curve is

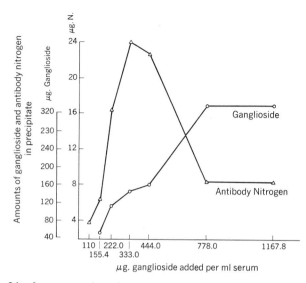

Figure 21. Amounts of antibody nitrogen and brain ganglioside in the precipitate in the quantitative precipitin test (65).

quite sharp. Because of the presence of neuraminic acid to the extent of 30 per cent by weight of the ganglioside, it was possible, by determining the neuraminic acid content, to determine the fate of ganglioside in both supernate and precipitate and thus to obtain some idea of the valence aspects of the precipitation phenomenon. The quantities in Figure 21 are uncorrected for solubility of specific precipitate. In the zone of antibody excess, about 50 per cent of the added ganglioside is precipitated, suggesting that there is more than one immunologically distinct component in this preparation of brain ganglioside. With increasing amounts of ganglioside (into the zone of antigen excess) the precipitate contains decreasing amounts of antibody and increasing amounts of ganglioside. At the peak of the zone of maximum precipitation of antibody, the precipitate contains approximately equal weights of brain ganglioside and antibody protein.

The antisera thus obtained have been used with the fluorescent antibody technique (142) to demonstrate the nerve cell body localization of brain ganglioside in bovine brain (91). This method should be applicable to the histological localization of any normal or abnormal brain constituent to which antisera can be prepared. The fact that non-specific staining may be obtained in brain needs to be considered in the interpretation of these observations, however.

The presence of a precipitin for brain ganglioside in mammalian serum, the titre of which is increased by successive injections of ganglioside, relates this normal brain constituent to other somatic or cellular antigens and blood group substances immunologically as well as structurally. It may be that the antigenic and membrane roles of brain gangliosides are pertinently related in a manner which suggests the general function of the cellular substances which contain hexosamine or derivatives thereof, e.g. muramic acid and neuraminic acid. This function is here postulated to be the maintenance of the structural integrity and individuality of the specific cell in which they reside, by the fact that their physico-chemical interaction with other molecules determines which enter and which leave the cell (65).

A recent statement by an immunologist points to the convergence of these concepts from the biochemical, developmental, and immunological points of view (114):

> Very recently there have been a number of indications that immunological recognition may be derived from an aspect of the processes by which all multicellular animals succeed in maintaining a characteristic morphological and functional unity. In its most general formulation this capacity must involve an interchange of "information" between cells. A cell seems to be able to "recognize" whether another cell is in contact with it or not and in some instances whether the adjacent cell is of its own type or another. For the appropriate reactions to take place, . . . one must postulate a rather elaborate structure of effector and receptor patterns, chains of stimulation and of feed-back controls. Effector and receptor patterns as factors in morphogensis have been sponsored . . . for many years, with a mutual relation of antigen-antibody type. Here then is a potential basis on which a specialized

recognition function of lymphoid cells may have been evolved.

One group of investigators (98) was unable to produce antibodies to brain ganglioside alone unless they first coated it on red cells before injection. Thereby they obtained an excellent antibody response, and came to the conclusion that ganglioside must be considered as a hapten rather than as a complete antigen. On the other hand, more recently a second group (403) was able to obtain good precipitating antibody in 23 out of 24 rabbits by injection of brain ganglioside into the peritoneum in rabbits. They were able, furthermore, to distinguish between normal ganglioside and Tay-Sachs' ganglioside by means of immunochemical tests such as double diffusion. This group therefore confirmed our findings that brain ganglioside can act as an antigen when injected uncomplexed to red cells.

There is a point of interest with regard to the different methods used in immunizing rabbits with ganglioside by the above three groups of investigators. We injected ganglioside into the toe pads of the rabbits (65), and in the last-mentioned study (403) ganglioside was injected intraperitoneally with adjuvant. It seems likely in either case that a protein carrier might be picked up by the highly acidic ganglioside. Thus, it would become a meaningless question to ask whether ganglioside *per se* on injection is antigenically sufficient to produce an antibody response. That is, ganglioside probably does not get to the antibody producing sites uncomplexed. At any rate, all three groups agree that it is possible to produce precipitating antibody to brain ganglioside, whether one injects it into the toe pads, combines it with adjuvant, or coats red blood cells with ganglioside prior to injection.

The antiganglioside antiserum obtained (569) did not cross-react with asialoganglioside coated on red cells, suggesting that the sialic acid residues are major immunologic determinants in ganglioside. In contrast, in the case of desialized orosomucoid, the sialic acid residues in this serum glycoprotein were not an important determinant antigenic group (20). There is some question as to what the actual structure of the asialoganglioside is after hydrolysis. For one thing, with mild acid hydrolysis not all of the neuraminic acid residues are readily removed, and for another, it is unlikely that even mild acid hydrolysis removes only the sialic acid residues without breaking some of the other glycosodic bonds as well. At any rate, a partially degraded ganglioside which has lost much of or all of its sialic acid is a different hapten. Asialo-ganglioside antibodies do not cross-react with naturally occurring globosides of red cells (485). A search for antiganglioside antibodies was made in the serum of patients with various neurological conditions (568). No antibodies were found in the serum of normal individuals; however, evidence was found for the existence of anti-ceramide-lactose antibodies. In 20 to 30 per cent of the cases of patients with multiple sclerosis, amytrophic lateral sclerosis, and brain tumors, some degree of antiganglioside antibody activity could be detected.

The immunological specificity of brain gangliosides is further supported by the demonstration that they act as inhibitors of the reaction of $Rh_0(D)$ antibody with $Rh_0(D)$ erythrocytes, show M and N blood group activity, and may act as pyrogens in the manner of bacterial lipopolysaccharides (550).

By utilizing sensitive complement fixation techniques, the immunological properties of the galactocerebroside of myelin fragments have also been studied (433).

Antigenic Constituents of Protein Extracts of Human Cortical Gray Matter

A systematic program of identification of discrete brain antigens has been undertaken (425-429) from the "protein view" as well.

The reactions of basic and acidic protein groups with rabbit antiserum prepared against the original whole "Extract A" (see page 116) in double-diffusion tests, suggested the presence of a minimum total of thirteen distinct antigens between them. These results are supported by immuno-electrophoretic findings, which indicate the basic group to contain five, and the progressively acidic group seven to eight distinct antigens. These antigens do not appear to be human serum proteins.

Antigens belonging to the BE class (resistant to boiling and relatively soluble in ethanol) are present among the progressively acidic proteins, and possibly among the basic proteins also (425).

A minimum of three distinct basic proteins were chromatographically separated from "Extract A" of human gray matter, using a discontinuous eluant series. These chromatographic subfractions were characterized by gradient elution chromatography and each subfraction analyzed for distinct antigentic characteristics.

Evidence was adduced for the presence of a minimum of three distinct basic protein antigens, all of which may be specific to human brain but not to human liver. None of them appear to be human serum proteins (429).

A minimum of eight thermostable, ethanol-insoluble antigens also were prepared from aqueous extracts of human cortical gray matter. Immuno-diffusion studies indicated one of these to be identical with BE antigen derived from the same source. This component is resistant to autoclaving as opposed to the other members of the group. Separate gray matter pools from two individual human brains were chromatographically separated into three basic and four progressively acidic subfractions. Immuno-diffusion studies indicated that, in one case, all the thermostable antigens were present only among the more basic proteins, and in the other, all were present only among the more acidic subfractions. Possible bases for this variable chromatographic behavior of thermostable antigens from individual human brains are of interest to questions of heterogeneity and individuality in nervous system proteins (63).

The more direct demonstration of the relationship of a given nervous system antigen to memory function cannot simply be made by experiments that show an interference with transmission function when the antigen is blocked *in situ* (465), although this finding indicates the feasibility of such an approach. Interference with encoding function does not necessarily imply interference with transmission function. Nonetheless such experiments could be extended to the learning situation itself in a fairly precise manner, provided that the union of antigen and antibody could be effected without procedural trauma or gross lysis or cell destruction on antigen-antibody union.

Summary

Experiments with purified brain gangliosides, and with a number of brain glycoproteins, suggest that "recognition" functions, detectable by classical immunological techniques, might operate in some brain mucoids. That a substance can act as a partial or complete antigen of course does not prove that it does so act *in situ*. However, now that purified brain antigens are being identified, it is becoming feasible to test the importance of this function in learning and memory by means of blocking experiments with specific antibodies.

CNS MUCOIDS AS SPECIFIC RECEPTORS IN THE VIROLOGICAL SENSE

Inhibition of Viral Hemagglutination by Brain Ganglioside
Numerous inhibitors of the viral hemagglutination reaction have been described (250, 251, 225). The fact that some mucoproteins are effective as inhibitors of the viral hemagglutination reaction led to the suggestion (299) that neuraminic acid might be identical with the red cell receptor for the attachment of viruses. It was noted (224, 297) that when virus was incubated with inhibitor mucin, neuraminic acid was among the dialyzable substances liberated. A brain mucolipid fraction (448) was shown to be an inhibitor of virus hemagglutination. It was of interest that, while neuraminic acid appeared to play a central role in the inhibitory process, sialic acid alone possessed no inhibitory action (392).

A viral hemagglutination method (254) was used with Influenza PR8 virus. The virus was heat inactivated by incubation at 55°C. for 30 minutes. Weekly, chick red blood cells were bled into citrate. After washing four times by suspension in 20 volumes of saline and centrifugation, the cells were kept in 10 per cent suspension of saline, and diluted to 2 per cent for use. Hemagglutination titer was obtained by serial twofold dilutions of virus in 0.15M NaCl buffered to pH 7.2 with phosphate. In the test for inhibitor activity, serial twofold dilutions of inhibitor were prepared in o.2 ml. of buffered saline, then one unit of hemagglutination activity of virus in o.2 ml. and o.1 ml. of 2 per cent chick red blood cells were added to each tube. The tubes were placed in a water bath at 2°C. for 2 hours, then read.

Aqueous solutions (10.0 per cent and o.25 per cent) of ash-free brain ganglioside (59) were found to totally inhibit virus hemagglutination in the system employed in an absolute concentration of from 20 mg. to as little as o.3 μg.

Heating of a 2 per cent aqueous solution of ash-free brain ganglioside (pH 3.1) at 100°C. without added acid (autohydrolysis), for exactly 20 minutes, resulted in the cleavage of neuraminic acid fraction I (203, 54). This fraction was separated by exhaustive dialysis at 4°C. against distilled water. The non-dialyzable balance of the brain ganglioside was lyophilized (Residue A). The dialyzable material, neuraminic acid fraction I, accounted for 20.8 per cent by weight of the original ganglioside, and contained nitrogen 4.42 per cent and reducing sugar 61.4 per cent. It accounted for approximately 60 per cent of the neuraminic acid of the intact ganglioside, but contained in addition some hexose (o.74 per cent as galactose) and galactosamine 2.5 per cent. The dialyzable fraction was capable of acting as a complete inhibitor in absolute concentrations of 500 μg. with partial inhibition at 125 μg.

Crystalline neuraminic acid was separated from neuraminic acid fraction I by partition with cold methanol (54, 203). If neuraminic acid fraction I was washed with cold methanol and centrifuged, crystalline neuraminic acid was collected as the methanol-insoluble fraction. Galactosamine and hexose were completely absent, and the nitrogen was 4.5 per cent. This crystalline neuraminic acid had no inhibitory activity.

That galactosamine alone is not the active material was shown by the fact that a purified sample of galactosamine hydrochloride in concentrations of from 8 μg. to 20 mg. had no inhibitory activity.

Brain ganglioside which had been treated with periodic acid for 2 minutes was considerably less active as an inhibitor, but still inhibited at a concentration of 460 μg. It is possible that a trace of unoxidized ganglioside was present.

A preparation of neuraminic acid fraction I which had been treated with periodic acid for 2 minutes was totally inactive as an inhibitor.

Residue A, which was obtained as described above by the auto-hydrolysis of ash-free brain ganglioside, represented the balance of the ganglioside remaining after neuraminic acid fraction I had been removed. It represented approximately 80 per cent by weight of the original ganglioside, contained essentially all of the hexose, 95 per cent of the galactosamine, and approximately one-third of the neuraminic acid of the intact ganglioside. Although completely water-soluble, it was more viscous in aqueous solution than the original ganglioside. Residue A was devoid of inhibitory activity.

The crystalline glucostearocerebroside, because of its insolubility in water, was not tested for inhibitory activity.

Thus, this purified mucoid appears to behave as a competitive receptor for influenza PR8 virus in a system with red blood cells present (55). The neuraminic acid present on the red cell surface is the natural receptor in this system, and brain ganglioside its imitator. The neuraminic acid portion of the mucoid was shown to be the essential specific constituent of the ganglioside in this function as it was in the immunological reactions of recognition just discussed.

Brain gangliosides have also been shown to have receptor properties for tetanus toxin and for staphylococcal and diphtheria toxins (46).

Influence of Brain Ganglioside upon the Neurotoxic Effect of Influenza Virus in Mouse Brain

A purified preparation of brain ganglioside was also shown to inhibit the neurotoxic effect of influenza PR8 and NWS viruses *in vivo* and to suppress the development of hemagglutinins in tissue culture in concentrations comparable to those at which it inhibited the hemagglutination reaction (86). In mouse brain the inhibition of the neurotoxic effect may be due to a competition of added brain ganglioside with the cellular brain ganglioside for the infecting virus.

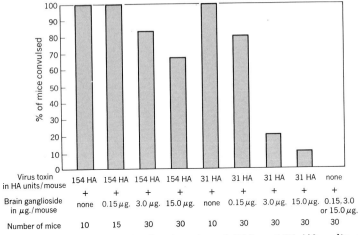

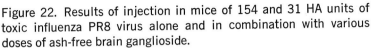

Figure 22. Results of injection in mice of 154 and 31 HA units of toxic influenza PR8 virus alone and in combination with various doses of ash-free brain ganglioside.

Figure 22 shows the results of an experiment in which both 154 and 31 HA units of toxic influenza PR8 virus were injected alone and in combination with three different doses of ash-free brain ganglioside. Both 154 and 31 HA units injected intracerebrally resulted in grand mal convulsions in 90 per cent of the mice at 30 hours and 100 per cent of the mice at 48 hours. The inclusion of 3.0 to 15 μg. of brain ganglioside resulted in a reduction of the toxic effect, which was more pronounced with the smaller virus dosages. Brain ganglioside injected alone resulted in no convulsions. A comparison of results at 30 and 48 hours showed that, while the neurotoxic effect of the virus increased with time, the inhibitory effect of brain ganglioside also increased with time.

Ganglioside salt (brain ganglioside from which cations had not been removed by dialysis in the cold with acid) was equally effective as an inhibitor.

There was a reduction in the percentage of mice convulsing when brain ganglioside was injected prior to the injection of 307 HA units of toxin, and a possible effect with 77 units. On the other

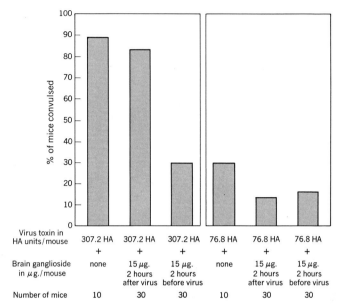

Virus toxin in HA units / mouse	307.2 HA +	307.2 HA +	307.2 HA +	76.8 HA +	76.8 HA +	76.8 HA +
Brain ganglioside in μg./ mouse	none	15 μg. 2 hours after virus	15 μg. 2 hours before virus	none	15 μg. 2 hours after virus	15 μg. 2 hours before virus
Number of mice	10	30	30	10	30	30

Figure 23. Effect on mice of intracerebral inoculation of brain ganglioside two hours prior to and two hours after injection of PR8 virus.

hand, the injection of brain ganglioside 2 hours after toxin had been inoculated intracerebrally had little or no effect against 307 units of virus, and possibly a small effect with 77 HA units (Figure 23).

A neurotropic virus strain (NWS) (491) was also tested for neurotoxic effects and for possible inhibition of these effects by brain ganglioside. There was a very definite contact inhibitory effect upon the 160 HA units of virus, but not upon 640 units. There was also definite inhibition even when the ganglioside was given 2 hours after the virus (160 HA units).

It was interesting to note that the range of concentration of brain ganglioside that was effective as inhibitor in the hemagglutination reaction was also effective in the inhibition of the neurotoxic effects of the above viruses. Furthermore, the interaction of brain ganglioside with influenza PR8 virus in tissue culture was shown to occur at comparable concentration ranges. Inhibition of HA production was present at 48 hours, but the inhibitory effect was partially or completely overcome by 72 hours, depending on the concentration of ganglioside present. Recovery from the inhibitory effect may have been due to metabolic destruction of the ganglioside and/or due to multiplication of uninhibited virus.

Subsequent investigations were directed toward the occurrence of other natural neuraminic-acid-containing substances in host systems and the part that they might play in virus infection. This study resulted in the detection, in chorioallantoic fluid of the intact host egg, of the accumulation within the first few minutes of bound neuraminic acid in response to influenza viral infection. This substance(s) was distinguished from free neuraminic acid as liberated by neuraminidase since it was bound presumably through its aldehydic group in a glycosidic linkage which is hydrolyzed by 0.1 N sulphuric acid at 80°C. for 1 hour. It was distinguished from interferon by its content of neuraminic acid and by the time of its appearance. It was named "sialoresponsin," since it appeared as an immediate response to the introduction of virus (82).

The almost instantaneous response of the organism to virus introduced into the extracellular fluid, i.e. the release of sialoresponsin, may represent one of the earliest defense mechanisms of the host. This sialic acid substance(s), whatever its function, may be viewed as resulting in the provision of a natural receptor "decoy," akin to that exogenously added in the form of brain ganglioside in earlier work in this laboratory (86). In the balance achieved between host sialoresponsin and viral sialidase may rest one of the determinants of whether certain invading viruses are inactivated extra-cellularly or gain entry into the host cells. Subsequent experiments demonstrated that sialoresponsin was freely dialyzable, thus clearly distinguishable from the interferons and other large molecular weight viral inhibitors; that it could be preserved and obtained in yields double that described by immediately shaking the freshly withdrawn chorioallantoic fluid with chloroform; that it was separable from free neuraminic acid and other dialyzable constituents on Dowex-1-formate; that it was produced by influenza PR8 virus which had been purified by red cell adsorption and by ultracentrifugal concentration; that its production and hydrolysis were demonstrable in chorioallantoic fluid *in vitro* as well as *in vivo*; and that its production was related to the HA concentration of virus (81, 83).

Summary

Gangliosides have been shown to be capable of receptor properties in the classical virological sense, and chemically related substances have been shown to participate in the immediate chemistry of host response to foreign agents. If certain brain mucoids act as surface cell receptors for foreign agents such as viruses, it is conceivable that they serve other daily related receptor and recognition functions for endogenous substances in the brain.

CNS MUCOIDS CAN INFLUENCE NEUROMUSCULAR EVENTS ON CONTACT WITH SUITABLE RECEPTORS

The consideration of the possible membrane and transport role that brain ganglioside might have in the central nervous system led to the investigation (77) of the effect of this substance upon the heart of a clam (*Venus mercenaria*). This organ has been used in the bioassay of acetyl choline, 5-hydroxytryptamine, and other substances with known or suspected neurohumoral function (553, 208).

The clam heart system employed was essentially that described elsewhere (208), with the exception that a 5 ml. bath was used. The bathing fluid consisted of sea water, with and without added benzoquinonium ("Mytolon"). Most preparations functioned well up to 10 and 15 hours, and stable function was established for at least 1 hour before test substances were added. All hearts were highly responsive to 5-hydroxytryptamine creatine sulphate in the usual doses (77).

Both brain ganglioside salt and its ash-free derivative were employed (59). Brain ganglioside salt in concentrations as low as 0.06

μg./cc. of suspension fluid produced a definite increase in the amplitude of contraction (12 to 30 per cent). At doses greater than 0.4 μg./cc. an increase in amplitude of contraction was accompanied by an increase in rate as well. At doses between 40 and 200 μg./cc. a tetanic state of contraction was observed. All the above effects were readily reversed by washing the heart with sea water. However, there appeared to be a cumulative effect in individual hearts on repeated administration of large doses of brain ganglioside, evidenced by a diminished responsivity to subsequent doses of brain ganglioside, although the heart retained normal responsivity to 5-hydroxytryptamine. Even while the heart was responding to brain ganglioside present in the bathing fluid, the addition of 5-hydroxytryptamine produced a superimposed stimulatory effect.

All these responses were observed whether or not benzoquinonium (6 μg./cc.) was present in the fluid. Since equivalent responses were obtained with both brain ganglioside salt and ash-free brain ganglioside, the stimulatory effect does not appear to be dependent upon either the presence of a free or neutralized carboxyl group in the neuraminic acid of brain ganglioside. Neuraminic acid itself, obtained by hydrolytic cleavage of ash-free brain ganglioside (59), in doses of 60-120 μg./cc., produced a small increase in the amplitude of contraction comparable to the response obtained with only 0.06 μg./cc. of the intact brain ganglioside.

The active concentrations of brain ganglioside were low. Considering that the functional unit of this macromolecular substance is its structural repeating unit (molecular weight approximately 3,314), then brain ganglioside is active in this system at concentrations of 10^{-8} molar. If, on the other hand, the functional unit is considered to be that indicated by the molecular weight determination of aqueous brain ganglioside (minimal molecular weight 250,000), then brain ganglioside as active at concentration of 10^{-10} molar.

These findings, taken together with other observations on the gangliosides, suggested the possibility that brain ganglioside may play a part in transmission phenomena in the central nervous system.

The effects of brain ganglioside and of neuraminic acid were then studied in clam heart once more, and further on various pharmacological test preparations (87). In concentrations of 10 μg./ml. or more, ganglioside stimulated the isolated guinea-pig ileum; graded responses were usually obtained. Various substances, known to antagonize the actions of other stimulant substances, fail to affect the response to ganglioside. For both the heart of *Venus mercenaria* and guinea-pig ileum, the activity demonstrated by brain ganglioside is specifically a property of the whole molecule, since neither neuraminic acid itself nor a preparation of brain ganglioside from which only two-thirds of its neuraminic acid had been removed are active.

Ganglioside caused a contraction of guinea-pig ileum, the threshold concentration being about 10μg./ml. Fivefold concentrations always caused a response which usually consisted of an increase in tone but frequently also of an increase in the amplitude of spontaneous movements. The response reached its maximum within 20 to 45 seconds. After washing it could be repeated at intervals of 3 minutes, but the responses of some preparations were rather variable. However, graded responses were usually obtained, and an increase in concentration by 30 per cent was detectable. During the course of an experiment the responses were likely to increase as the spontaneous activity increased.

The influence of various substances on the response of the ileum to ganglioside was studied. Mepyramine maleate (0.005 μg./ml., three experiments) and chlorprophenpyridamine maleate clearly antagonized histamine, but had no obvious effect on the response to ganglioside. Cocaine hydrochloride had no consistent effect on the response of the ileum to ganglioside and, if at all, affected similarly the response to histamine. Hexamethonium chloride reduced the response to nicotine by 50 to 75 per cent, but the response to ganglioside was unaltered or slightly increased, as was the spontaneous activity of the ileum. Dihydroergotamine methane sulphonate reduced the response to ganglioside by 30 to 60 per cent. The responses to histamine, acetylcholine, and nicotine were reduced to about the same extent by this dose. Papaverine hydrochloride abolished the response of the ileum to ganglioside, histamine, acetylcholine, and nicotine. Ganglioside itself (in doses from 1 to 100 μg./ml.) did not affect the response of the ileum to histamine and acetylcholine when it was left in the bath for 20 to 30 minutes.

Neuraminic acid in concentrations of up to 250 μg./ml. had no effect on the isolated guinea-pig ileum (in seventeen experiments). The stimulant effect of ganglioside on the guinea-pig ileum was lost when two-thirds of the neuraminic acid moieties were removed by autohydrolysis at 100°C. (Residue A) (59).

Experiments with specific inhibitors thus indicated that acetylcholine and histamine receptors are not involved in the response of the ileum to ganglioside. That the receptors for histamine, acetylcholine, and 5-hydroxytryptamine are not involved was also indicated by the observation that ganglioside itself did not change the response of the ileum to these substances. The site of action of ganglioside differs from that of 5-hydroxytryptamine, since dihydroergotamine had not the specific effect against ganglioside which it is known to have against 5-hydroxytryptamine (209). The failure of cocaine and of hexamethonium to change the response of the ileum to ganglioside is an indication that the nervous elements of the ileum are not involved in this response.

Direct evidence of the lack of effect of ganglioside on at least some autonomic ganglia was obtained in experiments in which this substance and neuraminic acid were injected into the blood supply of the superior cervical ganglion of the cat. Both substances failed to stimulate the ganglion or to modify ganglionic transmission; they also had no action on a neuromuscular junction, since they failed to modify the response of the frog rectus abdominis muscle to acetylcholine. On the other hand, the activity of ganglioside on excitability in brain slices (27) demonstrated that ganglioside has an effect at certain sites of the nervous system.

The results obtained on the isolated heart of Venus mercenaria indicate that the slowly developing response of this heart to ganglioside is not due to the release by ganglioside of endogenous 5-hydroxytryptamine or of other related hydroxyindoles. It is unlikely to be due to the liberation of histamine or of catecholamines, because these compounds are much less effective on this tissue (208). Neither the stimulant effect of 5-hydroxytryptamine nor the inhibitory effect of acetylcholine was changed by ganglioside. While brain ganglioside is not known to be a native constituent of any of the tissues tested, its activity in Venus mercenaria heart and in guinea-pig ileum, and its lack of activity in other preparations (frog rectus abdominis and superior cervical ganglion of the cat), indicate some selectivity of pharmacological action, the basis of which is at present obscure.

The mechanism of action of brain ganglioside is unknown. Because of the presence of both water- and lipid-soluble groups, and the demonstration of viral receptor properties, a function of brain ganglioside at interphases (membrane, receptor, and transmission functions in the nervous system) has been suggested (59, 77). The acidic groups of both phospho- and glyco-lipids form salts with cations. These salts are water- and lipid-soluble, and it has been suggested that their action on smooth muscle is due to an increased permeability to the bound cations as compared to the free ones (526, 527). That the neuraminic acid of ganglioside exerts its action simply as a binder of cations is not supported by the fact that the free neuraminic acid itself, which is also able to bind cations through the ionizable carboxyl group, is inactive alone. On the other hand, brain ganglioside from which two out of three of the terminal neuraminic acid residues have been removed (i.e. Residue A) (59) is also totally inactive. Thus, while the terminal neuraminic acid constituent is necessary for the activity, it is not sufficient; the activity is a property of the whole brain ganglioside. The fact that Residue A, comprising 80 per cent of the whole molecule with the bulk of both carbohydrate and lipid constituents still present in covalent linkage, is inactive also strongly supports the specificity of the stimulatory function of the intact molecule.

Other evidence (550) that gangliosides are serotonin-receptors is also of interest in this regard.

Summary

The pharmacological specificity of the action of gangliosides on neuromuscular receptors would further support their recognition function. Thus in immunological, virological, and pharmacological experimental terms, brain gangliosides exhibit specificity of an order consonant with requirements for their postulated function as recognition molecules in the nervous system.

6. Biosynthesis and regenerative potential of CNS mucoids

BIOSYNTHESIS OF CEREBROSPINAL FLUID (CSF) GLYCOPROTEINS

Only a few radioactive studies have been published on the synthesis of the glycoproteins of liver and of serum, and none on the synthesis of the glycoproteins of the nervous system. Recent advances in the methods of separating and identifying the constituent carbohydrates of glycoproteins facilitate and make opportune a systematic quantitative approach to these problems.

Both glucosamine and randomly labeled glucose were injected intravenously in chronic schizophrenic patients, and the incorporation of radioactive carbon was determined at 5 hours in the CSF and blood glycoproteins.

Table XII summarizes the fractionation procedures that were undertaken (89, 90). Analysis was carried out as follows: dry weight, nitrogen, hexose, hexosamine, and neuraminic acid were determined in each fraction. Each hydrolytic fraction was separated in duplicate on paper chromatography, one was stained, and one was eluted spot-by-spot, and the radioactivity was determined.

Thus, on the administration of uniformly labeled ^{14}C-glucose and 1-^{14}C-glucosamine to human subjects, followed by the isolation of glycoproteins from both serum and CSF at 5, 12, and 24 hour intervals, incorporation of ^{14}C into the carbohydrate constituents of these glycoproteins has been demonstrated both in the whole glycoprotein and in the hydrolytic carbohydrate residues isolated therefrom.

The glycoprotein fractions were hydrolyzed once to provide essentially distinct carbohydrate and protein fractions, and the radio-

Table XII. Stepwise hydrolysis of human serum and CSF glycoproteins for carbohydrate moieties (89)

FRACTION	PRODUCTS
Whole serum or CSF	
↓ Quantitative dialysis	
Non-dialyzable constituents	
0.3 N TCA, 100°C., 8 minutes	
Dialysis ———→ Dialyzate I	Neuraminic Acid
Non-dialyzable Residue I	
2 N HCl, 100°C., sealed tube, 4½ hours	
Dialysis ———→ Dialyzate II	Galactosamine, glucosamine (and N-acetyl derivatives), galactose, glucose, mannose; oligosaccharides
Non-dialyzable Residue II	
6 N HCl, 100°C., 16 hours	
Dialysis ———→ Dialyzate III	Amino acids, some hexosamines, and hexoses
Non-dialyzable Residue III	

activity was found to be almost exclusively in the carbohydrate portion. Subsequent to this a more refined stepwise hydrolysis procedure was initiated (Table XII).

Some examples of the incorporation already observed for both glucose and glucosamine are given in Table XIII. It may be seen that both glucose and glucosamine are incorporated biosynthetically into the glycoproteins of both cerebrospinal fluid and serum in man. Glucosamine carbon appears to pass into the hexoses of the glycoproteins of cerebrospinal fluid more readily than into those of serum.

BIOSYNTHESIS OF BRAIN MUCOIDS

The incorporation of labeled carbohydrate precursors into the brain gangliosides has demonstrated some of the pathways by which

Table XIII. Specific activity of hydrolytic carbohydrate constituents of human serum and cerebrospinal fluid glycoproteins 5 hours after I.V. injection of U-^{14}C-glucose or 1-^{14}C-glucosamine (90)

SOURCE	PRECURSOR	ISOLATED FRACTION OR CONSTITUENT	SPECIFIC ACTIVITY COUNTS PER MINUTE /μmole	/mg.
Cerebrospinal fluid	U-^{14}C- Glucose (90 μc.)	Non-dialyzable Res. I (as mg. hexose)	40.6	226.0
	(45 μc.)		13.9; 19.6	77.0; 109.0
	1-^{14}C-Glucosamine (90 μc.)	Neuraminic acid	99.0	320.0
		Glucosamine, galactosamine	72.0	400.0
		Galactose, glucose, mannose	7.9	43.8
Serum	U-^{14}C- Glucose (90 μc.)	Non-dialyzable Res. I (as mg. hexose)	34.8	193.0
	1-^{14}C-Glucosamine (90 μc.)	Neuraminic acid	740.0	2.395.0
		Glucosamine, galactosamine	437.0	2,430.0
		Galactose, glucose, mannose	1.5	8.1

these substances can be synthesized, and their constituent sugars exchanged (383, 550, 115). Puromycin, which interferes with memory, had been thought to do so only through inhibition of protein synthesis, but recent evidence (284a) demonstrates that incorporation of carbohydrate precursors into brain gangliosides is also inhibited.

The injection of ^{14}C-glucose intravenously in pigeons has been shown to result in incorporation into non-dialyzable mucoids of brain (75). There is considerable difference between the various brain protein groups in terms of the time course and the degree of turnover in the resting state, and further differences which accompany training. From the point of view of requirements for coding functions, the brain glycoproteins show an active turnover of

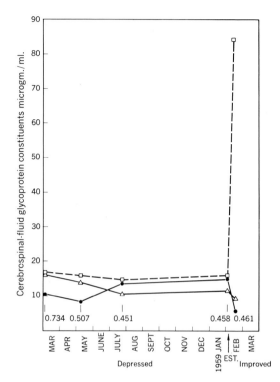

Figure 24. Cerebrospinal fluid glycoprotein constituents. Note: The neurochemical values are plotted on a monthly time scale. The figures on the abscissa represent the total concentration of glycoprotein "fraction G" as milligrams per milliliter of cerebrospinal fluid. ●——● represents fraction G neuraminic acid, △——△ fraction G hexosamine, and □————□ fraction G hexose. It is important to note that each of the last three constituents is non-dialyzable, protein-bound, and free of low-molecular-weight dialyzable contaminants. The arrows indicate the point at which therapy was begun. Abbreviations are as follows: adm. = admission; cat. = catatonic; ch. = chronic; depn. = depression; EST = electroshock therapy; impr. = improved; mod. = moderately; mark. = markedly; par. = paranoid; schiz. = schizophrenic; sl. = slight.

carbohydrate constituents. These studies will be discussed later in this chapter when the concentration of CNS mucoids in learning is considered (p. 185).

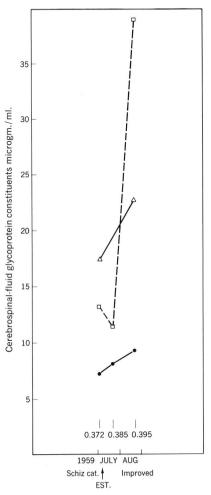

Figure 25. Cerebrospinal fluid glycoprotein constituents. See Note, Figure 24.

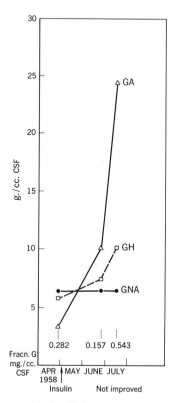

Figure 26. The change in absolute concentration of macromolecular (bound) hexose, hexosamine, and neuraminic acid of fraction G with time in a patient with the diagnosis of paranoid schizophrenia who received insulin therapy and showed no improvement. The symbols are as in Figure 24. Compare with Figure 27.

Summary

Data on the biosynthesis of the brain mucoids is still meager, and some are discussed later in this chapter. Preliminary data indicate that an active turnover of carbohydrate moieties of these constituents is possible. The fact that puromycin has been shown to inhibit the incorporation of carbohydrate precursors into brain gangliosides is relevant to the mucoid-memory hypothesis.

7. CNS mucoids change with behavioral change

The observation that the concentration of neuraminic acid in cerebrospinal fluid is related to behavioral status (56, 57, 58) led to

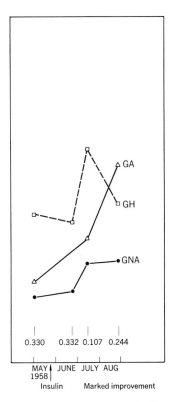

Figure 27. The change in absolute concentration of macromolecular (bound) hexose, hexosamine, and neuraminic acid of fraction G with time in a patient with the diagnosis of paranoid schizophrenia who received insulin therapy and showed marked improvement. The symbols are as in Figure 24. Compare with Figure 26.

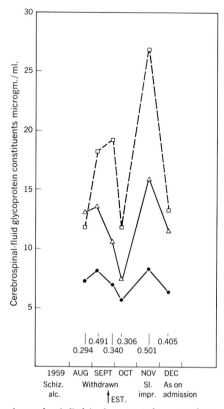

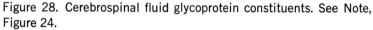

Figure 28. Cerebrospinal fluid glycoprotein constituents. See Note, Figure 24.

a series of studies on the glycoproteins of this compartment of the nervous system.

The determination of the glycoprotein constituents in a large group of individuals had demonstrated a high degree of chemical individuality in terms of absolute concentrations and molar ratios of these substances (63). In addition to the range of patterns available, there was an indication of a grouping of concentrations of particular constituents in relation to particular psychiatric disorders (62).

Patients who were followed longitudinally demonstrated neuro-chemical changes temporally coincident with and qualitatively and occasionally quantitatively related to changes in behavioral status (Figures 24 through 29) (78, 79). Figure 30 shows the relationship of increase or decrease in absolute amounts of CSF glycoprotein constituents in 65 instances of clinical improvement, worsening, and no change in 47 patients examined in double-blind, longitu-dinal studies. It is clear from the data that a significant correlation exists for changes in some of these constituents in the first three categories of clinical change listed (P values in Figure 30 refer to comparison with values in the "no change group"). In cases where

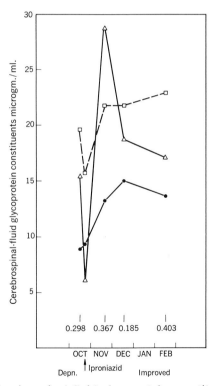

Figure 29. Cerebrospinal fluid glycoprotein constituents. See Note, Figure 24.

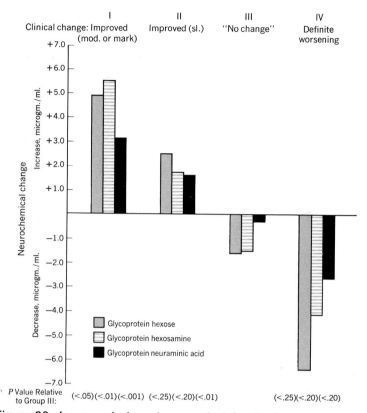

Figure 30. Increase (+) or decrease (—) in absolute amounts of glycoprotein constituents in 65 instances of improvement, "no change," or worsening in the clinical status of 47 schizophrenic patients during entry into and recovery from a psychotic state.

no significant clinical change was reported there was a tendency for glycoprotein hexose and hexosamine to be somewhat lowered, suggestive of slight worsening in at least some of these patients.

Table XIV summarizes the presence or absence of correlation in terms of direction of change in neurochemical and clinical values in 75 instances of entry into and recovery from psychosis. The extent of the close correlation is apparent.

Table XIV. Summary of 75 instances* of improvement, worsening, and no change in the first 57 cases** studied

PRESENCE OR ABSENCE OF CORRELATION OF CLINICAL AND NEUROCHEMICAL DATA	NUMBER	TOTAL NUMBER
1. PRESENCE OF CORRELATION		70
a) Neurochemical Changes Coincident with Clinical Improvement	45	
b) Neurochemical Changes Coincident with Clinical Worsening	12	
c) No significant Changes in either Clinical or Chemical Status	13	
2. ABSENCE OF CORRELATION		5
a) Clinical Improvement but No Coincident Neurochemical Change	3	
b) Clinical Improvement but Neurochemical Changes Indicative of Worsening	2	

NOTE: These were combined double-blind and neurochemical studies.
* The total number of examples of presence or absence of correlation exceeds the total number of cases, since in 18 of the cases studied, instances of both clinical improvement and worsening were observed.
** Data for each of the first 24 cases are reported in reference 78, those for each of the subsequent 33 cases in reference 74.

Differences in technique may explain the conflicting reports of other investigators on cerebrospinal fluid glycoproteins; some confirmed the earlier findings (132, 131, 400) while others did not (278, 440) or were in only partial agreement (21, 228). Only two of these studies used the same chemical methods, and none of them employed the quantitative dialysis methods originally described (58, 79). From an examination of the thiobarbituric acid method for neuraminic acid in CSF, used by some of the above investigators, it was concluded that the method does not reliably determine the amount of bound sialic acid in cerebrospinal fluid (124, 188, 80, 14). (For a detailed discussion see (124).

A further group of 131 hospitalized psychotic patients was studied clinically and neurochemically over a period of from one to six months (124). There was an inverse linear relationship between amount of glycoprotein neuraminic acid and the severity or degree of psychotic illness (Figure 31). This confirmed the earlier findings (70, 74, 78) that the more severe the illness, the lower the absolute amount of neuraminic acid.

These findings also supported much of the earlier work, in that a positive relationship was observed between clinical improvement in psychiatric patients and increases in absolute amount of glycoprotein neuraminic acid in cerebrospinal fluid. Concordance of ratings of severity of illness, family history, and changes in condition during the period of observation was similarly high. These findings appear to be of particular significance in that the clinical

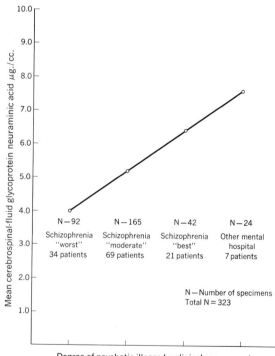

Degree of psychotic illness by clinical assessments

Figure 31. Relationship between degree of psychotic illness and cerebrospinal fluid glycoprotein neuraminic acid. Statistics in (124).

population was totally removed geographically from the chemical laboratory, so that neither clinical raters nor chemical analysts had any knowledge of the others' findings, and strict double-blind procedure was maintained throughout.

Summary

The mucoids of at least one compartment of the nervous system, the cerebrospinal fluid, thus appear to be related to behavior. The precise nature of the relationship is unknown, but it may be stated in the least that these substances are "behavior-sensitive"; thus they change in concentration in accompaniment with behavioral change.

8. Pigeon CNS mucoids in learning situations

CHANGE IN THE CONCENTRATION OF CERTAIN PIGEON BRAIN GLYCO-PROTEINS IN LEARNING

The recent development of more quantitative and more exhaustive methods for the extraction of brain proteins, and concomitant evidence for their marked heterogeneity, made it of interest to examine directly the brain proteins in learning situations. Indirect evidence has been obtained for the relationship of brain proteins to learning through the effect on learning of puromycin, an inhibitor of protein synthesis. In addition, some evidence of total protein changes in separated brain cells in learning have been reported, but no direct physico-chemical evidence has been obtained for changes in specific brain protein species with learning. Furthermore, most of the reports to date have not excluded the biochemical effects of stressful conditions and aversive stimuli used in the training situation. In addition to the methodological problems in both the experimental psychology and the biochemical aspects of these studies, there is a complexity in the conceptualization of the multiple mechanisms required for processing of information in the nervous system, since these must include sensory reception, association, storage, retrieval, and discharge (69) (See Table I.)

Male white Carneaux pigeons were studied in such a manner that stress and unphysiological learning conditions were minimal or absent. In these experiments, both control and experimental pigeons, matched for age and general experience before coming to the laboratory, were maintained together in comfortable air-conditioned quarters in which they could observe and hear activities of laboratory personnel; hence, they were minimally stimulated rather than isolated. Control pigeons from one to eleven months of age were sacrificed alternately with experimental pigeons, after being allowed to recover from the transportation to the laboratory and to accommodate to the laboratory for a period of ten days. A second control group, six months of age, was kept in the laboratory with no experiments performed, from the sixth to the eleventh month, then sacrificed. Since the results of these two groups were not significantly different both were grouped together as a single control group designated CP.

The experimental pigeons (EP) were divided into two subgroups. The members of the subgroup EPII, all six months of age on arrival in the laboratory, were allowed to rest for a ten-day period then exposed to learning experiments in the standard operant conditioning experimental chamber for pigeons (191). The chamber contained two response keys and a feeder that gave 3-second access for food reinforcement. Pecks of at least 10-gram force operated a relay in the chamber and provided auditory feedback. Except when the feeder was in operation, each of the response-keys was transilluminated by a 7-watt red bulb.

EPII pigeons were trained in two phases. First, EPII were trained to respond for food reinforcement. A peck on either of two response-keys operated the feeder for 3 seconds, during which period the pigeon could attain a few pieces of grain. After five sessions of exposure on the initial training procedure the second training phase commenced, in which the pigeons were placed on an auditory discrimination task. A trial began with a 2-second dark interval. An auditory stimulus (buzz) of 1-second duration might be present or absent during this interval. The trials were programmed so that in approximately 50 per cent the dark intervals contained auditory stimuli. After the 2-second interval, the response-keys were transilluminated for 4 seconds. If the auditory stimulus was present, a peck on the right-side response-key was reinforced; otherwise, a peck on the left-side response-key was reinforced. If a response failed to occur for 4 seconds after the onset of the key light, or a response was emitted on an incorrect response-key, the chamber remained dark for 10 seconds. A trial ended with either a reinforcement or a period of 10 seconds during which the chamber was dark, and another trial began. Sessions were terminated after 100 trials, and 17 daily sessions were given for all pigeons. The ratio of the right (or correct) responses over the total responses emitted for the final three sessions (per cent right) was taken as a measure against which to compare the amounts of brain protein in each fraction for each pigeon.

Another experimental group (EPI) was trained in three stages. First, the pigeons were trained to peck on a single key for food reinforcement. In the second phase, two response keys were installed and the pigeon learned to peck both sides equally often in order to maximize reinforcement. By staggering the time in which a peck on each key was reinforced, it became possible to obtain 2 reinforcements per minute (variable interval schedule). Phase two was completed when 50% $\pm$ 5% was the distribution of pecking for each key. In phase three, one key only was reinforced and it was necessary for the pigeon to learn this discrimination within only two experimental sessions. The final accuracy varied from 50 to 94 per cent in terms of the pigeons' performance, and this "per cent right" was compared with the amount of protein in each fraction. The pigeons in EPI were sacrificed immediately after the second session of the third phase.

Thus the pigeons of EPII were allowed to rest without exposure to the chamber after their final test session for from three to eleven months, whereas the pigeons of EPI were sacrificed immediately after the series of test sessions. EPII can therefore be considered to be a "remote memory (or learning)" group, and EPI a "recent memory (or learning)" group. The two groups, EPI and EPII, were combined in a single group (EP total) for comparison with

CP pigeons in order to examine the possibility that the training situation alone and not the learning itself is responsible for given chemical changes.

Fifteen experimental and twenty-one control pigeons were sacrificed by immersing the heads in a dry ice acetone bath. The entire frozen brain was removed from the skull, weighed and extracted by the "modified procedure" described on pp. 122 and 123. It was found that four homogenizations routinely extracted all of the proteins available from pigeon brain by these methods. Briefly, the four successive extracts were combined, dialyzed against 0.005 molar phosphate buffer pH 7, and chromatographed on DEAE cellulose (Cellex D) columns with solvent changes as previously described. The recovery from column chromatography was high, as shown in Table XV. Three EP and three CP brains had to be discarded from the comparison because their recoveries on DEAE chromatography fell below the arbitrary limit preset at 85 per cent (final EP, N = 12; CP, N = 18). Fractions were automatically collected as previously described. Each effluent tube was analyzed for content of protein by means of a Technicon Autoanalyzer programmed for the Folin-Lowry quantitative protein determination. After protein analysis the effluent tubes were combined into thirteen main groups as described, with groups 8, 10, and 11 being divided into A and B fractions, and 10B being further subdivided into 10BI and 10BII. The groups were lyophilized, dissolved, and dialyzed exhaustively against solution 1. Determination of the protein content was repeated and 500 micrograms of protein concentrated for each run on disc gel electrophoresis. The remainder was used for carbohydrate analysis (59). The amount of protein in each group was calculated from the original data back to the weight of the whole pigeon brain from which they were extracted, thus giving a yield in terms of mg./g. which could be compared between pigeons. Disc gel electrophoresis was performed as described.

There is a high degree of reproducibility in the crucial groups which are being examined, i.e. 10B and 11A, the position varying in most samples by only one or two tubes out of 350. Indeed, it has become possible to distinguish clearly between subgroups 10BI and 10BII in most specimens (Figures 32, 33, and 34).

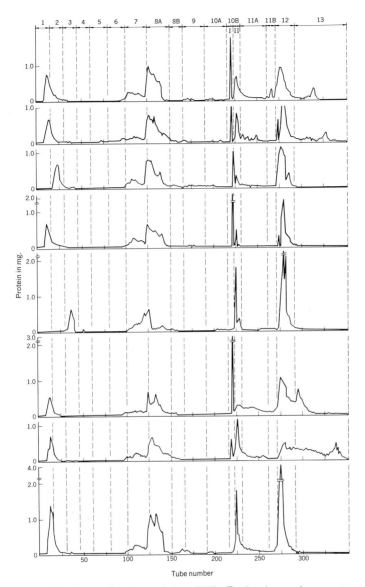

Figure 32. Pigeon brain proteins (CP). Each chromatogram represents one brain.

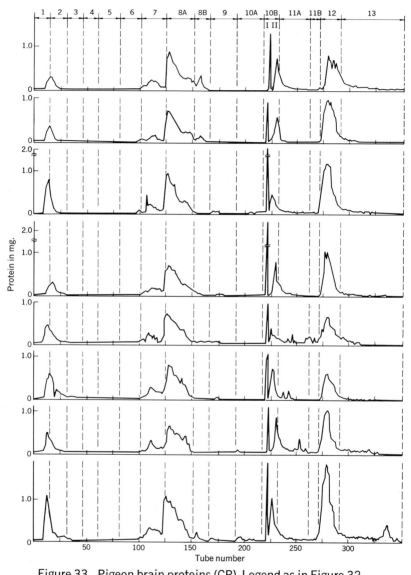

Figure 33. Pigeon brain proteins (CP). Legend as in Figure 32.

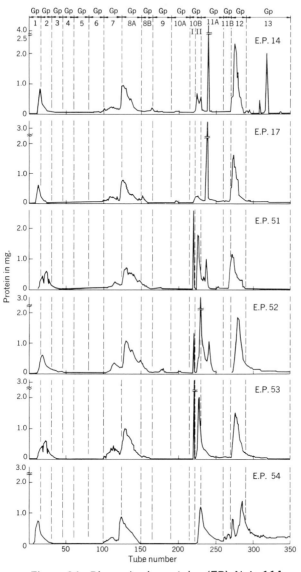

Figure 34. Pigeon brain proteins (EP). Note 11A.

Table XV shows that the brain weights were the same in the experimental and control groups and that the recovery on DEAE column chromatography was the same for both groups. Any differences between the groups therefore, cannot be ascribed to differences in column chromatography. The total protein extracted was significantly greater in EPI as compared to the CP.

Table XVI compares the protein in mg./g. shown to be present in each brain protein group in each of the EPI, EPII, and CP pigeon groups. The brain-to-brain variability in the CP is sufficiently small so as to permit comparison with brain proteins of EP. All of the protein groups are essentially the same in the three groups of pigeons, with certain statistically significant exceptions. First, the concentration of 11A is higher in the EPI, EPII, and EP total than in the CP. Second, the content of 10B-11A in EPI, and possibly in EP total, is greater than in the CP. Third, the concentration of protein group 2 is higher in EPI and EP total, but the same in EPII, when compared to the CP.

For both 11A alone, and for 10B-11A, there is a suggestion that there is a linear relationship between the amount of learning expressed as per cent right and the mg./g. of protein in the brain (Figure 35).

Group 10B, which is seen in Table XVI to be significantly elevated in EPI, seems to be decreased in EPII. This accounts for the drop of 10B-11A values to control CP levels in EPII despite the persistent elevation of 11A in EPII.

In contrast to the suggested linearity between the increase in 10B-11A and 11A itself and the per cent right achieved, no such relationship is found when group 2 protein values are plotted against per cent right in either EPI or EPII. Also, the increase in group 2 proteins occurs only in EPI, and is absent in EPII. Hence, the group 2 increase does not correlate with the amount learned, nor does it persist with time.

Since this learning situation has contained no aversive stimuli and no abnormally intense sensory stimuli, it can be assumed as a preliminary conclusion that this increase represents either some chemical changes accompanying the encoding process itself, one of the other primary mechanisms, or the immediately related supporting reactions (see Table I).

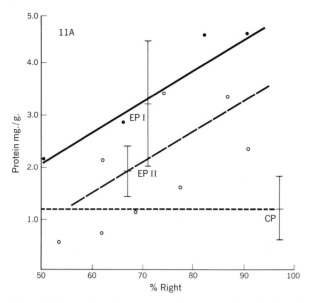

Figure 35. Relationship of amount of brain protein in fraction 11A to the per cent right in learning experiments, in two experimental groups (EPI and EPII) and in control pigeons (CP). The heavy horizontal bars indicate the means, the vertical lines indicate the standard deviations of the means. Each circle represents the data for a single pigeon, the solid circles representing members of EPI, the open circles members of EPII.

In all the experimental pigeons the amount of 11A and of 10B-11A related neither to the age of the pigeon, nor to the number of days in the laboratory, nor to the total number of experimental sessions, nor to the total number of all responses (right or wrong) of each pigeon in the experimental chamber. Hence, the increase in 11A and 10B-11A was not related to the special conditions of exposure to the training situation, but rather appears to be related to the phenomenon of learning itself. In contrast to this, the increase in group 2 proteins, seen only in EPI, does not correlate with the amount learned, and, therefore, is apparently related to exposure to the training situation rather than to the phenomenon of

Table XV. Comparison of brain weight, protein extracted, and protein recovered after column chromatography, in experimental and control pigeons

		BRAIN WEIGHT, G.	TOTAL PROTEIN EXTRACTED, MG./G. BRAIN	RECOVERY OF PROTEIN FROM DEAE CHROMATOGRAPHY, AS %
EXPERIMENTAL PIGEONS	EP Total	2.25 (±0.10)	26.0** (±6.02)	95.5 ±4.03)
	EP II	2.26 (±0.10)	23.7 (±3.14)	94.4 (±4.3)
	EP I	2.22 (±0.01)	32.0** (±6.58)	96.7 (±2.00)
CONTROL PIGEONS	CP	2.26 (±0.13)	21.5 (±3.31)	95.1 (±4.02)

** Significantly different from CP at the 0.01 level or better.

learning itself. However, among the many factors as yet unknown are those dealing with the question of "special effort" or even stress effects of the training situation. For example, liver glycoproteins are now being studied in the same pigeons in which brain glycoproteins are examined.

The proteins of 10B-11A are acidic proteins, eluted from DEAE at pH's below 4. The minimum number of individual protein species recognized to date by disc gel electrophoresis of groups 10B and 11A are three in group 10B (10B:0.52, 10B:0.74, and 10B:1.00), and two in group 11A (11A:0.80 and 11A:1.00) (relative mobilities as in reference 72) (See Figure 36.) These proteins are rich in bound carbohydrate components (e.g. sialic acid up to 7.0 per cent of protein in human brain proteins; hexose up to 12.7 per cent in man and up to 27.2 per cent in pigeon brain). The increase in their amount (and possibly in their heterogeneity) is considered to be supportive evidence for the experiential code hypothesis referred to previously. (68, 69). That is, the glycoproteins of the nervous system represent the mnemic substances in which experiential information is encoded.

Table XVI. Concentration of brain proteins in experimental and control pigeons in mg./g., mean and standard deviation

PROTEIN GROUP	PIGEON GROUP			
	EPI	EPII	EP TOTAL	CP
1	0.92 (±0.62)	1.01 (±0.54)	0.98 (±0.57)	1.08 (±0.70)
2	1.10** (±0.48)	0.75 (±0.48)	1.20** (±0.80)	0.73 (±0.36)
3	0.71 (±0.52)	0.27 (±0.21)	0.42 (±0.40)	0.39 (±0.44)
4	0.60 (±0.76)	0.15 (±0.09)	0.30 (±0.49)	0.15 (±0.09)
5	0.73 (±0.94)	0.17 (±0.09)	0.35 (±0.61)	0.17 (±0.12)
6	0.34 (±1.14)	0.28 (±0.14)	0.46 (±0.72)	0.27 (±0.19)
7	2.06 (±0.44)	1.75 (±0.63)	1.85 (±0.60)	1.94 (±0.55)
8A	5.81 (±1.08)	3.52 (±1.00)	4.29 (±1.60)	4.20 (±0.93)
8B	0.52 (±0.27)	0.43 (±0.20)	0.50 (±0.23)	0.35 (±0.32)
9	0.39 (±0.18)	0.51 (±0.27)	0.47 (±0.25)	0.37 (±0.12)
10A	0.28 (±0.08)	0.41 (±0.10)	0.36 (±0.11)	0.38 (±0.13)
10B	4.27** (±1.44)	1.43** (±0.29)	2.38 (±1.61)	2.07 (±0.51)
11A	3.24** (±1.20)	1.94* (±1.04)	2.56** (±1.34)	1.23 (±0.58)
10B-11A	7.50** (±1.62)	3.37 (±1.00)	4.75* (±2.31)	3.25 (±0.83)
11B	0.63 (±0.46)	0.61 (±0.28)	0.62 (±0.35)	0.29 (±0.16)
12	5.83 (±1.21)	6.23 (±1.47)	6.10 (±1.40)	4.96 (±1.65)
13	2.78 (±2.69)	2.37 (±2.70)	2.50 (±3.50)	1.97 (±1.58)

** Significantly different from CP at the 0.01 level.
* Significantly different from CP at the 0.05 level.

Further studies planned in this laboratory to examine this problem include experiments to define the discreteness structurally, and to define the specific cellular localization of given brain protein species by means of hydrolytic and immunochemical techniques, and experiments to demonstrate the influence of "enriched" and "restricted" environments and the influence of acute and chronic stress on these proteins.

IDENTIFICATION AND CONCENTRATION OF SUGARS BOUND GLYCOSIDI-
CALLY IN NONDIALYZABLE MUCOIDS OF PIGEON BRAIN: AT REST, AND
TRAINING

The demonstration that certain pigeon brain proteins change quantitatively in training and learning situations, taken together with

CP   EP

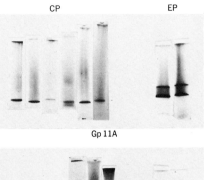

Gp 11A

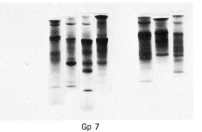

Gp 10B

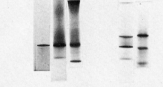

Gp 7

Figure 36. Disc gel electrophoresis of control (CP) and experimental (EP) pigeon brain proteins. Constant sample size of protein (Folin-Lowry protein, 0.5 mg.) and constant running time. Differences in gel size due to differences in photographic magnification. Individual gels differ in rate of movement of front-running dye marker, so that constant basis of comparison must be Rd (mobility of protein relative to mobility of dye marker), and Rd has been shown to be a reliable and reproducible index for a given protein (72).

the fact that many of these proteins were found to contain glyco-sidically-bound carbohydrate moieties, made it of interest to define in greater detail the sugar constituents of the pigeon brain mucoids, and to examine whether these are constant constituents or whether they vary quantitatively and/or qualitatively, when resting and training pigeons are compared. Thus, it is possible that only the amino acid components of the mucoids change in concentration, as demonstrated above, or that both the protein and the carbohydrate constituents change with training and learning.

A variety of methods exist for the liberation of constituent sugars of glycoproteins by hydrolysis and for their demonstration on various forms of chromatography. However, it was desirable to develop a method (75) which was both sensitive and permitted the separation of a wide variety of sugars on a single carrier with a view to their identification, and with the possibility of quantitative isolation of individual constituent sugars and determination of radio-activity in each sugar in incorporation experiments (75).

One-Dimensional Two-Step Thin-Layer Chromatography of Carbohydrates

Thin-layer chromatographic analysis was done on carefully cleaned glass plates. The plates were coated with NM 300 cellulose powder which had been washed in a solvent mixture of ethyl alcohol: carbon tetrachloride:water, 6:3:1, to remove a brownish impurity, then deionized water. The plates were allowed to stand for 4 to 6 hours at room temperature before they were oven-dried, then they were activated by heating for 30 minutes at 60°C., and stored in a desiccator until used.

The chromatographic plates were irrigated at 23°C. in the ascending direction in two-step organic solvents: system A consisted of butanol:acetic acid:pyridine:water, 60:45:4:30 v/v/v; system B consisted of ethyl acetate:isopropanol:pyridine:water, 7:3:2:2 v/v/v/v. The developing solvent was prepared just prior to chromatography. The plate was developed first in the solvents system A for 3.5 hours, then after drying for 15 minutes was developed in system B for 1 hour and 40 minutes in the same ascending direction. The development was stopped each time the solvent front had reached the

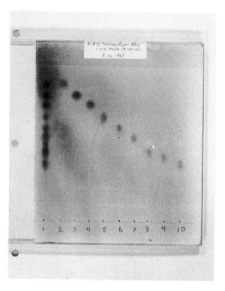

Figure 37. Thin-layer chromatography of sugars (standards): 1. Mixture of standards; 2. L-Rhamnose; 3. D-Ribose; 4. D-Xylose; 5. D-Mannose; 6. D-Glucose; 7. D-Galactose; 8. D-Mannosamine; 9. D-Glucosamine; 10. D-Galactosamine (75, 85).

top edge of the plate. After the two-step development, the plate was dried, then sprayed with a suitable detection reagent: aniline phthalate; o.5 per cent ninhydrin in acetone and 2 to 3 drops of collidine (for free amino groups); o.2 per cent tetrazolium blue and 10 per cent NaOH (1:2 by volume), and one drop of collidine (for deoxysugars, pentoses, hexoses, and hexosamines).

Standard sugars were spotted in 25 μg. amounts, but could be observed in as little as 5 μg. amounts (see Table XVII and Figure 37).

Individual pigeon brain protein groups were dialyzed exhaustively against distilled water, then hydrolyzed at 100°C. in 2N HCl for 4½ hours in sealed tubes. The hydrolyzate was then dialyzed and both dialyzate and dialysand separately collected and lyophilized. The dialyzate was analyzed for the quantitative content of hexoses and hexosamines, and after desalting, the sugars were separated by

Table XVII. R_f values for some sugars in one-dimensional two-step thin-layer chromatography (85)

L—Rhamnose	0.74	D—Mannose	0.58	D—Mannosamine 0.41
D—Ribose	0.68	D—Glucose	0.52	D—Glucosamine 0.38
D—Xylose	0.62	D—Galactose	0.47	D—Galactosamine 0.33

thin-layer chromatography as described above.

Table XVIII shows the deoxysugars, pentoses, hexoses, and hexosamines identified to date on thin-layer chromatography. Three spots remain unidentified as yet: one, a fast-moving spot running well ahead of rhamnose, and close to the solvent front; and the others, slow-moving spots with R_f approximately 0.10, which may be disaccharides or similar small carbohydrate-containing fragments. The results in parentheses indicate combined groups of pigeons, between 4 and 12 in each group; those not in parentheses indicate data from a single pigeon. The presence of rhamnose in non-dialyzable mucoids of brain has not previously been reported in human brain, but, as is shown in Table XVIII, it appears to be present in pigeon brain. Xylose, reported to be present in human brain, is probably also present in pigeon brain, although there is still some uncertainty in the chromatographic identification. Ribose and fucose have been observed less frequently in our pigeon brain studies to date. Pentoses are most likely to be destroyed under these hydrolytic conditions, and milder hydrolysis will need to be employed to check for their presence.

Mannose, glucose, and galactose occur in appreciable amounts in almost all of the brain protein groups. Mannosamine, glucosamine, and galactosamine occur in several protein groups as well. Since none of these sugars has as yet been identified through crystallization or properties of derivatives, conclusive identification must await these procedures.

Relation of Brain Mucoid Sugars to Function

Table XVIII also shows the presence of these various sugars with regard to the functional state of the pigeon, whether at rest or training. R is for resting pigeons (includes CP and EPII of last

Table XVIII. Sugars Bound Glycosidically in Non-dialyzable Mucoids of Pigeon Brain: at Rest (R), and Training (T) (see text, p. 199, for details)

	BRAIN PROTEIN GROUPS															
	1	2	3	4	5	6	7	8A	8B	9	10A	10B	11A	11B	12	13
Rhamnose	(R)	(R)R	(R)	R	(R)	(R)	(R)	R	(R)R	(R)	R	R		(R)	R	(R)
	(R)	R	R R	(R)	(R)	(R)(T)(R)										RR
Fucose	R	R	R R	R				R	R							
Ribose	R	R	R	(T)R				R	T R	R						R
										(R)						
Xylose	(R)	(R)R	(R)R	(R)	(R)	(R)	(R)	(R)	(R)	(R)(R)	(R)	(R)		R		
	(R)	(R)	(R)		(T)	T	(R)			(R)	T					
Mannose	(R)	(R)	(R)	(R)	(R)	(R)(R)	(R)	(R)	(R)	(R)(R)	(R)				R	R
	(R)	(R)	(R)	(R)	(R)	T	T	T	T	(R)	T				R	R
Glucose	(R)	(R)	(R)	(R)	(R)R	(R)R	(R)	(R)R	(R)R	(R)(R)	(R)		R	(R)		R
Galactose	T	T	T	(R)	T	T	T	T	T	(R)	T		R	R	(R)	R
	(R)(R)	(R)	(R)(R)	(R)	(R)(R)	(R)(R)	(R)	(R)(R)	(R)(R)	(R)(R)	(R)(R)	(R)	R	T	T	T
	T	T	T					T	T		T			R	R	
Mannosamine		R R	R	RR				R R	R R				R	R		R
		T	T						T							
Glucosamine	T	R	RR	RR R				R	R R				(T)	(T)	(T)	(T)
		R				T							T	T		T
Galactosamine	R	R	R	R		T		R	R	R	R		R	R RT	(T)	RT

experiment) and T for training pigeons (EPI). It may be seen that rhamnose, fucose, and xylose have only rarely been observed in training pigeon brain. Mannose and glucose of groups 1, 2, and 3, and mannose, glucose, and galactose of groups 11B, 12, and 13, have only been observed in resting pigeon brain to date.

There is an indication from these results, therefore, that there may be a selective preference for the existence of particular sugar residues attached to protein in the brain mucoids, depending on whether the pigeon is at rest or is in a training situation, but much more work needs to be done in this regard before definitive conclusions can be reached.

Table XIX shows that while the concentration of protein of group 11A increases in the learning situation, the bound hexose concentration increases even more, with a resultant elevation of the per cent hexose of this fraction. Thus the bound hexose is also "training or learning-sensitive." On the other hand, there is a decrease in the per cent hexose of groups 2 and 10B in the learning situation.

Further study of the concentration of hexose in the total of all fractions of the brain mucoids revealed that there are over-all differences between the resting and training situations. Table XX shows that the total hexose bound in brain mucoids is essentially the same in resting pigeons who have never been trained, and those resting 3 to 11 months after training (0.63 and 0.69 mg./g. brain, respectively). However, the concentration is much greater at all times during the training period (2.4-10.0 mg./g.; mean 6.0). Since data relating the concentration of mucoid hexose to the amount learned are not yet available, as they are in the case of the protein moiety of 11A, a specific relationship of the carbohydrate moieties to learning itself cannot be distinguished from a relationship of these carbohydrates to generally increased brain activation or alerting phenomena.

INCORPORATION OF 1-^{14}C-GLUCOSE INTO PIGEON BRAIN MUCOIDS

The determination of incorporation of radioactivity in intact *in situ* glycoprotein has obvious advantages when the intracellular

Table XIX. Hexose (as per cent of protein) in three brain protein groups

PROTEIN GROUP	RESTING	TRAINING
2	11.6	2.7
10B	4.5	2.2
11A	6.8	27.2

Table XX. Total concentration of bound hexose in brain mucoids of resting and training pigeons

	NUMBER OF PIGEONS*	MUCOID HEXOSE mg./g. WET WT. BRAIN
Resting, never trained	(21)	0.63
Resting, 3 to 11 months post-training	(11)	0.69
Training:		
10 minutes	1	9.0
20 minutes	1	8.8
30 minutes	5	10.0, 9.8, 3.9, 3.5, 2.7
45 minutes	1	3.5
60 minutes	2	7.8, 5.5
60 minutes	(3)	2.4

* Numbers in parentheses indicate number of individual brains from which individual groups were pooled, bound hexose determined, then added. Other numbers indicate individual brains separately determined for bound hexose.

localization of the protein is known. Ninety μc. of $1\text{-}^{14}\text{C}$-glucose was injected intravenously into pigeons prior to a rest or training period, and the pigeons were sacrificed at intervals thereafter. The proteins were then extracted and chromatographed from each pigeon brain as previously described, and radioactivity of the resultant fractions determined on a scintillation counter. After exhaustive dialysis of the isolated brain protein groups, singly or combined, total radioactivity of the fraction was determined, then the fraction was subjected to stepwise acid hydrolysis with dialysis

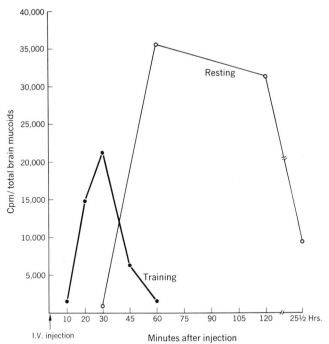

Figure 38. ¹⁴C-glucose incorporation into pigeon brain mucoids.

to free liberated sugars and other constituents. These were separated by thin-layer chromatography as above, and the stained spots, together with blanks, removed by vacuum suction, were counted (75).

Figure 38 shows the pattern of incorporation of ¹⁴C into the brain mucoids of pigeons resting or training, with time. First, incorporation of substantial amounts of ¹⁴C can be demonstrated. Second, there is a marked difference in the patterns of incorporation of resting pigeons when compared to training pigeons as indicated by the early peak of incorporation in the training pigeon brain mucoids. These preliminary results do not permit conclusions, but two of the possibilities to account for these differences which will need to be considered in subsequent experiments are the following: first, the precursor pool may be markedly different in resting as opposed to training pigeon brain; and, second, the carbohydrate moieties of the brain mucoids may be involved in functional activity of the brain in such a way that either (a) they are depleted during activity and replenished during rest, or (b) they are not depleted, but simply not available to exchange reactions while involved in some integral way with brain function in the training pigeon.

Table XXI. ^{14}C in dialyzable constituents released by 2N HCl hydrolysis for 4½ hours (cpm/protein group/pigeon brain).

PROTEIN GROUP	30 MINUTES RESTING	60 MINUTES RESTING	60 MINUTES TRAINING
1	—	0	70
2	259	56	73
3	0	56	77
4	0	73	0
5	0	56	10
6	0	21	0
7	0	38	73
8A	0	94	171
8B	0	94	133
9	0	21	168
10A	—	—	10
10B1	0	94	0
10B2	0	56	161
11A	0	56	91
11B	0	21	45
12	0	133	312
13	0	38	28

Table XXI shows that protein group 2 is the first protein group to have its hydrolyzable (2N HCl, 4½ hours) carbohydrate (only one-third to one-half of the total is released by this hydrolysis) labeled in the resting pigeon brain. Figure 39 demonstrates that the first labeled carbohydrate in group 2 is mannosamine, plus an unidentified slow-moving substance, probably disaccharidic; the other seven carbohydrate constituents of this fraction show no radioactivity at these levels of concentration of material. Among the readily hydrolyzable constituents of groups 8A and 8B, at 1 hour of training, only galactosamine has been labeled (see Figures

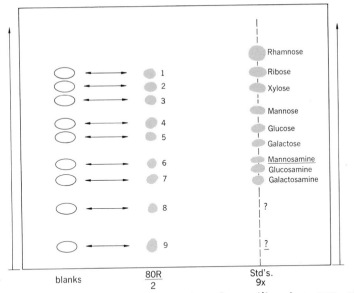

blanks	$\dfrac{80R}{2}$	Std's. 9x

Figure 39. Thin-layer chromatography of constituent sugars of brain mucoids of group 2 of pigeon 80R (see p. 204).

40 and 41). The complete survey of order of labeling of constituents has just begun.

The quantitative difference between resting and training brain is shown in Figure 42. The first appreciable labeling in resting brain is seen at 30 minutes, and occurs in fractions (1-2) and 11B. In contrast, at only 10 minutes of training, the total specific activity is approximately 15 times that in resting brain at 30 minutes. Nonetheless, the same fractions, (1-2) and 11B, show the highest specific activity.

There are now three types of evidence for early biochemical changes in training: (1) quantitative increase of group 2 protein, which does not persist with time (Table XVI); (2) increase in total brain mucoid hexose in the first 10 or 20 minutes of training (Table XX); and (3) rapid early incorporation of ^{14}C-glucose into groups 2 and 11B bound carbohydrates (Figure 42). It may become possible experimentally to separate these early changes from more persistent changes such as those in group 11A protein.

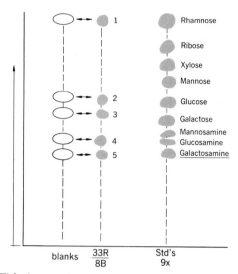

Figure 40. Thin-layer chromatography of constituent sugars of brain mucoids (see p. 204).

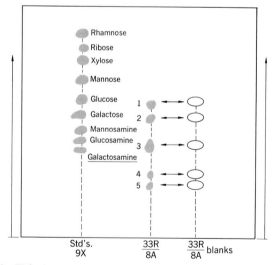

Figure 41. Thin-layer chromatography of constituent sugars of brain mucoids (see p. 204).

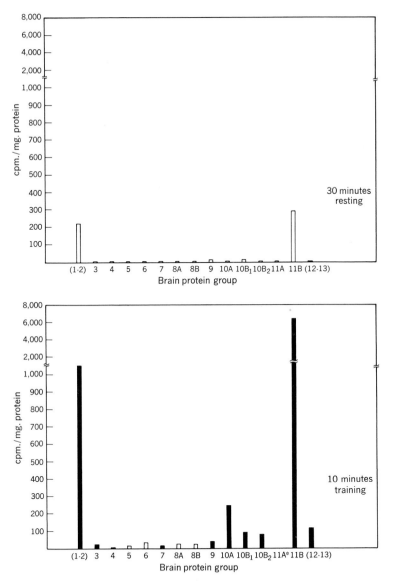

Figure 42. Comparison of incorporation of ^{14}C-glucose in 30-minute resting and 10-minute training pigeon brain mucoids. Predominant labeling in both instances is in groups 1-2 and 11B; however, note difference in extent of labeling (73).

Summary

Certain brain proteins, especially groups 10B, 11A, 11B, 12, and 13, are seen to be associated with membranous structures, and some of these proteins, 10B and 11A, and Group 2, show quantitative changes in pigeon brain with training and learning. These proteins are rich in bound carbohydrate moieties, which have received preliminary identification by thin layer chromatography. Group 10B protein, increased over the normal in glial tumors, appears to be a glial membrane component. The incorporation of ^{14}C-glucose into these brain mucoids has been demonstrated. A beginning has been made in differentiating the order in which the constituents are labeled, and in noting the differences in incorporation patterns between resting and training pigeon brain. The quantitative changes in the amino acid portion of these brain mucoids with learning are exceeded by the quantitative changes in their bound hexose residues. The hypothesis, which suggests that brain mucoids are involved in the coding of experiential information, is not contradicted, and appears to be supported by the above findings.

This chapter has listed some requirements for prospective coding molecules, and has reviewed the relevant experimental data available. The correctness of the hypothesis here proposed, after all, will be determined by this and future data. The level of certainty of the conclusion for each requirement varies considerably, not because the data is conflicting, for it is all remarkably positive to date, but because there is as yet insufficient data on many of the requirements. In sum, however, the data appears to be adequate for hypothesis formation. The brain mucoids demonstrate sufficient heterogeneity, fixed location, appropriate development, change with pathology, recognition functions, biosynthesis (resting, training, and puromycin-sensitive), change with behavior, and change with learning, all consistent with the notion that they are directly involved in the biochemistry of learning and memory. Some specific ways in which they might be so involved are considered next.

VII

Toward a comprehensive biochemical theory of memory

Because the field of memory stretches from the storage of simple numbers to the recall of the most abstract concepts and events, with all of the accompanying sense impressions and affects which enrich them, it is likely that the nature of memory will not yield to any single formulation, no matter how correct.

Certain basic requirements for the memory process, each of which may well demand quite discrete molecular mechanisms for their performance, have been discussed in Chapter II (Table I). In addition to the molecular requirements for these phases of the memory process, which must include sensory reception, transduction, coding for transmission, coding for storage, retrieval and non-retrieval, association, discharge, and supporting reactions for each, the following additional characteristics of memory and learning will require molecular understanding before we have achieved anything resembling a comprehensive biochemical theory of memory.

Time dependency and hierarchies of storage

There may well be different mechanisms for the retention of information which is to be held temporarily, but not "stored": that is, held for seconds or minutes, as in the case of certain telephone numbers, or held only for minutes or hours, as in the case of the departure time of an airplane. Both of these types of temporary

209

retention of information may differ in quite fundamental or in only superficial ways from those which deal with storage for longer periods of time.

For long-term storage there may be distinctions between the mechanisms used for data which must always be readily available, and those used for data which may be required months or years later. It is clear that long-term information is stored out of consciousness. One cannot be thinking of all that one knows at once; it is neither desirable nor possible. However, there is probably a hierarchy of information storage, from permanent storage with ready retrievability, through permanent storage with retrievability only by great conscious effort, or by association, to permanent storage without retrieval throughout the lifespan.

Are there macromolecules of the same or different types whose biosynthetic half-lives correspond to these various needs, or are there different anatomic subsystems performing these different functions, or both? That there is some anatomic localization of memory process is supported by the data of Chapter III.

Repair and sleep

If one considers the macromolecular configuration that corresponds to a particular long-term storage requirement to be akin to the structural permanence of a brick wall which requires repair with time, is renewal "whole-wall-at-a-time"; or "brick-by-brick" without disturbing the wall's organizational structure or its existence as a functional unit for even a moment in the life of the organism?

From early exchange data on the brain mucoids (see p. 203) it may be that exchange, even though it be "brick-by-brick," is not possible when the molecule is functioning. Thus, "repair" may require the resting state. Indeed, the need for these reparative processes may underlie the need for sleep, and its survival function.

Plasticity, redundancy, and economy

The entire synaptic region on both sides of the interface provides graded, nonpropagated responses (48).

> The receptive surfaces of the next-order neurons must synthesize conflicting as well as consonant data from a number of sources (varying from one or a few to perhaps tens of thousands) and code them into new patterns of action potentials which will then be distributed to the next further constellation of synaptic stations. . . . Plasticity in the central nervous system is apparently achieved by this means. Reliability is apparently provided through a redundancy of signals and circuits (337).

> . . . neurons are functionally related to each other not only through synaptic articulations, but also by electrotonic field forces [which] . . . influence the level of excitability among neighboring neurons, even though no strictly anatomical connections may exist between them (48).

> As the experience is repeated many times, there develops a significant economy in terms of the extent of brain involvement. Perhaps recognizable signals can eventually be reduced to quite a small number of impulses, representing minuscule abstractions of reality (337).

Another indication of the abstracting capacity of the brain is the following:

> The time required for initial transfer of a replicated trace from one hemisphere to another is considerably shorter than that required for the complete fixation of the replicated trace in the previously "naïve hemisphere" (361).

Organizers

In addition to the concept of organizers in the development of the nervous system (551), the full nature of "meaning," of "relevance," of "sense of fit," of "elegance," and of "pleasure" probably require, in addition to preferred pathways and arrangement, some orienting systems here briefly referred to as organizers. Affective components are present in perception, association, repression, and derepression. Whether sense impressions "last" may relate to the strength of the stimuli, or to the quality, as with an accompanying sense of danger or pain. Whether these experiences remain available in forms readily retrievable into consciousness, or only through the signal anxiety they provoke when reawakened by new experiences which the organism judges to be relevant, there is no doubt that they are stored, and like the non-affective components of the event, stored in some unconscious form. These affective components probably enter into the function of the organizers and indeed may themselves represent one major organizing system. The day-to-day function of the organizers is doubtless tested in the balance of survival value to the individual and to the species. The organizers are themselves probably those characteristics which are most individual about a given nervous system, and perhaps most subject to pathology. The potential complexity of such systems is staggering, but not inconceivable (see pp. 29-31).

Development

No stimulus can enter upon a *tabula rasa*. All of the sense organs themselves maintain a steady state of activity even in the absence of recognizable stimuli. Afferent influx contributes to the "spontaneous" central nervous activity. Each neuronal constellation in the brain shows some activity even during sleep, hibernation or deep anesthesia (337).

From what is known of morphogenesis and repair in the nervous system (551) the following statements appear to be most in accord with anatomic and physiologic evidence of how the nervous system develops (481):

It now appears that the complicated nerve fiber circuits of the brain grow, assemble, and organize themselves through the use of intricate chemical codes under genetic control. Early in development the nerve cells, numbering in the billions, acquire, and retain thereafter, individual identification tags, chemical in nature, by which they can be recognized and distinguished one from another.

Lasting functional hookups are established only with cells to which the growing fibers find themselves selectively matched by inherent chemical affinities.

By selective chemical preferences the respective nerve fibers are guided correctly to their separate channels at each of the numerous forks or decision points which they encounter as they travel through what is essentially a multiple Y-maze of possible channels.

It remains an open question whether the effects of function —that is, learning and memory—add or subtract any actual fiber structures or synaptic connections to the established morphology. It is possible, though not particularly indicated, that the neural changes implanted by learning and memory are essentially physiological in nature; membrane or other micro or molecular changes could affect excitatory threshold, conductance, and resistance to impulse transmission, endogenous discharge properties all within the already established morphological networks. Between the strictly inherited organization of the behavioral networks and the strictly acquired, we recognize an important intermediate realm of nervous development in which function and growth go on simultaneously with mutual interactions. The anatomical effects of functional influence during these stages may not be large or even visible under the light microscope, but the minute differences may be critical in terms of behavior, especially with reference to human childhood.

The computer models for memory described in Chapter V can be directly superimposed upon these morphogenetic formulations, with a resultant organizational structure, which, although vague in its detail, might well be relevant to the nervous system.

Among what has been referred to as the "remaining problems" in the above formulation is the following: what is "the underlying chemistry" of these affinities that is responsible for which cells of the nervous system can and do interact and which do not?

The function of the brain mucoids

Brain mucoids might be involved in some way in all of the aspects of memory discussed above.

The recent evidence of similarity in the amino acid chain of structural membrane proteins derived from such diverse sources as mitochondrial and red cell membranes (151) offers little chance for a purely protein structural specificity based on amino acids alone. On the contrary, this sameness of protein leads to the conclusion that specificity is more likely to be a property of the end groups, carbohydrate, lipid, or other attached to the protein backbone.

THE "SIGN-POST" MECHANISM

One example of a possible specific molecular mechanism underlying memory is that which follows. A single carbohydrate end group might determine whether or not transmission of an impulse is facilitated between neuron A and B. Consider that on the presynaptic membrane belonging to neuron A there is a glycoprotein, glycoprotein A^1, whose carbohydrate end group can be of two types, which determine whether contact is or is not taking place with the postsynaptic membrane belonging to neurone B. Thus, for example, glycoprotein A^1 may exist with its end group a galactosamine residue, but with the postsynaptic membrane B possessing the specific receptor B^1 (possibly, but not necessarily, also a glycoprotein) specific only for a galactose residue. In the "resting" state, A^1 does not combine with B^1, and no synaptic contact results. Thus, although transmission is possible between A and B, it may not occur, or it may occur without facilitation. To state it another way, the threshold for transmission between neurons A and B may be an inverse function of the amount of physical contact between the membranes of A and B: the more the contact, the lower the threshold.

A synthetic mechanism, a galactose transferase here taken as only one example, could be present at or in A, which could upon the proper stimulus attach a galactose residue to the galactosamine end group of A^1, thus changing the galactosamine end group to a galactose end group for A^1. This galactose end group of A^1 would combine immediately with receptor B^1, ionically or covalently, the contact between A and B would be increased, the threshold lowered, and transmission between A and B facilitated. It is possible that the "proper stimulus" for the attachment of galactose is the passage of an excitatory impulse of sufficient intensity through A. The question of whether A can fire B will depend upon (1) whether the synthetic reaction necessary to attach the correct end group on A^1 is at hand and immediately available, or if repressed, is able to be derepressed; and (2) whether the receptor B^1 is at hand to react with A^1-galactose. These paired configurations might be laid down with complete or relative specificity by genetic coding mechanisms and realized in the morphogenesis of the nervous system. Thus the chemical specificities of A and B which allow them to grow together in synaptic contact in the first place would be the same specificities determining their contact and the transmission of an impulse between them throughout the life of the organism.

The influence of experience would enter in terms of (1) The frequency of stimuli, or strength of stimuli, or both, passing through A causing it to fire B. That is, the potential to synthesize A^1-galactose may require the activation by strong and/or repeated stimulation. (2) The competitive pathways available. That is, neuron A could transmit to neuron C, A to D, A to E, etc. All might be programmed genetically as possibilities, then a combined selection-instruction mechanism brought to bear by experience to determine which pathway is selected, or which alternative pathways are preferred, and their order of preference. A DNA-specified repression-derepression type of induction requiring experiential input for activation could well be invoked for the A^1-galactose transferase reaction. The potential of the system may be quite extensive, as genetically programmed, but each component would require experiential realization in order to perform. That is, the degree of derepression in each instance would be a direct function of experiential input.

For A^1-galactose, it might be necessary to substitute A^1-(glycosaminoglycan)$_n$-galactose, "n" representing the number of residues actually required to bridge the synaptic cleft so that the molecule A^1 may reach B^1.

Even greater complexity and selectivity could be achieved by having more than one specific glycoprotein and receptor present per synapse, thus, A^1, A^2, A^3, A^n and B^1, B^2, B^3, and B^n.

Chemical coding of information in the brain would thus be visualized as a specific set of instructions determining whether, and under what conditions, each neuron will fire any other accessible neuron. The actual information coded in glycoprotein A^1 could be no more than that required to define whether or not B^1 would be contacted. The mucoids would thus act as switching mechanisms, "sign-posts" which route transmission. The mucoids would thus be the chemical basis of the make-break mechanisms of the brain's circuitry, the chemical basis of the establishment of the cluster of specific circuits which constitute a memory trace. They might also underlie specificities of contact between glia and neurons.

The informational content of a memory would rest in an inactive state until activated by the appropriate recall or retrieval mechanisms. The ability of the impulse to enter into many parts of the circuit would correspond with the ability to reach a given memory by a number of different associative pathways.

The mechanism for retrieval in unconscious function may be only slightly different, or it may differ markedly, from that for retrieval in conscious function.

The different duration-stabilities of different memories could be a direct function of the stability of the A^1-galactose and similar linkages. This would leave open the question of whether even stable configurations would require constant or periodic replacement of the galactose residue by exchange reactions, or whether all of the exchange reactions are only for the laying down of temporary configurations. Sleep might be necessary only to synthesize stable A^1-galactose end groups to replace the temporary configurations which have held the information each day. Since the amount of sleep required daily does not always seem to be justified by the amount learned each day, however, it may be that even stable memories need their determinant groups exchanged periodically. It should be noted once again that the galactose residue is only chosen here as one possible example of the many specific carbohydrate end groups which could function in this way.

There seems to be little indication to theorize further with greater specificity along this one approach at this time, but it can be seen that many features of learning and memory could be accounted for in this way.

THE "SPELL-OUT" MECHANISM

A second theoretical approach might minimize the importance of circuitry of the brain for long-term storage, and apply circuitry only to temporary holding, categorizing, and retrieval mechanisms. The major basis of the chemical coding of information in long-term storage would thus be the fine structure of the millions of possible molecular species and configurations of the brain mucoids. In computer terms, every "bit" of information and every abstract structure would be "spelled out." That is, each "bit" would have a corresponding mucoid to represent it, either by means of the primary structure of each, or by the configurational change in the protein induced by changing the carbohydrate side chains. Each mucoid might be represented many times both in different molecular groupings or clusters and in the same grouping occurring in many different sites in the brain.

COMBINED MECHANISM

These two theoretical approaches are not necessarily conflicting; both could be partially or wholly correct. Indeed, both the "signpost" and the "spell-out" mechanisms could function simultaneously, and this would offer a solution to the conflict between the computer and molecular coding schools of memory.

Many other specific postulates are possible for the manner in which the brain mucoids might mediate memory. Enough has been stated to indicate that the basic hypothesis lends itself both to further detailed sub-hypotheses and to experimental tests.

Stated in general terms, the evidence reviewed in the preceding chapter for the ability of mucoids to qualify as coding macromolecules in brain, taken together with their known function as a determinant of contact properties elsewhere, makes it seem reasonable that they fulfill similar roles in the nervous system for the handling of information. Thus brain mucoids exhibit heterogeneity, location, development, pathology, recognition functions, biosynthesis, and change with behavior consistent with requirements for coding molecules. The experimental evidence on the state of the brain mucoids in the learning situation reinforces the sense of correctness of the hypothesis.

However, what has seemed eminently reasonable in the past has on occasion been shown to be false, or difficult of proof. With this caution in mind, it appears worthwhile to consider the brain mucoid-memory hypothesis further, and to gather more experimental data of relevance to it.

There is a tendency in viewing the complex products of higher nervous system activity to question how hypotheses such as these can possibly be relevant when they are based upon relatively simple principles underlying molecular contact reactions. Yet biology is one, and its most advanced manifestation, the nervous system, may well be an organization in magnificent complexity of just such principles.

References

1. Adey, W. R., Dunlop, C. W., and Hendrix, C. E. *AMA Arch. Neurol.*, 3, 74, 1960.
2. Agin, D. *Macromolecules and Behavior*, J. Gaito (ed.), New York: Appleton-Century-Crofts, 1966, p. 14.
3. Agranoff, B. W. *Neurosciences Res. Prog. Bull.*, 4, 2, 1966, p. 158.
4. Agranoff, B. W., Davis, R. E., and Brink, J. J. *Proc. Nat. Acad. Sci.*, 54, 788, 1965.
5. Albert, D. J. *Neuropsychologia*, 1, 79, 1966.
6. Albert, D. J. *Neuropsychologia*, 1, 49, 1966.
7. Alpern, E. B., Finkelstein, N., and Gantt, W. H. *Bull. Johns Hopkins Hosp.*, 73, 287, 1943.
8. Altman, J. *Macromolecules and Behavior*, J. Gaito (ed.), New York: Appleton-Century-Crofts, 1966, p. 103.
9. Altman, J. *Protides of the Biological Fluids*, H. Peeters (ed.), Amsterdam: Elsevier, 1966, p. 127.
10. Altman, J., and Das, G. D. *Nature*, 204, 1161, 1964.
11. Altman, J., and Das, G. D. *Nature*, 207, 953, 1965.
12. Altman, J., Das, G. D., and Chang, J. *Intnl. J. Physiol. Behavior*, 1, 111, 1966.
13. Altman, J., and Das, G. D. *Intnl. J. Physiol. Behavior*, 1, 105, 1966.
14. Aminoff, D. *Biochem. J.*, 81, 384, 1961.
15. Amoore, G. E. *Cold Spring Harbor Symp. on Quant. Biol.*, Vol. 30, 1965, p. 623.
16. Anderson, B. *Acta Physiol. Scand.*, 28, 188, 1953.
17. Anderson, B., and McCann, S. M. *Acta Physiol. Scand.*, 33, 333, 1953.
18. Anderson, B., and Wyrwicka, W. *Acta Physiol. Scand.*, 41, 194, 1957.

19. Ariens-Kappers, C. U., Huber, G. C., and Crosby, E. C. *The Comparative Anatomy of the Nervous System of Vertebrates, Including Man*, New York: The Macmillan Company, 1936.
20. Athineos, E., Thornton, M., and Winzler, R. *J. Proc. Soc. Exp. Biol. Med.*, *111*, 353, 1962.
21. Atwood, R. P., and Green, J. P. *Fed. Proc.*, *18*, 364, 1959.
22. August, C. S., Kies, M. W., Hzuby, S., and Shaw, C. H. *Fed. Proc.*, *25*, 356, 1966.
23. Babich, F. R., Jacobson, A. L., Bubach, S., and Jacobson, A. *Science*, *49*, 656, 1965.
24. Babich, F. R., Jacobson, A. L., and Bubach, S. *Proc. Nat. Acad. Sci.*, *54*, 1299, 1965.
25. Bailey, B. F. S., and Heald, P. J. *J. Neurochem.*, 6, 342, 1961.
26. Ibid. 7, 81, 1961.
27. Balackrishnan, S., and McIlwain, H. *Biochem. J.*, 81, 72, 1961.
28. Balazs, E. A., and Jeanloz, R. W. *The Amino Sugars*, Vol. II A, New York: Academic Press, 1965.
29. Barbizet, H., Victor, M., and Yakovlev, P. I. *Neurology*, *5*, 394, 1955.
30. Barondes, S. H. *Nature*, *205*, 18, 1965.
31. Barondes, S. H., and Jarvik, M. E. *J. Neurochem.*, *11*, 187, 1964.
32. Barondes, S. H., and Cohen, H. D. *Science*, *151*, 594, 1966.
33. Barondes, S. H., and Cohen, H. D. *Brain Res.*, *4*, 44, 1967.
34. Barron, K. D., Bernsohn, J. I., and Hess, A. *J. Histochem. and Cytochem.*, *9*, 656, 1961.
35. Bauer, H., Matzelt, D., and Schwarze, I. *Klin. Wochschr.*, *40*, 251, 1962.
36. Beckwith, W. C. *Proc. of the XXVII Intnl. Cong. of Psychology, Acta Psychologica*, *23*, 172, 1964.
37. Bennett, E. L., Crossland, J. D., and Rosenzweig, M. R. *Nature*, *187*, 787, 1960.
38. Bennett, E. L., Diamond, M. C., Krech, D., and Rosenzweig, M. R. *Science*, *146*, 610, 1964.
39. Bennett, E. L., Diamond, M. C., Morimoto, H., and Hebert, M. *J. Neurochem.*, *13*, 563, 1966.
40. Bennett, E. L., Hebert, M., Rosenzweig, M. R., and Krech, D. *Absts. of 6th Intnl. Cong. Biochem.*, *New York*, 1964, p. 224.
41. Bennett, E. L., Diamond, M. C., Krech, D., and Rosenzweig, M. R. *Science*, *146*, 610, 1964.
42. Bennett, E. L., Rosenzweig, M. R., Krech, D., Caarlsson, H., Dye, N., and Ohlander, A. *J. Neurochem.*, *3*, 144, 1958.

43. Bennett, M. V. L. *Cold Spring Harbor Symp. on Quant. Biol.*, Vol. 30, 1965, p. 245.
44. Berger, B. D., Margules, D. L., Fenichel, R. L., and Stein, L. *Science, 153*, 658, 1966.
45. Berman, E. R., and Gatt, S. *Cerebral Sphingolipidoses*, S. M. Aronson and B. W. Volk (eds.), New York: Academic Press, 1962, p. 237.
46. Bernheimer, A. W., and Van Heyningen, W. E. *J. Gen. Microbiol., 24*, 121, 1961.
47. Bernsohn, J., Barron, K. D., and Hess, A. R. *Proc. Soc. Exp. Biol. Med., 107*, 773, 1961.
48. Bishop, G. H. *Physiol. Rev., 36*, 379, 1956.
49. Bleuler, E. *Dementia Praecox or the Group of Schizophrenias*, New York: International Universities Press, 1950.
50. Blix, G. *Skand. Arch. Physiol., 80*, 46, 1938.
51. Blix, G., and Odin, L. *Acta Chem. Scand., 9*, 1541, 1955.
52. Bogen, J. F., and Voge, P. J. *Bull. Los Ang. Neurol. Soc., 27*, 169, 1962.
53. Bogoch, S. *Am. J. Psychiat., 111*, 108, 1954.
54. Bogoch, S. Ph.D. Thesis, Harvard University, 1956.
55. Bogoch, S. *Virology, 1*, 458, 1957.
56. Bogoch, S. *Am. J. Psychiat., 114*, 122, 1957.
57. Bogoch, S. *AMA Arch. Neurology and Psychiatry, 80*, 221, 1958.
58. Bogoch, S. *Am. J. Psychiat., 114*, 1028, 1958.
59. Bogoch, S. *Biochem. J., 68*, 319, 1958.
60. Bogoch, S. *Proc. IV Intnl. Cong. Biochem.*, Vienna, F. Brucke (ed.), New York: Pergamon Press, 1959, p. 196.
61. Bogoch, S. *First Intnl. Cong. Neurol. Sci., Brussels*, Vol. 1, L. Van Bogaert (ed.), *Exerpta Medica*, 1957, p. 54.
62. Bogoch, S. *Am. J. Psychiat., 116*, 743, 1960.
63. Bogoch, S. *J. Biol. Chem., 235*, 16, 1960.
64. Bogoch, S. *Neurology, 10*, 439, 1960.
65. Bogoch, S. *Nature, 185*, 392, 1960.
66. Bogoch, S. *Cerebral Sphingolipidoses*, S. M. Aronson and B. W. Volk (eds.), New York: Academic Press, 1962, p. 249.
67. Bogoch, S. *Proc. 8th Intnl. Cong. Neurol.*, Vienna, *Excerpta Medica*, Amsterdam: Elsevier, 1965, p. E 139.
68. Bogoch, S. *Neurosciences Res. Prog. Bull., 3*, 38, 1965.
69. Bogoch, S. *Proc. IV World Congress of Psychiatry*, September 1966, *Excerpta Medica*, in press.

70. Bogoch, S. *Biological Treatment of Mental Illness,* M. Rinkel (ed.), New York: Farrer, Strauss, and Giroux, 1966, p. 406.
71. Bogoch, S. Chapter 5, "Proteins of the Nervous System," *Handbook of Neurochemistry,* Vol. I, A. Lajtha (ed.), New York: Plenum Press, 1968, in press.
72. Bogoch, S., and Belval, P. C. In *Inborn Disorders of Sphingolipid Metabolism,* S. M. Aronson and B. W. Volk (eds.), New York: Pergamon Press, 1966, p. 273.
73. Bogoch, S., Belval, P. C., Sacks, W., and Neuringer, A. Unpublished results.
74. Bogoch, S., Belval, P. C., Dussik, K. T., and Conran, P. *Am. J. Psychiat.,* 119, 128, 1962.
75. Bogoch, S., Belval, P. C., Sweet, W. H., Sacks, W., and Korsh, G. *Proc. XVth Colloq., Brugge, Protides of Biological Fluids,* H. Peeters (ed.), Amsterdam: Elsevier, 1968, p. 129.
76. Bogoch, S., Belval, P. C., and Winer, D. *Nature,* 190, 152, 1961.
77. Bogoch, S., and Bogoch, E. S. *Nature,* 183, 53, 1959.
78. Bogoch, S., Dussik, K. T., and Conran, P. *New Eng. J. Med.,* 264, 521, 1961.
79. Bogoch, S., Dussik, K. T., Fender, C., and Conran, P. *Am. J. Psychiat.,* 117, 409, 1960.
80. Bogoch, S., and Evans, P. *Nature,* 195, 180, 1962.
81. Bogoch, S., Gilfillan, R. F., Chess, L., and Kraysler, S. *Bact. Proc. Abst. 63rd Ann. Mtg. Am. Soc. Microbiol.,* 1963, p. 150.
82. Bogoch, S., Gilfillan, R. F., and Evans, P. *Nature,* 196, 649, 1962.
83. Bogoch, S., and Kaufman, J. *Bact. Proc., Abst. 65th Ann. Mtg.,* April 1965, p. 101.
84. Bogoch, S., and Korsh, G. *Nature,* 212, 509, 1966.
85. Bogoch, S., and Korsh, G. Unpublished results.
86. Bogoch, S., Lynch, P., and Levine, A. S. *Virology,* 7, 161-9, 1959.
87. Bogoch, S., Paasonen, M. K., and Trendelenburg, U. *Brit. J. Pharmacol.,* 18, 325, 1962.
88. Bogoch, S., Rajam, P. C., and Belval, P. C. *Nature,* 204, 73, 1964.
89. Bogoch, S., Sacks, W., and Simpson, G. *Neurology,* 13, 355, 1963.
90. Bogoch, S., Sacks, W., and Simpson, G. Unpublished results.
91. Bogoch, S., and Szulman, A. E. Unpublished results.
92. Bogoch, S., and Whittaker, V. P. Unpublished results, 1966-67.

93. Bonner, J. *Macromolecules and Behavior*, J. Gaito (ed.), New York: Appleton-Century-Crofts, 1966, p. 158.
94. Bovet, D., Bignami, G., and Robustelli, F. *Compt. Rend. Acad. Sci.*, 276, 778, 1963.
95. Bovet, D., McGaugh, J. L., and Oliverio, A. *Life Sciences*, 5, 1309, 1966.
96. Bownds, D. Unpublished data, quoted in R. Hubbard, D. Bownds, and T. Yoshizawa, *Cold Spring Harbor Symp. on Quant. Biol.*, Vol. 30, 1965, p. 301.
97. Bownds, D., and Wald, G. *Nature*, 205, 254, 1965.
98. Brady, R. O., and Trams, E. G. *Ann. Rev. Biochem.*, 33, 75, 1964.
99. Breen, R. A., and McGaugh, J. L. *J. Comp. Physiol. Psychol.*, 54, 498, 1961.
100. Brierly, J. B. *Gerontol. Clinica*, 3, 97, 1961.
101. Brink, J. J., Davis, R. E., and Agranoff, B. W. *J. Neurochem.*, 13, 889, 1966.
102. Brown, H. M. Unpublished Ph.D. Thesis, University of Utah, 1964, quoted in J. V. McConnell, *Ann. Rev. Physiol.*, 28, 107, 1966.
103. Brown, K. T., and Murakami, M. *Nature*, 204, 739, 1964.
104. Brown, K. T., and Watanabe, K. *Nature*, 193, 958, 1962.
105. Brown, S., and Schafer, E. A. *Phil. Trans. Roy. Soc. (London)*, 179, 303, 1888.
106. Brunngraber, E. G., and Aguilar, V. J. *J. Neurochem.*, 9, 451, 1962.
107. Brunngraber, E. G., and Bejnarowicz, E. A. *XIIIth Colloq. Prot. Biol. Fluids*, H. Peeters (ed.), Amsterdam: Elsevier, 1966, p. 201.
108. Buchwald, J. S., Standish, M., Eldred, E., and Halas, E. S. *EEG Clin. Neurophysiol.*, 16, 585, 1964.
109. Buendia, N., Sierra, G., Goode, M., and Segundo, J. P. *EEG Clin. Neurophysiol. Suppl.*, 24, 199, 1963.
110. Bullock, T. H. *Neurosciences Res. Prog. Bull.*, 4, 2, 116, 1966.
111. Bullock, T. H. *Neurosciences Res. Prog. Bull.*, 4, 115, 1966.
112. Bullock, T. H. *Neurosciences Res. Prog. Bull.*, 4, 119, 1966.
113. Bullock, T. H. *Neurosciences Res. Prog. Bull.*, 4, 160, 1966.
114. Burnet, F. M. *The Integrity of the Body, A Discussion of Modern Immunological Ideas*, Cambridge: Harvard University Press, 1963.

115. Burton, R. M., Garcia-Bunuel, L., Golden, M., and Belfour, Y. M. *Biochem.*, 2, 580, 1963.
115a. Handa, S., and Burton, R. M. *1st Intnl. Mtg., Strasbourg, Intnl. Soc. for Neurochem.*, 1967, *Abst.* p. 91.
116. Bures, J., Bohdanecky, A., and Weiss, T. *Psychopharmacologia*, 3, 254, 1962.
117. Byrne, W. L., and Samuel, D. *Science*, 154, 418, 1966.
118. Byrne, W. L., Samuel, D., Bennett, E. L., Rosenzweig, M. R., and Wasserman, E. *Science*, 153, 658, 1966.
119. Byzov, A. L. *Cold Spring Harbor Symp. on Quant. Biol.*, Vol. 30, 1966, p. 547.
120. Cameron, D. E. *Am. J. Psychiat.*, 114, 943, 1958.
121. Cameron, D. E. *Proc. IV World Congress of Psychiatry*, Madrid, September 1966.
121a. Nodine, J. H., Shulkin, M. W., Slap, J. W., Levine, M., and Frieberg, K. *Am. J. Psychiat.*, 123, 1257, 1967.
122. Cameron, D. E., Solyom, L., and Beach, L. *Neuropsychopharmacology*, 2, 351, 1961.
123. Cameron, D. E., Sved, S., and Barik, H. *Am. J. Psychiat.*, 120, 320, 1963.
124. Campbell, R., Bogoch, S., Scolaro, M. J., and Belval, P. C. *Am. J. Psychiat.*, 123, 952, 1967.
125. Caravaglios, R., and Chiaverini, P. *Experientia*, 12, 303, 1956.
126. Cardo, G. *J. Physiol. (Paris)*, 5, 845, 1959.
127. Carlton, P. L. *Brain Chem. Behavior Res. Project Newsletter*, 9, 2, 1964.
127a. Chamberlain, T. J., Rothschild, G. H., and Gerard, R. W. *Proc. Nat. Acad. Sci.*, 49, 918, 1963.
128. Cheng-tung Mei. *Scientia Sinica*, 13, 524, 1964.
129. Cherkashin, A. N., and Sheimann, N. Academy of Sciences, USSR; personal communication from Dr. J. V. McConnell.
130. Chiapetta, L., and Jarvik, M. E. *Science*, 153, 658, 1966.
131. Chistoni, G., and Zappoli, R. *Riv. Sper. Freniatria*, 83, 1283, 1959.
132. Chistoni, G., and Zappoli, R. *Am. J. Psychiat.*, 117, 246, 1960.
133. Chorover, S. L. *Neurosciences Res. Prog. Bull.*, 4, 134, 1966.
134. Chorover, S. L., Holt, C. E., and Schiller, P. H. *Science*, 153, 658, 1966.
135. Chung, S. H., and Neuringer, A. *Psychon. Sci.*, 8, 25, 1967.
136. Clausen, J. *Proc. Soc. Exp. Biol. Med.*, 107, 170, 1961.

137. Cohen, H. D., and Barondes, S. H. *J. Neurochem.*, 13, 207, 1966.

138. Cohen, H. D., and Barondes, S. H. Submitted for publication; personal communication.

139. Cohen, H. D., Irving, G., and Barondes, S. H. *Science*, 154, 1557, 1966.

140. Cohen, M. J., and Jacklet, J. *Science*, 148, 1237, 1965.

141. Cone, R. A. *Nature*, 204, 736, 1964.

142. Coons, A. H., and Kaplan, M. H. *J. Exp. Med.*, 91, 1, 1950.

143. Coons, E. E., and Miller, N. E. *J. Comp. Physiol. Psychol.*, 53, 524, 1960.

144. Cori, G. T., and Cori, C. F. *J. Biol. Chem.*, 151, 57, 1943.

145. Cori, G. T., and Cori, C. F. *J. Biol. Chem.*, 199, 661, 1952.

146. Corning, W. C., and John, E. R. *Science*, 131, 1363, 1961.

147. Corning, W. C., and John, E. R. *Science*, 134, 1363, 1961.

148. Corson, G. A., and Enesco, H. E. *Science*, 153, 658, 1966.

149. Crain, S. M. *Science*, 141, 427, 1963.

150. Crain, S. M. *Neurobiol.*, 9, 1, 1966.

151. Criddle, R. S. *XVth Colloq. Prot. Biol. Fluids*, H. Peeters (ed.), Amsterdam: Elsevier, 1968, in press.

152. Cumings, J. N., Goodwin, H., Woodward, E. M., and Curzon, G. T. *J. Neurochem.*, 2, 289, 1957-58.

152a. Dain, J., Weicker, H., Schmidt, G., and Thannhauser, S. J. *Cerebral Sphingolipidoses*, S. M. Aronson and B. W. Volk (eds.), New York: Academic Press, 1962, p. 289.

153. Darkan, N. A. *Pharmacol. Rev.*, 16, 223, 1964.

154. Davis, R. E., and Agranoff, B. W. *Proc. Nat. Acad. Sci.*, 55, 555, 1966.

155. Davis, B. J., and Ornstein, L. *Ann. N.Y. Acad. Sci.*, E. Wroblewski (ed.), 94, 655, 1961.

156. Davison, P. F., and Schmitt, F. O. *J. Gen. Physiol.*, 43, 801, 1960.

157. Delgado, J. M. R. *J. Neurophysiol.*, 18, 261, 1955.

158. Demling, J., Kinzelmeier, H., and Henning, N. *J. Exp. Med.*, 122, 416, 1954.

159. Deul, D. H., and McIlwain, H. *J. Neurochem.*, 8, 246, 1961.

160. Deutsch, J. A., Hamburg, M. D., and Dahl, H. *Science*, 151, 221, 1966.

161. Dews, P. B. *Brit. J. Pharmacol.*, 8, 46, 1953.

162. Dews, P. B. *J. Pharmacol. Exp. Therap.*, *115*, 380 and 393, 1955.
163. Diamond, M. C., Law, F., Rhodes, H., Lindner, B., Rosenzweig, M. R., Krech, T. T., and Bennett, E. L. *J. Comp. Neurol.*, *128*, 117, 1966.
164. Dingman, W., and Sporn, M. B. *J. Neurochem.*, *4*, 154, 1959.
165. Dingman, W., and Sporn, M. B. *J. Psychiat. Res.*, *1*, 1, 1961.
165a. Dische, Z. *XIIIth Colloq. Prot. of Biol. Fluids*, H. Peeters (ed.), Amsterdam: Elsevier, 1966, p. 1.
166. Dott, N. M. *The Hypothalamus: Morphological, Functional, Clinical and Surgical Aspects*, Edinburgh: Oliver and Boyd, 1938, p. 131.
167. Doty, B. A., and Doty, L. A. *J. Comp. Physiol. Psychol.*, *57*, 331, 1964.
168. Drachman, D. A., and Adams, R. D. *Arch. Neurol.*, *7*, 45, 1962.
169. Eccles, J. C. *Brain Mechanisms and Learning*, J. F. Delafresnaye (ed.), Oxford: Blackwell Scientific Publications, 1961, p. 335.
170. Eccles, J. C. *The Anatomy of Memory*, Vol. 1, D. P. Kimble. (ed.), Palo Alto, Calif.: Science and Behavior Books, 1965, p. 231.
171. Eccles, J. C. *The Anatomy of Memory*, Vol. 1, D. P. Kimble (ed.), Palo Alto, Calif.: Science and Behavior Books, 1965, p. 12.
172. Edelman, G. M., and McClure, W. *Neurosciences Res. Prog. Bull.*, *3*, 10, 1966.
173. Edström, J. E., and Grampp, W. *J. Neurochem.*, *12*, 735, 1965.
174. Edström, J. E., and Pigon, A. *J. Neurochem.*, *3*, 95, 1958.
175. Edström, J. E., Grampp, W., and Schor, N. *J. Biophys. Biochem. Cytol.*, *11*, 549, 1961.
176. Egyhazi, E., and Hyden, H. *J. Biophys. Biochem. Cytol.*, *10*, 403, 1961.
177. Eisenstein, E. M. Quoted in *Neurosciences Res. Prog. Bull.*, *4*, 173, 1966.
178. Eisenstein, E. M., and Cohen, M. *J. Anim. Behavior*, *13* (Suppl. 1), 104, 1965.
179. Elson, L. A., and Morgan, W. T. *J. Biochem.*, *28*, 988, 1934, as modified in S. Bogoch. *J. Biochem.*, *68*, 319, 1958.
180. Engstrom, H., Ades, H. W., and Kakins, J. E., Jr. *J. Acoust. Soc. Am.*, *34*, 1356, 1962.
181. Essman, W. B. *Fed. Proc.*, March-April, 1966, p. 208.
182. Ewing, P. L., Moore, B. M., and Moore, W. T. *J. Pharmacol. Exp. Therap.*, *105*, 343, 1952.

183. Eyzaguirre, C., and Koyano, H. *Cold Spring Harbor Symp. on Quant. Biol.*, Vol. 30, 1965, p. 227.
184. Faillace, L. A., and Bogoch, S. *Biochem. J.*, 82, 527, 1962.
185. Fair, C. M. *Neurosciences Res. Prog. Bull.*, Vol. 3, 1965, p. 43.
186. Ibid. p. 41.
187. Ibid. p. 27.
188. Falbe-Hansen, I., and Balazs, E. A. Personal communication; to be published.
189. Feldberg, W. S. *Proc. Assoc. Res. Nerv. Ment. Dis.*, 36, 401, 1958.
190. Ferrier, D. *The Functions of the Brain*, London: Smith Elder, 1876.
191. Ferster, C. B., and Skinner, B. F. *Schedules of Reinforcement*, New York: Appleton-Century-Croft, 1957.
192. Fisher, A. E. *Science*, 124, 228, 1956.
193. Fjerdomgstad, J., Nissen, T. H., and Roigaard-Petersen, H. H. *Scand. J. Physiol.*, 6, 1, 1965.
194. Flexner, L. B., and Flexner, J. B. *Proc. Nat. Acad. Sci.*, 55, 369, 1966.
195. Flexner, L. B., Flexner, J. B., Roberts, R. B., and DelaHaba, G. *Proc. Nat. Acad. Sci.*, 55, 1165, 1964.
196. Flexner, L. B., Flexner, J. B., DelaHaba, G., and Roberts, R. B. *J. Neurochem.*, 12, 535, 1965.
197. Flexner, L. B., Flexner, J. B., and Roberts, R. B. *Proc. Nat. Acad. Sci.*, 56, 730, 1966.
198. Flexner, J. B., Flexner, L. B., and Stellar, E. *Science*, 141, 57, 1963.
199. Flexner, J. B., Flexner, L. B., Stellar, E., DelaHaba, G., and Roberts, R. B. *J. Neurochem.*, 9, 595, 1962.
200. Flock, A., and Aumdquist, P. *Cold Spring Harbor Symp. on Quant. Biol.*, Vol. 30, 1965, p. 115.
201. Folch, J., and Lees, M. *J. Biol. Chem.*, 191, 807, 1951.
202. Folch, J., and LeBaron, F. N. *Metabolism of the Nervous System*, D. Richter (ed.), New York: Pergamon Press, 1957, p. 67.
203. Folch, J., Meath, J., and Bogoch, S. *Fed. Proc.*, 15, 254, 1956.
204. Folch-Pi, J. *Brain Lipids and Lipoproteins and the Leucodystrophies*, J. Folch-Pi and H. Bauer (eds.), Amsterdam: Elsevier, 1963, p. 18.
205. Freed, C., and Horowitz, S. D. *Worm Runner's Digest*, 6, 3, 1964.

206. Freud, S. *Project for a Scientific Psychology, 1895, The Standard Edition of Complete Psychological Works of Sigmund Freud,* Vol. 1, London: Hogarth Press, 1966, pp. 300, 301.
207. Freud, S. *Project for a Scientific Psychology, 1895, The Standard Edition of Complete Psychological Works of Sigmund Freud,* Vol. 1, London: Hogarth Press, 1966, p. 299.
208. Gaddum, J. H., and Paasonen, M. K. *Brit. J. Pharmacol.,* 10, 474, 1955.
209. Gaddum, J. H., and Picarelli, Z. P. *Brit. J. Pharmacol.,* 12, 323, 1957.
210. Gaito, J. *Proc. XXVII Intnl. Cong. Psych., Acta Physiologica,* 23, 172, 1964.
211. Gaito, J. *Macromolecules and Behavior,* J. Gaito (ed.), New York: Appleton-Century-Crofts, 1966, p. 100.
212. Gaito, J. In *Macromolecules and Behavior,* J. Gaito (ed.), New York: Appleton-Century-Crofts, 1966, p. 89.
213. Galambos, R. *Fed. Proc.,* 20, No. 2, 603, 1961.
213a. Galambos, R. *Proc. Nat. Acad. Sci.,* 17, 129, 1961.
214. Galambos, R. Personal communication, 1967.
215. Gatt, S., and Berman, E. R. *Neurochem.,* 10, 43, 1963.
216. Gelber, B. *J. Anim. Behavior,* 13, *Suppl.* I, 21, 1965.
217. Geller, E., Yuwiler, A., and Zolman, J. *Abst. Intnl. Neurochem. Conf., Oxford, England,* July 1965.
218. Gerard, R. *Am. J. Psychiat.,* 106, 161, 1949.
219. Ghent, L., Mishkin, M., and Teuber, H. L. *J. Comp. Physiol. Psychol.* 55, 705, 1962.
220. Glasky, A. J., and Simon, L. N. *Science,* 151, 702, 1966.
221. Goldman, D. E. *Cold Spring Harbor Symp. on Quant. Biol.,* Vol. 30, 1965, p. 59.
221a. Gombos, G., Vyemura, K., Tardy, J., and Vincedon, G. *1st Intnl. Neurochem. Mtg.,* Strasbourg, *Intnl. Soc. for Neurochem.,* 1967, *Abst.,* p. 86.
222. Gonzalez, R. C., and Ross, S. J. *Comp. Physiol. Psychol.,* 54, 645, 1961.
223. Gordon, N. W., Deanin, G. G., Leonhardt, H. L., and Gwinn, R. H. *Am. J. Psychiat.,* 122, 1174, 1966.
224. Gottschalk, A. *Nature,* 176, 881, 1955.
225. Gottschalk, A. *The Chemistry and Biology of Sialic Acids and Related Substances,* Cambridge, England: Cambridge University Press, 1960.

226. Graziadei, P.   *Cold Spring Harbor Symp. on Quant. Biol.*, Vol. 30, 1965, p. 45.
227. Green, D. E., Tisdale, H. D., Criddle, R. S., Chen, P. Y., and Bock, R. M.   *Biochem. Biophys. Res. Commun.*, 5, 109, 1961.
228. Green, J. P., Atwood, R. P., and Freedman, D. X.   *AMA Arch. Gen. Psychiat.*, 12, 90, 1965.
229. Gross, C. G., and Carey, F. M.   *Science*, 150, 1749, 1965.
230. Grossman, S. P.   *Am. J. Physiol.*, 202, 872, 1962.
231. Ibid. 202, 1230, 1962.
232. Grossman, S. P.   *A Textbook of Physiological Psychology*, New York: John Wiley & Sons, 1967.
233. Gutekunst, R., and Youniss, J.   *Perceptual Motor Skills*, 16, 348, 1963.
234. Haddad, R. K., and Rabe, A.   *IIIrd World Congress of Psychiatry*, Toronto: University of Toronto Press, Vol. I, 1961, p. 658.
235. Haldane, J. B. S.   *Behavior*, 6, 256-270, 1954.
236. Halsall, T. G., Hirst, E. L., and Jones, J. K. N.   *J. Chem. Soc.*, 1399, 1947.
237. Harris, G. W., and Michael, R. P.   *J. Physiol. (London)*, 171, 275, 1964.
238. Hassid, W. Z., Cori, G. T., and McCready, R. M.   *J. Biol. Chem.*, 148, 89, 1943.
239. Haughton, G.   *Ann. N.Y. Acad. Sci.*, 101:131, 1962.
240. Haworth, W. N., Hirst, E. L., and Isherwood, E. A.   *J. Chem. Soc.*, 577, 1937.
241. Haynes, R. C.   *J. Biol. Chem.*, 233, 1220, 1958.
242. Heald, J. P.   *Nature*, 193, 451, 1962.
243. Heath, R. G., and Krupp, I. M.   *Am. J. Psychiat.*, 123, 1499, 1967.
244. Hebb, D. P.   *The Organization of Behavior*, New York: John Wiley & Sons, 1949.
245. Hechter, O., and Halkerston, I.   *Neurosciences Res. Prog. Bull.*, 1, 1, 1963.
246. Hechter, O., and Halkerston, I.   *Perspectives in Biol. Med.*, 1, 183, 1964.
247. Hernnstein, R. J.   W. K. Honig, *Operant Behavior: Areas of Research and Application*, New York: Appleton-Century-Crofts, 1966.
248. Herz, A.   *Arch. Exp. Pathol. Pharmakol.*, 236, 110, 1959.
248a. Hess, H. H., Bass, N. H., and Still, C. N.   *1st Intnl. Mtg.*, Strasbourg, *Intnl. Soc. for Neurochem.*, 1967, Abst. p. 96.

249. Hillyard, S. A., and Galambos, R. *EEG Clin. Neurophysiol.*, 22, 304, 1967.
250. Hirst, G. K. *Science*, 94, 22, 1941.
251. Hirst, G. K. *J. Exp. Med.* 87, 301, 1948.
252. Hofman, G., and Schinko, H. *Klin. Wochschr.* 34, 86, 1956.
253. Horridge, G. A. *Nature*, 193, 697, 1962.
254. Howe, C., MacLennan, J. D., Mandl, I., and Kabat, E. A. *J. Bacteriol.*, 74, 365, 1957.
255. Hoyle, G. J. *Exp. Biol.*, 44, 429, 1966.
256. Hubbard, R., Bownds, D., and Yoshizawa, T. *Cold Spring Harbor Symp. on Quant. Biol.*, Vol. 30, 1965, p. 301.
257. Huneeus-Cox, F. *Science*, 143, 1036, 1964.
258. Hyden, H. *Sci. Amer.*, 205, 62, 1961.
259. Hyden, H. *Endeavor*, 21, 144, 1962.
260. Hyden, H. *Neurosciences Res. Prog. Bull.*, 2, 33, 1964.
261. Ibid. *11*, 33, 1964.
262. Hyden, H. *The Anatomy of Memory*, Vol. 1, D. P. Kimble (ed.), Palo Alto, Calif.: Science and Behavior Books, 1965, p. 212.
263. Ibid. p. 179.
264. Hyden, H., and Egyhazi, E. *Proc. Nat. Acad. Sci.*, 48, 1366, 1962.
265. Ibid. 49, 618, 1963.
266. Ibid. 52, 1030, 1965.
267. Hyden, H., and Lange, P. W. *Proc. Nat. Acad. Sci.*, 523, 946, 1965.
268. Hyden, H., and McEwen, G. *Proc. Nat. Sci.*, 55, 354, 1966.
269. Izquierdo, I., Wyrwicka, W., Sierra, G., and Segundo, J. P. *Actualitées Neurophysiologiques*, Sixth Series, Paris: Masson et Cie, 1965, p. 277.
270. Jacobson, A. L. *Psychol. Bull.*, 60, 74, 1963.
271. Jacobson, A. L. *Discovery*, February 1966, p. 11.
272. Jacobson, A. L. *J. Anim. Behavior*, in press.
273. Jacobson, A. L., Babich, F. R., Bubash, S., and Goren, C. *Psychonom. Sci.*, 4, 3, 1966.
274. Jacobson, A. L., Babich, F. R., Bubash, S., and Jacobson, A. *Science*, 150, 636, 1965.
275. Jakoby, R. K., and Warren, L. *Neurology*, 11, 232, 1961.
276. Jarvik, M. E. *Ciba Foundation Symp. Animal Pharmacologia and Drug Action*, Boston: Little, Brown and Co., 1964, p. 44.

277. Jarvik, M. E., and Essman, W. B. *Psychol. Rep.*, 6, 290, 1960.
278. Jenner, F. A., Kerry, R. J., Fowler, D. B., and Graves, E. W. *J. Ment. Sci.*, 108, 822, 1962.
279. Jensen, D. D. *J. Anim. Behavior*, 13, 9, 1965.
280. Jerne, N. K. *Macromolecules and Behavior*, J. Gaito (ed.), New York: Appleton-Century-Crofts, 1966, p. 151.
281. John, E. R. *Ann. Rev. Physiol.*, 23, 451, 1961.
282. John, E. R. *Frontiers in Physiological Psychology*, New York: Academic Press, 1966, p. 149.
283. Kabat, E. A. *Blood Group Substances, Their Chemistry and Immunochemistry*, New York: Academic Press, 1956.
284. Kandel, E. R., and Tauc, L. *J. Physiol.*, 181, 1, 1965.
248a. Kanfer, J. N., and Richards, R. L. *J. Neurochem.*, 14, 513, 1967.
285. Kaps, G. *Arch. Psychiat. Nervenkrankh*, 192, 115, 1954.
286. Karcher, D., van Sande, M., and Lowenthal, A. *J. Neurochem.*, 4, 135, 1959.
287. Kety, S. S. *Neurosciences Res. Prog. Bull.*, 5 (1), 81, 1967.
288. Keupl, W. *Confinia Neurol.*, 18, 117, 1955.
289. Kies, N. W. *Ann. N.Y. Acad. Sci.*, 122, 161, 1965.
290. Kies, M. W., Alvord, E. C., and Roboz, E. *J. Neurochem.*, 2, 261, 1958.
291. Kies, M. W., Thompson, E. B., and Alvord, E. C. *Ann. N.Y. Acad. Sci.*, 122, 148, 1965.
292. Kimble, J., and Kimble, D. P. *Worm Runner's Digest*, 8, 32, 1966.
293. Klenk, E. *Z. physiol. Chem.*, 235, 24, 1935.
294. Klenk, E. *Z. physiol. Chem.*, 262, 128, 1939-40.
295. Klenk, E. *Z. physiol. Chem.*, 268, 50, 1941.
296. Klenk, E. *Z. physiol. Chem.*, 273, 76, 1942.
297. Klenk, E. *Biochemistry of the Developing Nervous System*, H. Waelsh (ed.), New York: Pergamon Press, 1955.
298. Klenk, E., and Gielen, E. *Z. physiol. Chem.*, 319, 283, 1960.
299. Klenk, E., and Lauenstein, K. *Z. physiol. Chem.*, 291, 249, 1952.
300. Klenk, E., and Lauenstein, K. *Z. physiol. Chem.*, 295, 164, 1953.
301. Klenk, E., and Gielen, W. *Z. physiol. Chem.*, 323, 126, 1961.
302. Klenk, E., and Gielen, W. *Z. physiol. Chem.*, 330, 218, 1963.
303. Klenk, E., and Gielen, W. *Z. physiol. Chem.*, 330, 162, 1963.

304. Klenk, E., and Kuna, W. Z. physiol. Chem., 335, 275, 1964.
305. Klenk, E., and Rennkamp, F. Z. physiol. Chem., 273, 253, 1942.
306. Klenk, E., and Wolter, H. Z. physiol. Chem., 291, 259, 1952.
307. Klopfer, P. H., and Gottlieb, G. J. Comp. Physiol. Psychol., 55, 126, 1962.
308. Kluver, H., and Bucy, P. C. Arch. Neurol. and Psychiat., 42, 979, 1939.
309. Konorski, J., and Miller, S. J. Gen. Physiol., 17, 405, 1937.
310. Kopp, R., Bohdanecky, A., and Jarvik, M. E. Science, 153, 1547, 1966.
311. Korey, S., and Stein, A. Life Sciences, 3, 296, 1963.
312. Korey, S., and Terry, R. D. J. Neuropath. Exp. Neurol. 22, 2, 1963.
313. Krivanek, J. Fed. Proc. Trans. Suppl., 24, 178, 1965.
314. Krylov, O. A., Danylova, R. A., and Tongur, V. S. Life Sciences, 4, 1313, 1965.
315. Krylov, O. A., Danylova, R. A., and Tongur, V. S. J. High Nerv. Act., 15, 79, 1965.
316. Kuffler, S. W., and Nicholls, J. G. Rev. Physiol. Biochem. and Expt. Pharmacol., 57, New York: Springer-Verlag, 1966, p. 1.
317. Kuhn, R., and Weigandt, H. Z. Naturforsch., 186, 541, 1963.
318. Kuhn, R., and Egge, H. Chem. Ber., 96, 3338, 1963.
319. Kuhn, R., and Weigandt, H. Z. Naturforsch., 196, 80, 1964.
320. Kujota, K. J. Neurochem., 4, 202, 1959.
321. Lajtha, A. International Review of Neurobiology, Vol. 6, C. C. Pfeiffer and J. R. Smithies (eds.), New York: Academic Press, 1964, p. 1.
322. Landsteiner, K., and Levene, P. A. J. Immunol., 10, 731, 1925.
323. Landsteiner, K., and Van Der Scheer, J. J. Exp. Med., 42, 123, 1925.
324. Larrabee, M. G., and Nagata, Y. J. Physiol. Soc. Jap., 26, 39, 1964.
325. Lashley, K. S. Psychobiol., 1, 141, 1917.
326. Lashley, K. S. Sym. Soc. Exp. Biol., 4, 454, 1950.
327. Leaf, R. C., Deutcher, J. D., Horovitz, P., and Carlson, P. L. Science, 153, 658, 1966.
329. LeBaron, F. N., and Rothleder, E. E. Proc. 4th Intnl. Cong. Biochem., Vienna, 1958, p. 206.
330. Leloir, E. F., and Cardini, G. E. J. Am. Chem. Soc., 79, 6340, 1957.

331. Lettvin, J. Y., Maturana, H. R., McCullock, W. S., and Pitts, W. *Proc. I.R.E.*, 47, 1940, 1959.
332. Lettvin, J. Y., and Gestelan, D. R. C. *Cold Spring Harbor Symp. on Quant. Biol.*, Vol. 30, 1965, p. 217.
333. Leukel, E. J. *Comp. Physiol. Psychol.*, 50, 300, 1957.
334. Levine, S. *The Anatomy of Memory*, Vol. 1, D. P. Kimble (ed.), Palo Alto, Calif.: Science and Behavior Books, 1965, p. 224.
335. Levi-Montalcini, R. *Science*, 143, 105, 1964.
336. Livingstone, R. B. In *Handbook of Neurophysiology*, Vol. I, Baltimore: Williams and Wilkins, 1959, p. 741.
337. Livingstone, R. B. In *Psychology. A Study of a Science*, S. Koch (ed.), New York: McGraw-Hill, 1959, p. 94.
338. Lorente de Nó, R. *Physiology of the Nervous System*, J. F. Fulton (ed.), New York: Oxford University Press, 1949, p. 288.
339. Lorenz, K. *Evolution and Modification of Behavior*, University of Chicago Press, 1965.
340. Lowry, O. H., Rosebrough, N. J., Farr, L., and Randall, R. J. *J. Biol. Chem.*, 193, 265, 1951.
341. Lubinska, L. In *Mechanisms of Neural Regeneration Progress in Brain Research*, 13, M. Singer and J. P. Schaade (eds.), Amsterdam: Elsevier, 1964, p. 1.
342. Luco, J. V. In *Brain Function*, Vol. II, M. A. B. Brazier (ed.), Los Angeles: University of California Press, 1964, p. 135.
343. Lumry, R., and Eyring, H. *J. Phys. Chem.*, 58, 110, 1954.
344. Luttges, M., Johnson, T., Buck, C., Holland, J., and McGaugh, J. *Science*, 151, 834, 1966.
345. Maclean, P. D. *Am. J. Med.*, 25, 611, 1958.
346. Macht, B. I., and Bloom, W. *Proc. Soc. Ex. Biol. Med.*, 18, 99, 1921.
347. Magoun, H. W. *The Waking Brain*, Springfield, Ill.: Charles C Thomas, 1958.
348. Manuelides, E. E. *J. Neurosurg.*, 22, 368, 1965.
349. Mark, V. H., Ervin, F. R., and Hackett, T. P. *Arch. Neurol.*, 3, 351, 1960.
350. Masourovsky, G. B., and Noback, C. R. *Nature*, 200, 847, 1963.
351. Mathews, R. G., Hubbard, R., Brown, P. K., and Wald, G. *J. Gen. Physiol.*, 47, 215, 1963-64.
352. McConnell, J. V. *J. Neuropsychiat.*, 3, (Suppl. 1), 542, 1962.
353. McConnell, J. V. *Worm Runner's Digest, Editorial*, 1965.

354. McConnell, J. V.   *Ann. Rev. Physiol.*, 28, 107, 1966.
355. McConnell, J. V.   *The Chemistry of Memory, Proceedings of a Conference held at Michigan State University*, September 1966, W. Corning and S. Ratner (eds.), New York: Plenum Press, in press.
356. McConnell, J. V.   Personal communication.
357. McCulloch, W. S.   *Science in the Sixties*, D. L. Arm (ed.), Albuquerque: University of New Mexico Press, 1965, p. 73.
358. McCulloch, W. S., and Pitts, W.   *Bull. Math. Biophys.*, 5, 115, 1943.
359. McCulloch, W. S., and Pitts, W.   *Bull. Math. Biophys.*, 9, 127, 1947.
360. McGaugh, J. L.   *The Anatomy of Memory*, D. P. Kimble (ed.), Palo Alto, Calif.: Science and Behavior Books, 1965.
361. McGaugh, J. L.   *Science*, 153, 1351, 1966.
362. McGaugh, J. L., and Alpern, H. P.   *Science*, 152, 665, 1966.
363. McGaugh, J. L., and Madsen, M. C.   *Science*, 144, 182, 1964.
364. McGaugh, J. L., and Petrinovich, L. F.   *Intnl. Rev. Neurobiology*, 8, 139, 1965.
365. McGaugh, J. L., and Thomson, C. W.   *Psychopharmacologia*, 3, 166, 1962.
366. MsGaugh, J. L., Thomson, C. W., Westbrook, W. H., and Hudspeth, W. J.   *Psychopharmacologia*, 3, 352, 1962.
367. McGaugh, J. L., Westbrook, W. H., and Burt, G.   *J. Comp. Physiol. Psychol.*, 54, 502, 1961.
368. McIlwain, H.   *Chemotherapy and the Central Nervous System*, Boston: Little, Brown and Co., 1957.
369. McIlwain, H.   *The Chemical Exploration of the Brain*, Amsterdam: Elsevier, 1963.
370. Mendelhall, M. C.   *J. Comp. Psychol.*, 29, 257, 1940.
371. Meyer-Gross, W.   *Lancet*, 1943-II, 603, 1943.
372. Miller, N. E.   *Science*, 126, 1271, 1957.
373. Miller, N. E.   *Psychology: A Study of a Science*, S. Koch (ed.), Study I, Vol. 2, New York: McGraw-Hill, 1959.
374. Miller, N. E.   *Bull. Brit. Psychol. Soc.*, 17, 1, 1964.
375. Miller, N. E.   *Science*, 148, 328, 1965.
376. Miller, N. E.   *Proc. of the XVIIIth Intnl. Cong. of Psychology*, Moscow, 1966, in press.
377. Milner, B.   *NLM Psychiatric Research Reports*, No. 11, 43, 1959.

378. Milner, B., and Penfield, W. *Trans. Am. Neurol. Assn.*, 80, 42, 1955.
379. Monod, J. *Science*, 154, 475, 1966.
380. Monod, J., Changu, J. P., and Jacob, F. *J. Mol. Biol.*, 6, 306, 1963.
381. Moore, B. W. *Biochem. Biophys. Res. Commun.*, 19, 739, 1965.
382. Moore, B. W., and McGregor, D. *J. Biol. Chem.*, 240, 1647, 1965.
383. Moser, H. W., and Karnovsky, M. L. *J. Biol. Chem.*, 234, 1990, 1959.
384. Mountcastle, V. B. *J. Neurophysiol.* 20, 408, 1967.
385. Mountcastle, V. B., and Powell, T. P. S. *Bull. Johns Hopkins*, 105, 108, 1959.
386. Murray, R. W. *Cold Spring Harbor Symp. on Quant. Biol.*, Vol. 30, 1965, p. 233.
387. Nachmansohn, D. *Nerve as a Tissue*, K. Rodahl and E. Issekutz, Jr. (eds.), New York: Hoeber, 1966, p. 141.
388. Naftalin, L. *Cold Spring Harbor Symp. on Quant. Biol.*, 1965, p. 169.
389. Nakamura, S., Hayashi, Y., and Tanaka, K. *J. Biochem.*, 41, 13, 1954.
390. Nathans, D. *Proc. Nat. Sci.*, 51, 585, 1964.
390a. Newton, Isaac. *Opticks* (1717), 4th Ed., London: J. L. Ball and Sons, 1931.
391. Nielsen, J. M. *Clinical Neurology*, A. B. Baker (ed.), New York: Harper & Bros., 1962, p. 433.
391a. Nikaido, H. *The Specificity of Cell Surfaces*, B. D. Davis and L. Warren (eds.), Prentice-Hall, N. J., 1967, p. 3.
392. Odin, L. *Nature*, 170, 663, 1952.
393. Ojemann, R. G. *Neurosciences Res. Prog. Bull.*, May-June, 1964.
394. Olds, J. *Physiol. Revs.*, 42, 554, 1962.
395. Olds, J., and Milner, P. J. *Comp. Physiol. Psychol.*, 47, 419, 1954.
396. Olds, J., and Olds, M. E. *Brain Mechanisms and Learning*, J. R. Delafresnaye (ed.), Oxford: Blackwell Scientific Publications, 1961, p. 153.
397. Palay, S. *Nerve as a Tissue*, K. Rodahl and B. Issekutz (eds.), New York: Hoeber, 1966, p. 3.
398. Palladin, A. V. *Metabolism of the Nervous System*, D. Richter (ed.), New York: Pergamon Press, 1957, p. 456.

399. Palladin, A. V., and Vladimirov, G. E. In *Proc. Intnl. Conf. on Peaceful Uses of Atomic Energy*, Vol. 12, New York: United Nations, 1956.

400. Papadopoulos, N. M., McLane, J. E., O'Doherty, D., and Hess, W. C. *J. Nerv. Mental Dis.*, 128, 450, 1959.

401. Pare, W. J. *Comp. Psychol.*, 54, 506, 1961.

402. Park, J. T. *J. Biol. Chem.*, 194, 877, 1952.

403. Pascal, T. A., Saifer, A., and Gitlin, J. *Inborn Disorders of Sphingolipid Metabolism*, S. M. Aronson and B. W. Volk (eds.), New York: Pergamon Press, 1967, p. 289.

404. Pavlov, I. P. *Arch. Intnl. Physiol.*, 1, 119, 1904.

405. Pearlman, C. S., Sharpless, S. K., and Jarvik, M. E. *J. Comp. Physiol. Psychol.*, 54, 109, 1961.

406. Pearlman, C., and Jarvik, M. E. *Fed. Proc.*, 20, 340, 1961.

407. Penfield, W. *Res. Publ. Ass. Res. Nerv. Ment. Dis.*, 36, 210, 1958.

408. Penfield, W., and Milner, B. *AMA Arch. Neurol. Psychiat.*, 79, 475, 1958.

409. Petrinovich, L. *Psychopharmacologia*, 4, 103, 1963.

410. Petrinovich, L., Bradford, D., and McGaugh, J. L. *Psychon. Sci.*, 2, 191, 1965.

411. Plotnikoff, N. *Science*, 151, 703, 1966.

412. Pollack, M., and Goldfarb, W. *AMA Arch. Neurol. & Psychiat.*, 77, 635, 1957.

413. Polyglase, W. J., Brown, D. M., and Smith, E. L. *J. Biol. Chem.*, 199, 105, 1952.

414. Porter, H., and Ainsworth, S. *J. Neurochem.*, 5, 91, 1959.

415. Porter, H., and Folch, J. *J. Neurochem.*, 1, 260, 1957.

415a. Pratt, R. T. C. *The Genetics of Neurological Disorders*, London: Oxford University Press, 1967.

416. Pribram, K. H. *EEG and Behavior*, G. H. Glaser (ed.), New York: Basic Books, 1963.

417. Pribram, K. H. *Macromolecules and Behavior*, J. Gaito (ed.), Appleton-Century-Crofts, 1966, p. 165.

418. Prieto, A., Kornblith, P., and Pollen, D. A. Unpublished data.

419. Quamina, A., and Bogoch, S. Unpublished results.

420. Quamina, A., and Bogoch, S. *Proc. XIIIth Colloq. Protides of Biological Fluids, Brugge*, H. Peeters (ed.), Amsterdam: Elsevier, 1966, p. 211.

421. Quartermain, D., Paoling, R. M., and Miller, N. E. *Science*, 149, 1116, 1965.

422. Radding, C. M., and Wald, G. *J. Gen. Physiol.*, 39, 909, 923, 1955-56.

423. Rahmann, H. *Arch. Ges. Physiol.*, 273, 247, 1961.

424. Rahmann, H. *Arch. Ges. Physiol.*, 276, 384, 1963.

425. Rajam, P. C., and Bogoch, S. *Immunology*, 11, 211, 1966.

426. Rajam, P. C., and Bogoch, S. *Nature*, 211, 1200, 1966.

427. Rajam, P. C., Bogoch, S., Driscoll, M. A., and Forrester, P. C. *Immunology*, in press.

428. Rajam, P. C., Bogoch, S., and Rushworth, M. A. *Nature*, 211, 1201, 1966.

429. Rajam, P. C., Bogoch, S., Rushworth, M. A., and Forrester, P. C. *Immunology*, 11, 217, 1966.

430. Rall, T. W., Sutherland, E. W., and Berthet, J. *J. Biol. Chem.*, 224, 463, 1957.

430a. Rambourg, A. *C. R. Acad. Sc. Paris*, 265, 1426, 1967.

430b. Rambourg, A., and Leblond, C. P. *J. Cell Biol.*, 32, 41, 1967.

430c. Rappoport, D. A., and Daginawala, H. F. *1st Intnl. Mtg. Strasbourg, Intnl. Soc. for Neurochem.*, 1967, *Abst.*, p. 175.

431. Rapport, M. M., Skipski, V. P., and Alonzo, N. F. *J. Lipid Res.*, 12, 438, 1959.

432. Rapport, M. M., Graf, L., and Alonzo, N. F. *J. Lipid Res.*, 1, 301, 1963.

433. Rapport, M. M., Graf, L., Autilio, L. A., and Norton, W. T. *J. Neurochem.*, 11, 855, 1964.

434. Ray, O. S. and Emley, G. *Science*, 144, 76, 1964.

435. Reinis, S. *Activatas Nervosa Superior*, 7, 167, 1965.

436. Reinis, S. *Worm Runner's Digest*, 8, 7, 1966.

437. Roberts, E. *Brain Research*, 2, 109, 1966.

438. Roberts, E. *Brain Research*, 2, 117, 1966.

439. Robertson, D. M. *J. Neurochem.*, 1, 358, 1957.

440. Robins, E., Croninger, A. B., Smith, M. K., and Moody, A. C. *Ann. N.Y. Acad. Sci.*, 96, 390, 1962.

441. Robinson, B. W. *Thirst*, M. J. Wayner (ed.), New York: Pergamon Press, 1964, p. 411.

442. Roboz, E., Henderson, N., and Kies, M. W. *J. Neurochem.*, 2, 254, 1958.

443. Robustelli, F. *Atti Accademia Nazl. Lincei Mem. Classe Sci. Fis. Mat. Nat.*, 34, 703, 1963.

444. Roderick, T. H. *Genetics*, 45, 1123, 1960.

445. Rose, J. E., Malis, L. I., and Baker, C. P. *Sensory Communica-*

tion, W. A. Rosenblith (ed.), New York: John Wiley & Sons, 1961.

446. Rosenberg, A., Binnie, B., and Chargaff, E. *J. Am. Chem. Soc.*, 82, 4113, 1960.
447. Rosenberg, A., and Chargaff, E. *Biochem. Biophys. Acta*, 21, 588, 1956.
448. Rosenberg, A., and Chargaff, E. *J. Biol. Chem.*, 232, 1031, 1958.
449. Rosenberg, A., and Chargaff, E. *Am. J. Dis. Child.*, 97, 739, 1959.
450. Rosenblatt, F., Farrow, J. T., and Rhine, S. *Proc. Nat. Acad. Sci.*, 55, 548, 1966.
451. Rosenblatt, F., Farrow, J. T., and Herblin, W. F. *Nature*, 209, 46, 1966.
452. Rosenheim, P. *Biochem. J.*, 7, 604, 1961; 8, 110, 1914.
453. Rosenzweig, M. R., Bennett, E. L., and Diamond, M. C. *Abst. Internl. Neurochem. Conf., Oxford, England,* July, 1965.
454. Rosenzweig, M. R., Krech, D., and Bennett, E. L. *Biological and Biochemical Basis of Behavior*, H. F. Harlow and C. H. Woolsey (eds.), Madison, Wis.: University of Wisconsin Press, 1958, p. 367.
455. Rosenzweig, M. R., Krech, D., and Bennett, E. L. *Psychol. Bull.*, 57, 476, 1960.
456. Ross, D. M. *J. Anim. Behavior, 13 (Suppl. 1)*, 43, 1965.
457. Rossiter, R. J. *Neurochemistry, the Chemistry of Brain and Nerve*, 2nd ed., K. A. C. Elliott, R. H. Page, and J. H. Quastel (eds.), Springfield, Ill.: Charles C Thomas, 1962, pp. 10-54.
458. Rubin, A. L., and Stenzel, K. H. *Neurosciences Res. Prog. Bull.*, 3, 24, 1965.
459. Santen, R. J., and Agranoff, B. W. *Biochem. Biophys. Acta*, 72, 251, 1963.
460. Samuels, S., Korey, S. R., and Gonatas, J. *J. Neuropath. and Exp. Neurol.*, 22, 81, 1963.
461. Scheibel, M. E., and Scheibel, A. B. *EEG Clin. Neurophysiol. Suppl.*, 24, 235, 1963.
462. Schmitt, F. O. *Macromolecular Specificity and Biological Memory*, F. O. Schmitt (ed.), Cambridge, Mass.: M.I.T. Press, 1962, p. 1.
463. Schmitt, F. O. *Neurosciences Res. Prog. Bull.*, 2, 43, 1964.
464. Schmitt, F. O. *Nerv. Sci.*, 23 (408), 643, 1964.

465. Schmitt, F. O. *Neurochem. (Japan)*, 4 (*Suppl.*) 96, 1965.

466. Schmitt, F. O., and Melnechuk, T. *Neurosciences Research Symposium Summaries*, Vol. I, Cambridge, Mass.: M.I.T. Press, 1966.

467. Schwartz, I. L., Rasmussen, M. A., Schoessler, M. A., Silver, L., and Fong, T. O. *Proc. Nat. Acad. Sci.*, 46, 1288, 1960.

468. Scoville, W. G. *Neurosurg.*, 11, 64, 1954.

469. Scoville, W. G. *J. Neurol. Neurosurg. Psychiat.*, 20, 11, 1957.

470. Scoville, W. G., and Milner, B. *J. Neurol. Neurosurg. Psychiat.*, 20, 11, 1957.

471. Shannon, L., and Rieke, J. *Worm Runner's Digest*, 6, 7, 1964.

472. Sharon, N. *Amino Sugars*, E. Balazs and R. Y. Jeanloz (eds.), New York: Academic Press, 1965, p. 2.

473. Sheng, P., and Tsao, T. *Scientia Sinica (Peking)*, 6, 309, 1957.

474. Sherrington, C. S. *Man on his Nature: The Gifford Lectures, Edinburgh, 1937-1938* (2nd Ed.), London: Cambridge University Press, 1951.

475. Skinner, B. F. *The Behavior of Organisms*, New York: Appleton-Century-Crofts, 1938.

476. Slotnick, B. M., and Jarvik, M. E. *Science*, 154, 1207, 1966.

477. Smith, S. J. *Worm Runner's Digest*, 5, 39, 1963.

478. Sober, H. A., Gutter, F. J., Wyckoff, M. M., and Peterson, E. A. *J. Am. Chem. Soc.*, 78, 756, 1956.

479. Sorensen, M., and Haugaard, G. *Biochem. Z.*, 206, 247, 1933.

480. Sperry, R. W. *Fed. Proc.*, 20, No. 2, 609, 1961.

481. Sperry, R. W. *Sci. Amer.*, 210, 42, 1964.

482. Sperry, R. W. *Brain and Conscious Experience*, J. Eccles (ed.), New York: Springer-Verlag, 1966, p. 314.

483. Sperry, R. W. *Neurosciences Res. Symposium Summaries*, Vol. 1, F. O. Schmitt and T. Melnechuk (eds.), Cambridge, Mass.: M.I.T. Press, 1966, p. 213.

484. Spiegel, A., Wycis, H. T., Orchinik, W., and Freed, H. *Science*, 121, 771, 1955.

485. Somers, J. E., Kanfer, J. N., and Brady, R. O. Quoted in R. O. Brady and E. C. Trams, *Ann. Rev. Biochem.*, 33, 78, 1964.

486. Stacey, M., and Barker, S. A. *Carbohydrates of Living Tissues*, Princeton: Van Nostrand, 1962.

487. Starr, A., and Livingston, R. B. *J. Neurophysiol.*, 26, 41, 1963.

488. Stary, A., and Arat, F. *Biochem. Z.*, 329, 11, 1957.

489. Steinbaum, E. A., and Miller, N. E. *Am. J. Physiol.* 208, 1, 1965.
490. Strumwasser, F. *Proc. Int. Union Physiol. Sci.* (*XIIIth Intnl. Cong.*), *Leiden*, 2, 801, 1962.
491. Stuart-Harris, C. H. *Lancet*, I, 497, 1939.
492. Suzuki, K., and Chen, G. C. *J. Lipid Res.*, 8, 105, 1967.
493. Suzuki, K., Suzuki, K., and Chen, G. C. *Abst.*, *1st Intnl. Mtg.*, *Strasbourg, Intnl. Soc. for Neurochem.*, 1967, p. 193.
494. Svennerholm, L. *J. Neurochem.*, 10, 613, 1963.
495. Svennerholm, L. *Acta Chem. Scand.* 17, 860, 1963.
496. Svennerholm, L. *J. Neurochem.*, 11, 839, 1964.
497. Svennerholm, L. *J. Lipid Research*, 5, 145, 1964.
498. Svennerholm, L. *The Amino Sugars*, E. A. Balazs and R. W. Jeanloz (eds.), New York: Academic Press, 1965, p. 381.
499. Svennerholm, L., and Raal, A. *Biochim. Biophys. Acta*, 53, 422, 1961.
500. Sweet, W. H., Talland, G. A., and Ervin, F. R. *Trans. Am. Neurol. Assn.*, 84, 76, 1959.
501. Szentágothai, J. *Information Processing in the Nervous System*, R. W. Gerard and J. W. Duyff (eds.), *Excerpta Medica*, Amsterdam, 1964, p. 119.
502. Szurek, S. A. In *Learning and Its Disorders*, I. N. Berlin and S. A. Szurek (eds.), Palo Alto, Calif.: Science and Behavior Books, 1965, p. 3.
503. Tauc, L., and Gerschenfeld, H. M. *J. Neurophysiol.*, 25, 236, 1962.
504. Terzian, H., and Ore, G. D. *Neurology*, 5, 373, 1955.
505. Tewari, H. B., and Bourne, G. H. *Pathol. biol. Semaine hop.*, 9, 919, 1961.
506. Thistlethwaite, D. L. *Psychol. Bull.*, 48, 97, 1951.
507. Thompson, R., and Dean, W. *J. Comp. Physiol. Psychol.*, 48. 488, 1955.
508. Thorndike, E. L. *Psychol. Rev. Monogr.*, *Suppl.* 2, 1898.
509. Thudichum, J. L. *A Treatise on the Chemical Constitution of the Brain*, trans. by David L. Drabkin (Facsimile Edition; first publ. 1884), Hamden, Conn.: Archon Books, 1962.
510. Trams, E. G., and Lauter, L. J. *Biochim. Biophys. Acta*, 60, 350, 1962.
511. Tryon, R. C. *Univ. of Calif. Publ. Psychol.*, 4, 71, 1929.
512. Tsukada, Y. *Neurosciences Res. Proc. Bull.*, 3, No. 6, 26, 1965.

513. Ungar, G. *Fed. Proc.*, 25, 207, 1966.
514. Ungar, G. *Nature*, 207, 419, 1965.
515. Ungar, G. *Proc. Cong. Int. Neuropsychopharmacol. Conf.*, Washington, March 1966, in press.
516. Ungar, G. *Neurosciences Res. Prog. Bull.*, 3 (6), 1965, p. 29.
517. Ungar, G., and Oceguera-Navarro, C. *Nature*, 207, 301, 1965.
518. Utina, I. A., and Byzov, A. L. *Biophysica (Moscow)*, 10, 1965.
519. Utina, I. A. *Biophysica (Moscow)*, 5, 626, 1960.
520. Uzman, L. L., and Rosen, H. *Arch. Biochem. Biophys.*, 76, 490, 1958.
521. VanDenter, J. M., and Ratner, S. C. *J. Comp. Physiol.*, 57, 407, 1964.
522. Van Heyningen, W. E., and Bernheimer, A. W. *J. Gen. Microbiol.*, 24, 121, 1961.
523. Velick, S. F., and Wicks, L. F. *J. Biol. Chem.*, 190, 741, 1951.
524. Verplanck, W. S. *Psychol. Rev.*, 64 (*Suppl.*) 1, 1957.
525. Victor, M., and Adams, R. Quoted in T. R. Harrison, *Principles of Internal Medicine*, New York: McGraw-Hill, 1962, p. 1841.
526. Vogt, W. *Arch. Exp. Path. Pharmakol.*, 240, 134, 1960.
527. Volk, B. W., Aronson, S. M., and Saifer, A. *Am. J. Med.*, 36, 481, 1964.
528. von Bechterew, W. V. *Neurol. cbl.*, 19, 990, 1900.
529. von Foerster, H. *The Anatomy of Memory*, D. P. Kimble (ed.), Palo Alto, Calif.: Science and Behavior Books, 1965, p. 388.
530. von Foerster, H. *Das Gedachtnis*, Vienna: Franz Deuticke, 1948.
531. von Foerster, H. *Currents in Modern Biology*, R. G. Grenell and R. Friedenberg (eds.), Amsterdam: North-Holland Publishing Co., 1967.
532. von Foerster, H., Inselberg, A., and Weston, P. *Memory and Inductive Inference*, Lecture, University of Illinois; personal communication, 1967.
533. Waelsch, H. *Biochemistry of the Developing Nervous System*, H. Waelsch (ed.), New York: Pergamon Press, 1955.
534. Waelsch, H., and Lajtha, A. *Physiol. Revs.*, 41, 709, 1961.
535. Wagner, A. R., Gardner, F., and Galambos, R. *Science*, 153, 658, 1966.
536. Wald, G., and Brown, P. K. *Cold Spring Harbor Symp. on Quant. Biol.*, Vol. 30, 1965, p. 345.

537. Wald, G., Brown, P. K., and Gibbons, I. R. *J. Opt. Soc. Amer.*, 53, 20, 1963.

538. Wald, G., and Brown, P. K. *J. Gen. Physiol.*, 35, 797, 1951-52.

539. Walker, A. E., and Jablon, S. *V.A. Medical Monograph*, 1961.

540. Walter, W. G. *Ann. N.Y. Acad. Sci.*, 112, 320, 1964.

541. Walter, W. G. *J. Psychosom. Res.*, 9, 51, 1965.

542. Walter W. G. *J. Psychosom. Res*, 9, 1, 1965.

543. Walter, W. G., Cooper, R., Aldridge, V. J., McCallum, W. C., and Winter, A. L. *Nature*, 203, 380, 1964.

544. Walz, E. *Z. Physiol. Chem.*, 166, 210, 1927.

545. Wardi, A. H., Allen, W. S., Turner, D. L., and Stary, Z. *Arch. Biochem. Biophys.*, 117, 44, 1966.

546. Warren, L. *J. Biol. Chem.*, 234, 1971, 1959.

547. Warren, L. *J. Biol. Chem.*, 234, 1971, 1959; as modified in S. Bogoch, R. F. Gilfillan, and P. Evans, *Nature*, 196, 649, 1962.

548. Watkins, W. N. *Science*, 152, 172, 1966.

549. Watson, J. D., and Crick, F. H. *Nature*, 171, 964, 1953.

550. Weigandt, H. *Revs. Physiol. Biochem. and Exp. Pharmacol.*, New York: Springer-Verlag, 57, 190, 1966.

551. Weiss, P. *Genetic Problems of the Development, Growth and Regeneration of the Nervous System and Its Functions*, Chicago: University of Chicago Press, 1950.

552. Wells, P. H. *Worm Runner's Digest*, 5, 58, 1963.

553. Welsh, J. H. *Arch. exp. Path. Pharmak.*, 219, 23, 1953.

554. Wersall, J., Flock, A., and Aumdquist, P. *Cold Spring Harbor Symp. on Quant. Biol.*, Vol. 30, 1965, p. 115.

555. Westerman, R. *Science*, 140, 676, 1963.

556. Westphal, O. *Ann. d'Institut Pasteur*, 98, 79, 1960.

557. Whelan, W. J., and Roberts, P. J. *Nature*, 170, 748, 1952.

558. Whitehouse, J. J. *Comp. Physiol. Psychol.*, 57, 13, 1964.

558a. Whittaker, V. P. *Ann. N.Y. Acad. Sci.*, 137, 982, 1966.

559. Whitty, C. W. M. In *Modern Trends in Neurology*, Washington: Butterworth & Co., 1962, p. 314.

560. Whitty, C. W. M., and Lewin, W. *Brain*, 83, 648, 1960.

560a. Williams, J., Bogoch, S., and Belval, P. C. Unpublished results.

561. Williams, M., and Pennybacker, J. *J. Neurol. Neurosurg. Psychiat.*, 17, 115, 1954.

561a. Wolfe, L. S. *Biochem. J.*, 77, 9P, 1960.

561b. Derry, D. M. and Wolfe, L. S. *1st Intnl. Mtg., Strasbourg, Intnl. Soc. for Neurochem.*, 1967, *Abst.*, p. 52.

562. Williams, M., and Zangwill, O. L. *J. Neurosurg. Psychiat.*, 15, 54, 1952.

563. Wolfrom, M. L., Lassetre, E. A., and O'Neil, A. N. *J. Am. Chem. Soc.*, 73, 595, 1951.

564. Wyman, J. *Cold Spring Harbor Symp. on Quant. Biol.*, Vol. 28, 1963, p. 483.

565. Yakovlev, P. Personal communication.

566. Yamakawa, T. and Suzuki, S. *J. Biochem.*, 39, 393, 1952.

567. Yamamoto, C., Yamamoto, Y., and Iwana, K. *J. Neurophysiol.*, 26, 403, 1963.

568. Yokoyama, M., Trams, E. G., and Brady, R. O. *Proc. Soc. Exp. Biol. Med.*, 111, 350, 1962.

569. Yokoyama, M., Trams, E. G., and Brady, R. O. *J. Immunol.*, 90, 372, 1963.

570. Zemp, J. W., Wilson, J. E., and Glassman, E. *1st Intnl. Mtg., Strasbourg, Intnl. Soc. for Neurochem.*, 1967, *Abot.*, p. 225.

571. Zerman, A., Kabat, L., Jacobson, R., and McConnell, J. V. *Worm Runner's Digest*, 5, 14, 1963.

Index

11A, protein fraction, 192
Abstract information, 12
Abstracting operations, 78
Abstraction, 11, 47
Alpha wave, 45
Abdominal ganglion, 15
Acetoxycycloheximide, 27, 36, 64
Acetylcholine, 44, 56, 125, 168, 170
Acetylcholinesterase, 53, 56, 57, 58
Acoustic transmission, 42
Actinomycin-D, 36, 38, 51, 54, 63
Action potential, 62
Action spectrum, 46
Activation effect, 29
Adenine, 50
Adenosine triphosphate, 11
Adrenals, 60
Adrenergic, 83
Affective accompaniments, 11
Afferent fibers, 40
Agraphia, 24
Ahexosamino-gangliosides, 99
Air-puff habituated donors, 72
Alexia, 24
Allosteric transformation, 45
All-trans retinal, 45
Ambient temperature, 70
Amines, biogenic, 89
Amino acids, 64, 94
Aminoglycolipid, 93, 99
    amino acids present, 107
    heterogeneity of, 111

hydrolysis of, 107
Aminopolysaccharides, 93, 95, 96
Ammonium sulfate fractionation of
    mucoids, 130
Amnesia, 26, 31, 33, 60
Amphetamine, 33
Amplification, 46
Amygdaloid complex, 29
Amyotrophic lateral sclerosis, 160
Anatomical organization of memory,
    21
Anosmias, 40
Anterior coxal adductor muscle, 15
Anterior horn cells, 49
Antibodies, 13, 88
    fluorescent antibody technique, 157
    zone of antibody excess, 157
    zone of maximum precipitation,
    157
Antigens, 62, 92
    ABO, 155
    BE, 160
    brain gangliosides as, 155, 160
    brain glycoproteins as, 160, 162
Antigen-antibody reaction, 121
Antigenic properties of gangliosides, 5,
    155
Antisera:
    to brain gangliosides, 156-62
    to brain proteins, 119
    to Tay-Sachs' disease proteins, 149
Anticeramide-lactose antibodies, 160

Aphasia, 25
Aplysia depilans, 15
Appetites, 25, 28
Apraxia, 25
Arabinose, 97
Arousal, 60
Artifacts, 77
Asialongangliosides, 98
Association, 11
Associative pathways, 216
Astrocytes, 60
Asymmetric center, 95
Atropine, 35
Attention, 25
Autopsy brain specimens, 123
Autoimmune disease, 13
Aversive stimuli, 192
Axon, 49, 78
Axoplasmic streaming, 62
8-Azaguanine, 37, 53, 63

10B, protein fraction, 62, 192
Bacteria, 95, 155
    agglutination of, 155
    cell wall constituents of, 5
    contact properties of, 155
    lipopolysaccharides of, 160
    motility of, 155
    toxins of, 6
    virulence of, 155
Barbiturates, 32
Behavioral states, 6, 29, 179, 217
Benzoquinonium, 168
Biopsy brain specimens, 123
Biosynthesis of mucoids, 173, 217
Bleaching of rhodopsin, 45
Blindness, 58
Blocking experiments with specific
    antibodies, 162
Blood, 57
Blood group substance, 5
Blood volume, 58
Bohr effect, 46
Brain damage, 25
Brain gangliosides, see Gangliosides
Brain-mind disorders, 13
Brain regions, 81
Brain slices, excitability in, 171
Brain stem, 53

Brain weight, 59, 194
Brightness discrimination, 73

Caffeine, 34
Cannibalism, 71
Capillamenta, 45
Carbohydrates:
    in brain proteins, 120
    protein-bound, in Tay Sachs' and
        Spielmeyer-Vogt disease, 140-50
    protein-ganglioside complex, 149
Cardiovascular function, 44
Care of the young, 37
Carotid body chemoreceptors, 44
Catecholamines, 171
Cell destruction, 161
Centers in brain, 28
Centriole, 42
Ceramide, 105
Ceramide-dihexoside, 97
Cerebellum, 53
Cerebral, 13
Cerebral cortex, 28, 35
Cerebral hemispheres, 53
Cerebronic acid, 94
Cerebroproteins, 115, 119
    specific antisera to, 119
Cerebroside, 5, 94, 97
    in genetic disorders, 150
Cerebrospinal fluid glycoproteins, 6,
    173, 176
Cerebrospinal fluid glycoprotein con-
    stituents, 177, 180, 181
Cervical sympathetic ganglia, 49
Cetylpyridinium bromide, 97
Changes in learning situations, 4
Chemical coding, 3, 11, 215
Chemical individuality in the nervous
    system, 110
Chemostimulation through fine can-
    nulae, 37
Chick egg, 5
Chicks, 33, 53
Chickens, 53
Chlorpromazine, 33
Chlorprophenpyidamine maleate, 170
Cholinergic, 83
Cholinesterase, 60
Chorioallantoic fluid, 167

Chronic stress, 60, 61
Cilia, 41
Ciliate culture, 17
Cingulate gyri, 25
Circuitry, 19, 77, 82
11-cis retinaldehyde, 45
Clam heart, 168
Click responses, 30
Cockroach, 15, 16
Coding of experimental information,
    3, 4, 7
    requirements for, 91
    specificity of, 121
Coding molecules, 91
    requirements for prospective, 91
Code, 3
Color blindness, 40
Colony rats, 58
Column chromatography:
    of brain proteins, 100, 111, 116,
        117, 192
    of Tay Sachs' disease protein, 143
Combined mechanism, mucoid-mem-
    ory hypothesis, 217
Commissures, anterior and hippo-
    campal, 25
Compartmentalization of information,
    13
Complement fixation techniques, 160
Complexity, limitations imposed by,
    17
Comprehension, 25
Computer, 18
Computer model, 79, 80, 86
Conditioned reflex, 55
Conditioning, 8, 9
Conditioning effects, 15
Cones, 40, 45, 48
Conditioned response, 69
Configuration, paired, 215
Conformational change in the recep-
    tor protein, 42
Conformational rearrangement, 46
Conscious thoughts, 29
Consolidation of memory, 82
Contact barrier, 85
    between cells, 214
Continuous light, 48
Cord, 13

Corpus callosum, 25
Cortex, 13, 25, 30
Cortical cell layers II and IV, 60
Counting test, 74
Critical period in development, 136
Critical periods, 18
Cuticle, 42
Cycloheximide, 36, 64
    effects upon puromycin, 67
Cylindrical cells, 41
Cytoplasmic RNA, 16
Cytolipin H, 97
Cytoside, 95, 98
Cytosine, 50

Death of cells, 14
Debilitation, 27, 65
Dedifferentation, 14
Deep nuclear structures, 31, 40
Defects in memory, 24
Definitions of learning, 8
Deiters' nerve cell, 50
Deiters' nucleus, 52
Dendrites, 86, 134
Dendritic nets, 18
Dendritic proliferation proteins, 134
Deoxyribonucleic acids, 47, 87
    chromosomal, 87
    genomal, 88
    hybridizable, 88
Dentate granule cell layers, 29
Derepression, 88, 89, 215
Detergents, 62
Development, 4, 212, 217
    embryonic, 135, 138
    prenatal and postnatal, 134, 152
Di- and tri-sialogangliosides, 104, 106
Diarrhea, puromycin-induced, 22, 54
Dietary habits, 24
Dihydroergotamine, 170, 171

Dihydrosphingosine, 94
Diisopropyl fluorophosphate, 36, 60
Diphenyldiazadamantanol, 34
Diphtheria toxins, 164
Discharge, 11
Discrimination, 33, 34, 186
Dissociation, pharmacological, 37
Drinking, 37

Drugs, 32
Duration-stabilities, 216

Early receptor potential, 45
Earthworms, 16, 69
Efferent response, 16
Effort, 194
Ehrlich's reagent, 99
Elasmobranch fishes, 44
Electric organs, 44
Electrical activity, 65
Electrical and chemical receptors, 44
Electrical means of studying learning
    and memory, 21, 26
Electrical phase of memory consoli-
    dation, duration of, 27
Electrical signal, 11
Electrical stimulation of tissue cul-
    tures, 13
Electroconvulsive shock, 3, 26
    amnesia in, 66
Electrode studies, 31
Electroencephalogram, "activation"
    effect in, 29
Electrophoresis, 100
    acrylamide gel, 111, 115, 144, 188
Electron microscopic studies of glia,
    37
Elegance, 211
Embryonic dorsal root ganglion cells,
    62
Emotions, 24, 25
Encoding for transmission, 11, 192
Emulsion fractionation method, 140
Engineers, 77
Engrams, 17, 77, 82, 89
Environment, enriched and restricted,
    57, 68, 84, 195
Erasing of circuit content, 26
Esterases, 119
Ether, amnesia induced by, 35
Expectancy of stimulus, 31
Excitation:
    presynaptic, 86
    postsynaptic, 86
Experiential biochemical code hy-
    pothesis, 194
Experimental allergic encephalomyeli-
    tis, 156

Experimental systems in studying
    learning and memory, 12
External limiting membrane of retina,
    48
External synaptic layer of retina, 48
Extinguished response, 70
Extract A, 161
Extraneural influences, 22

Facilitation, neuronal, 78
Facilitation of attention, 32
Facilitation of storage, 32
Fatiguability, 22
Fatigue, 70
    in computer units, 79
Fatty acids, 94, 105
Fiber tracts, 18
Fish, 41
Fixation of memory, 66
Fixation of postural asymmetry, 36
Fixation time, 37
Flaxedil, 16
Flickering light as stimulus, 48
Fluorescent antibody technique, 157
Food reinforcement, 186
Food-seeking, 50
Forgetting, 4, 11
Fornix, 24, 26
Frontal lobe, 25
Fucose, 94
Functional state, 118

Galactocerebrosides, 94
Galactosamine, 6, 94, 97, 105
Galactose, 6, 94, 97, 105
Galactose-1-phosphate, 150
Galactose transferase, 214
Galactosidosphingosine, 94
Gamma aminobutyric acid, 86
Ganglia, 15, 16
Gangliocerebroside, 94
Ganglion cells, 48
Ganglionic transmission, 171
Gangliosidase, 105
Gangliosides:
    accompanying amino acids, 107
    electrophoresis, 106
    membranous granules, 107
    metabolic destruction of, 167

Gangliosides: (*Cont.*)
 salt of, 165
 structure of, 99-107
 ultracentrifugation of, 106
Gaucher's disease, 150
Geometric order, 91
Glia, 52, 82
 and memory, 87
 multiplication of, 84
 to neuron ratio, 59
 and neuronal circuits, 87
 protein of, 153-5
Glioblastoma multiforme, 150-55
Globoside, 160
Globular molecule, 102
Glucocerebroside, 94
Glucose, 94, 105
1-^{14}C-glucosamine, 173
^{14}C-glucose, 173
Glucose-1-phosphate, 150
Glycogen, 96
Glycolipoproteins, 93
Glycolipid, 93, 94
Glycoprotein neuraminic acid and
 psychotic illness, 184
Glycoproteins, 95
 of brain, 111
 of cerebrospinal fluid, 111, 112
Glycosaminoglycans, 93
Glycosaminolipids, 93
Glycosidic linkage, 95
Goldfish, 49, 64, 65
Guanine, 50
Guinea-pig ileum, 170

Habituation to light, 70
Handling preinjection, 73
Hapten, brain ganglioside as, 156-60
Head trauma, 25
Hemagglutinins, 164
Hemoglobin, 46
Heterogeneity, 97, 161, 217
 of brain aminoglycolipids, 110
 of CNS aminoglycolipids, 107
 of CNS proteins, 66, 112, 125
 of CSF glycoproteins, 110, 112,
  125
Hexamethoniun chloride, 170
Heximide, 27

Hexokinase, 58
Hexosamines, 94, 98, 107
Hexoses, 94, 107
Hexuronic acid, 97
Hierarchy of information storage, 209
Hippocampus, 22, 26, 29, 36, 60, 63,
  65
Histamine, 170
Homogenization of brain, 113
Hormones, 121
Hunger, 28
Hunter's syndrome, 150
Hurler's syndrome, 150
Hydroxyindoles, 171
Hydroxylignoceric acid, 94
5-hydroxytryptamine, 168, 171
Hypoglycemia, 150
Hypothalamus, 28

Ileum, 170
Illness, drug induced, 54, 65
Immuno-diffusion, 161
Immuno-electrophoresis, 160
Immunology, 4, 12, 88
Implanted electrodes, 28
Imprinting, 33
Impulse frequency, 84
Impulse generation, 82
Individual variability, 118
Individuality, 160
 in brain aminoglycolipids, 107
 in brain glycoproteins, 111
 of cell, 158
 in glycoproteins of CSF, 110-11
Inductive operations, 77
Inference computer, 77
Influenza PR8 and NWS viruses, 5,
  164
Information:
 feed-back control of, 158
 interchange between cells, 158
 processing of, 77
Inhibition, 78
Inner nuclear layer of retina, 48
Inner synaptic layer of retina, 48
Instructional theory, 88
Instrumental learning, 9
Insular area of cortex, 28
Insulin therapy, 178, 179

Inter-cell geometry, 19
Integrity of cell, 158
Interferons, 167
Intracisternal injection, 54
Invariants in computer theory, 78
Iodopsin, 45
Ion transport, 41, 62

Kidney protein, 62
Kluver-Bucy syndrome, 24

Labile synapse, 84
Labyrinth of frog, 41
Language, 11
Latent learning, 9
Lateral or surround inhibition, 80
Lateral vestibular nucleus, 50
Leucine, 66
    radioactive, 63
Light deprivation, 58
Littermates, 57
Liver, 53
Local brain areas, 28
Location:
    of brain gangliosides, 125
    of brain glycoproteins, 126
    of CNS mucoids, 217
Locust, 15
Logical stability, 79
Long-term memory, 64
Looseness of associations, 13
Lumirhodopsin, 45
Lunar month, 70
Lymph, 12
Lysine, 45

M and N blood group activity, 160
Magnesium pemoline, 37
Mammillary bodies, 24, 26
Manic patient, 34
Mannose, 94
Mauthner nerve cells, 49
Maze-bright, 57
Maze-dull, 57
Maze-learning, 70
Meaning, 211
Mechanoreceptor, 40
Medial temporal lobes, 22
Membrane:
    integrity of, 6

mitochondrial, 214
potential, 49
pre- and post-synaptic, 19
proteins, 132
red cell, 214
Memory consolidation, 27, 33
Memory defects:
    arteriosclerotic, senile, 74
    with surgical lesions, 25
Memory trace, 216
Mental disorders, 26, 178, 179
Mepyramine maleate, 170
Messenger ribonucleic acid, 64
Metabolism, 4
Methamphetamine, 34, 37
Metarhodopsin I, 45
Metarhodopsin II, 45
Methathoracic ganglion, 15
Methylatropine, 35
Methylphenidate, 37
Methylscopolamine, 35
Mice, 24, 67
Micro-cybernetic unit, 86
Microelectrophoretic studies, 51
Mind-brain, 5
Midbrain reticular formation, 29
Miniaturization of components in the
    brain, 79
Mitochondria, 42, 214
Mnemic cells, 83
Mnemic substances, 194
Modulated frequencies, 87
Molecular weight, 93, 100
Mollusk, 15
Monkeys, 22
Monosialoganglioside, 105, 106
Mormyrids, 44
Mother surrogate object, 53
Motor activity, 53
Motor axons, 16
Motor response, conditioned, 16
Mouse, 13
Mucopolysaccharidoses, 150
Multiple sclerosis, 160
Myelin, 132
Mytolon, 168

NWS viruses, 5
N-acetyl galactosamine, 105
N-acetyl neuraminic acid, 105

"Naïve hemisphere," 211
Naïve mice, 72
Natural disease, 21
Negative feedback, 86
Neonatal, 13
Nerve cell, 14, 16, 79, 84
Nerve impulse, 40
Nerve nets, 4, 11, 79
Nest building, 37
Networks, with and without loops, 77, 79
Neural net field effects, 37
Neuraminidase, 105, 106, 167
Neuraminic acid, 5, 6, 94, 98, 106, 107
  aldolase, 142
  inhibitory activity, 163
  lipid-soluble, 125
  terminal, 172
Neuraminlactose, 95
Neurological conditions, 160
Neuromuscular events, 168
Neuron-glia, 82
Neurons, 78, 82
  internuncial, 85
  short-axoned, 85
  specific population of, 82
Neurophysiologists, 78
Neurotoxic effects of influenza virus, 164
Nicotine, 34, 170
Nitrous oxide, 34
Nodes, 12
Noise, 29
Non-dialyzable complexes in brain, 6
Nonlinear algebraic systems, 79
Non-retrieval, 4
Non-specific ascending systems, 29
N-retinyl-opsin, 45
Nucleases, 55
Nucleic acids, 89; see also Deoxyribonucleic acids, Ribonucleic acid
Nutritional lack, 22

Octopi, 41
Odor, 42
Olfactory bulb, 80
Olfactory receptors, 42
Oligodendrocytes, 60
Oligosaccharides, 93, 100

One-trial learning, 33
Operant conditioning, 18
Operational concept of learning and memory, 10
Opsin, 45
Optic nerves, 47
Optical rotatory dispersion, 45
Organ of Corti, 42
Organ-specific substances, 13
Organizers, 211
Orosomucoid, desialized, 159
Outer nuclear layer of retina, 48
Ox spleen, 97

Pacinian corpuscle, 41
Painful memories, 26
Papaverine hydrochloride, 170
Paper chromatography, 100, 173
Paradigm, experimental, 70
Paramecium, 17
Passive biochemical transfer of information, 37, 69
Passive cutaneous anaphylaxis, 156
Past, remote, 79
Pathological changes, 4, 118
pCO_2, 44
Peak effect of a drug, 65
Pentobarbital, 32
Pentylenetetrazole, 34
Peptides, 63, 93
Performance, 22, 187
Perikarya, 60
Periodate oxidation, 96, 106, 164
Phases of the memory process, 11
Phenol extraction, 73
Phosphoproteins, 62
Phosphorylases, 96
Photic stimulation, 49
Photoreceptors, 44, 45, 48, 49
Phrenosine, 95
Physostigmine, 35
Picrotoxin, 34
Pigeon brain mucoids, 7, 18, 55, 185
  controls, 186, 189, 190, 195, 196
  disc gel electrophoresis of, 196
  experimental, 186, 191, 193, 195, 196
  incorporation of 1-^{14}C-glucose into, 201, 203, 207

Pigeon brain mucoids (*Cont.*)
  sugars bound in, at rest and training, 195, 200
  thin-layer chromatography of bound sugars in, 197-201
  total concentration of bound sugar in, at rest and training, 202
Pigments, visual, 46
Pitch discrimination, 29
Planaria, 7, 55, 69, 70
Plasticity of the nervous system, 19, 77, 80, 211
Pleasure, 211
pO2, 44
Polydisperse, 96
Polymer, 102
Polypeptide chains, 63, 64
Polysaccharides, 44
Pompe's disease, 150
Posterior ectosylvian sulcus, 30
Postmortem change, 118
Postmortem measurements of the RNA, 49
Post-synaptic membranes, 15
Potassium chloride, 35
Precipitin test, quantitative, 156, 157
Pre-lumirhodopsin, 45
Process growth, 84
Processing of information, 11
Protease-digested, 97
Protein synthesis, 67, 68
Proteinases, 119
Proteolipids, 62
Psychoses, 6, 182
Psychosine, 94
Punishing effects of electroconvulsive shock, 33
Puromycin, 22, 36, 38, 54, 63, 69, 82, 208
Pyramidal cell, 29
Pyridoxal 5-phosphate, 96
Pyrogens, 160

Quaternary ammonium salts, 44

Rats, 13, 33, 57
Recall, 4, 11, 210, 216
Recent memory, 187
Receptor, 4, 92
  decoy, 167

sensitivity, 86
synthesis, 86
Recognition, 173, 217
  chemistry of, 155-73
  functions, 6, 155-73, 162
  functions in lymphoid cells, 159
  molecules, 173
Rectus abdominis muscle of the frog, 171
Red blood cells, 98
Redundancy, 65, 210, 211
Reinforcement, 88
Relevance, 211
Reliability, 211
Remembering, 4, 11
Remote memory, 7, 23, 187
Repair, 210
Repeating unit of brain ganglioside, 101
Repression, 89, 215
Reproducibility, 188
Required mechanisms for memory process, 11
Resection, bilateral, 23-4
Residue A of brain ganglioside, 164, 171
Respiration, 28, 44
Restricted experience, 57
Retina of frog, 48
Retinyl-opsin, 45
Retrieval function, 4, 11, 210, 216
Retrograde chromatolyses, 16
Retrograde facilitation, 34
Reversal training, 27
Rho(D) antibody, 160
Rho(D) erythrocytes, 160
Rhodopsin, 45
Rhythmic activity, 63
Ribonuclease, 55, 69
Ribonucleic acid, 37, 47, 62, 70-75, 87-9
  cytoplasmic, 49
  to deoxyribonucleic acid ratio, 53
  in glia, 51
  nuclear, 49, 53
  ^{32}P-labeled, 73
  polymerase, 37
Rods, visual, 40, 45, 48

S-100 protein, 62

Salinity stimuli, 44
Schiff base linkage, 45
Schizophrenia, 26, 178, 179
Scopolamine, 35
Sea anemones, 17
Sea hare, 15
Season, 70
Selective theory, 88
Senile dementia, 25
Sense of fit, 211
Sense impressions, 211
Sensitization to drugs, 38
Sensory hairs, 42
Sensory input reception, 11
Sensory receptors, 39
Sepia, 41
Septal forebrain region, 24
Serotonin, 6, 58
Serum albumin, 55
Serum proteins, 113
Sexual activity, 24, 37
Sexual centers, 28
Short-term consolidation, 66
Sialoresponsin, 167
Side effects of drugs, 65
Signal, 77
"Sign-post" mechanism, 214
Silica gel, 100
Skin, 80
Sleep, 29, 210, 216
Slime trails, 70
Slow-wave activity, 29
Slow-wave potential shift, 30
Social control, 58
Sodium amytal, 33
Sodium borohydride, 45
Solubility of brain proteins, 111
Somatic cells, 52
Somatosensory cortex, 29, 57, 80
Sound-habituated-rat-brain extracts,
    72
Species differences, 70
Specific site of protein synthesis, 66
"Spell-out" mechanism, 217
Sphingolipidoses, 142
Sphingosine, 94, 105
Spielmeyer-Vogt disease, 144-50
Spinal cord, 13, 36, 49
Spleen, 95
Spontaneous electrical events, 29

Spreading depression in cortex, 35
Squid axoplasmic protein, 62
Stages of learning, 11, 66
Staphylococcal toxin, 164
Starfish, 17
Startle response, 72
Stepwise hydrolysis:
    of brain ganglioside, 100
    of brain glycoproteins, 200, 204
    of human serum and CSF glyco-
        proteins, 174
Stimulation by light, 40
Stimulation of smooth muscle, 5
Stimulus configurations, 78
Stimulus-specific information transfer,
    72
Storage of memory, 4, 11, 47
Strain and species differences, 38
Stress, 58, 60, 68
Striate cortex, 83
Strychnine, 34
Subcellular distribution:
    of cerebroproteins, 127
    of gangliosides, 125
    of glial tumor cell proteins, 131
    of guinea-pig cortex proteins, 131
    of membrane proteins, 132
    of non-membrane proteins, 132
    of nuclear proteins, 132
Subcortex, 58
Subcortical regions, 30
Suicidal depressions, 26
Sulfhydryl groups, 45
Superior cervical ganglion of the cat,
    172
Swimming maze, 53
Synapses, 42
    activation of, 86
    atrophy of, 89
    contact at, 215
    glycoproteins at, chemically, 131-3
    glycoproteins at, by electron micro-
        scopy, 6, 133
    hypertrophy, 89
    inhibitory phenomena at, 86
    membranes of, 214
    new connections, 84, 85
Synaptosome, 132
    external membranes of, 125

Synchronization of the electroencephalogram, 29
Switching mechanism, 216

TCA supernate fraction, 67
T-maze learning, 29, 33, 54, 73
Taste, 42
Tay-Sachs' disease, 98, 139-50
    protein, 142-50
Temperature control center, 28
Temporal integration, 78
Temporal lobe, 24, 28, 82
Tetanic state of contraction, 169
Tetanus toxin, 6, 164
Thalamic areas, 7, 24, 26
Thermomechanical stimuli, 44
Thermostable antigens, 161
Thiamin deficiency, 22
Thinking disturbances, 13
Thin-layer chromatography, 100, 197-208
Thiobarbituric acid method for bound sialic acid in cerebrospinal fluid, 183
Thiopental, 33
Third ventricle, 24
Thirst center, 28
Thought processes, 11
Threshold for transmission, 214
Time:
    constants, 66
    of day or night, 70
    dependency and hierarchies of storage, 209
Tolerance to drugs, 38
Trace reflexes, 29
Transduction in sensory receptors, 12, 39-47
Transfer of information, passive:
    in humans, 74
    in planaria, 69
    in rats, 71
Transmission, interneuronal, 4, 11, 47, 121, 169, 215
Transmitter substance, 15, 83, 86
Transport, 4
Tranylcypromine, 51
1,1,3-tricyano-2-amino-1-propene, 36

Trigger mechanism, 29
Triton X-100, 62, 117, 122
Trypsin, 55
Tryptophane, 61, 66
Tryptophane transaminase, 60
Tumor, 24
    antisera to, 151, 160
    10B protein of, 150-55
    cell ghosts, 151-5
    glial, 124, 150-55
    immunospecific labeling of, 151
    mouse brain glial, 151
    neutron-capture therapy of, 151
    proteins of, 150-55
    tissue culture, 150-55
    transplanted, 151
Turnover of protein, 62
Tyrosine, 61
Tyrosine transaminase, 60

Unconscious, storage in, 210
Uncus, 22
Uracil, 50

Valine, 66
Variables in learning in planaria, 70
Venus mercenaria, 168, 171
Vertical internuncial chains, 80
Vesicular structures, 42
Vestibular nucleus, 50, 51
Vestibular sensory cells, 41
Viral hemagglutination, inhibition of, 162
Viral inhibitors, 167
Viruses, 5, 103
Visceral brain, 26
Visual cortex, 29, 59
Visual pattern discrimination, 68
Visual pigments, 45
Visually deprived rats, 68
Von Gierke's disease, 150

Wechsler test, 74
Worms classically conditioned, 69

Xylose, 94, 97

Y-maze, 17, 54